The Surface Chemistry of
Metals and Semiconductors

a
symposium
sponsored
by the
OFFICE OF NAVAL RESEARCH
and
THE ELECTROCHEMICAL SOCIETY
Columbus, Ohio, 1959

New York . London . JOHN WILEY & SONS, INC.

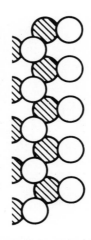

edited by **HARRY C. GATOS**

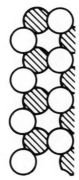

with the assistance of
J. W. FAUST, JR. and
W. J. LAFLEUR

The Surface Chemistry of Metals and Semiconductors

Chemistry Lib.

add

PREFACE

This volume contains the papers presented at the Joint Symposium of the Corrosion and Electronics Divisions of The Electrochemical Society on the Surface Chemistry of Metals and Semiconductors held in Columbus, Ohio, October 19-21, 1959. The symposium was sponsored by the Office of Naval Research and the Electrochemical Society. It was conceived as a medium for an effective exchange of theory and technology between the fields of metal surfaces and semiconductor surfaces. Dr. J. W. Faust, Jr., co-chairman of the Symposium shared with me the responsibility of its organization and planning.

The material of the volume is grouped into five parts. I. Chemistry and Physics of Surfaces; II. Imperfections and Surface Behavior; III. Electrode Behavior of Metals and Semiconductors; IV. Surface Reactions in Liquid Media; and V. Surface Reactions in Gaseous Media.

Discussion of the papers from the floor was an important part of the Symposium. After editing, the discussions were in most instances checked by the contributors. I am pleased to acknowledge here the contributors' prompt response. Some comments were received after the conference but I did not consider it essential to identify them as such in this volume.

I wish to acknowledge the facilities provided by the Lincoln Laboratory in the preparation of this volume. I wish

to thank Dr. H. Kolm for translating into English the manuscript "On the Mechanism of the Oxidation of Metals," and
Miss Joan Sweetser for handling much of the correspondence.
I am indebted to Mrs. P. M. Dougherty for coping patiently
with the typing of this volume.

May, 1960

                                        Harry C. Gatos

LIST OF CONTRIBUTORS

M. Boudart	Princeton University, Princeton, N. J.
K. Bohnenkamp	Max Planck Institute, Düsseldorf, Germany
W. H. Brattain	Bell Telephone Laboratories, Murray Hill, N. J.
T. M. Buck	Bell Telephone Laboratories, Murray Hill, N. J.
N. Cabrera	University of Virginia, Charlottesville, Va.
J. F. Dewald	Bell Telephone Laboratories, Murray Hill, N. J.
R. P. Eischens	Texaco Research Center, Beacon, N. Y.
H. J. Engell	Max Planck Institute, Düsseldorf, Germany
H. E. Farnsworth	Brown University, Providence, R. I.
J. W. Faust, Jr.	Westinghouse Research Laboratories, Pittsburgh, Pa.
H. C. Gatos	Lincoln Laboratory, Massachusetts Institute of Technology, Lexington, Mass.
H. Gerischer	Max Planck Institute, Stuttgart, Germany

J. J. Gilman — General Electric Research Laboratories, Schenectady, N. Y.

A. T. Gwathmey — University of Virginia, Charlottesville, Va.

N. Hackerman — University of Texas, Austin, Texas

P. Handler — University of Illinois, Urbana, Ill.

K. Hauffe — Kalle 8 Co. AG, Wiesbaden-Biebrich, Germany

H. J. Juretschke — Polytechnic Institute of Brooklyn, Brooklyn, N. Y.

C. V. King — New York University, New York, N. Y.

P. Lacombe — Ecole Nationale Supérieure des Mines, Paris, France

K. R. Lawless — University of Virginia, Charlottesville, Va.

J. V. Petrocelli — International Nickel Company Research Laboratories, Bayonne, N. J.

L. E. Samuels — Defense Standards Laboratories, Sydney, Australia

D. R. Turner — Bell Telephone Laboratories, Murray Hill, N. J.

CONTENTS

ix

CONTENTS xi

INTRODUCTORY
REMARKS

HARRY C. GATOS

Lincoln Laboratory,*
Massachusetts Institute
of Technology

Metal and Semiconductor Surfaces

METALS AND SEMICONDUCTORS exhibit significant differences in their chemical and physical characteristics consistent with the corresponding differences between the metallic bond and the covalent or ionic bond. Research and development on metals centers about their electrical, thermal, and particularly about their mechanical properties. Basic and applied studies of semiconductors, on the other hand, center about their electronic properties because the concentration of their mobile carriers is orders of magnitude smaller than in metals and can be varied at will within wide limits.

The surface properties of metals and of semiconductors reflect in certain respects the differences of the bulk characteristics; accordingly, the conventional approaches to studying these two classes of surfaces have been quite different. It is believed, however, that metal and semiconductor surfaces have many common characteristics and that an effective interchange of theory and technology between these two fields of study should advance the understanding of surface behavior.

The physical and chemical behavior of metal surfaces has been of interest ever since metals were put into use; thus metal surfaces have been studied for a much longer period and to a greater extent that semiconductor surfaces. Over the years, studies of metal surfaces played an important role in such fields as metallurgy, electrochemistry, catalysis, and

*Operated with support from the U. S. Army, Navy, and Air Force.

corrosion. This fact is well known and need not be amplified here. It should be pointed out, however, that studies of metal surfaces continue to be largely concerned with structural and chemical configuration.

Semiconductor surfaces first became of interest about twenty years ago, and came into sharp focus only in the late forties and early fifties when germanium and silicon surfaces were studied intensively by numerous large research and development groups in various countries. This unusually intense activity resulted from the discovery of the transistor by a team of scientists at the Bell Telephone Laboratories in 1948; but it is of interest to note that this discovery was itself a direct outgrowth of work on semiconductor surfaces by the same scientists. It is also of interest to note that just as work on semiconductor surfaces has contributed to modern solid state electronics, so work on metal surfaces has contributed heavily to vacuum-tube electronics. Outstanding in this case are Langmuir's studies on gas adsorption and vacuum techniques.

A high level of effort on the investigation of semiconductor surfaces was sustained by the growing realization that the electronic properties of semiconductor surfaces are quite different from the bulk properties, that they determine to a large extent the characteristics of semiconductor devices, and that they are very sensitive to the various ambients. It should also be kept in mind that fundamental electronic properties of the bulk are in many instances studied through contact with the surface.

The intensity of work on semiconductor surfaces appears to have diminished somewhat in the last few years; but this is certainly not an indication that all the pertinent problems have been solved, or that the subject has become less significant. In fact, this lull probably anticipates a new spurt of activity, perhaps directed at surface properties of intermetallic compound semiconductors, which present a far more difficult field of study than elemental semiconductors.

There are basic and direct advantages in carrying over to semiconductor surfaces our knowledge of metal surfaces, and vice versa. Many of the techniques developed over a period of years for preparing and studying metal surfaces can be applied directly or with some modifications to the investigation of semiconductor surfaces. Among these techniques are polishing, etching, metallography, adsorption in gaseous or liquid environments, surface diffusion, field emission, electrochemical techniques, work function measurements, and others. In addition, theoretical concepts of the structure and energetics of metal surfaces are relevant to the newer field.

While semiconductors have presented new challenges to workers in the field of surface phenomena, they have also provided materials of unusual purity, crystal perfection, and structural advantages for basic studies. Germanium, for example, is routinely available with impurities at the unprecedented low level of one part in 10^9 or even less. The degree of crystal perfection encountered in semiconductors is rarely attained in metals. The unusual properties of germanium oxides, such as their volatility at high temperatures and their solubility in aqueous solutions, allow the study of oxide-free surfaces in both aqueous and gaseous environments. The ease with which semiconductors are cleaved has made possible the preparation of virgin surfaces under high vacuum. Because of their directional bonding, semiconductors lend themselves to basic structural studies of surfaces, including nucleation and crystal growth phenomena, which should be considered as reciprocal to dissolution and etching processes.

It must also be emphasized that electrical or electronic techniques developed for the characterization of semiconductor surfaces constitute powerful tools for the worker in surface phenomena. In many respects, the understanding of semiconductor surface behavior is further advanced than the understanding of metal surfaces although the interest in the properties of semiconductors is relatively recent. Germanium is undoubtedly studied more and understood better than any other solid material.

In summary, striking progress in the understanding of semiconductor surfaces can be advantageously made use of in the field of metal surfaces. Similarly, advanced techniques developed in the study of metal surfaces can be exploited to a far greater extent in the study of semiconductor surfaces than they are at present. This volume was designed to meet the

compelling need for intergrading the present knowledge of metal
and semiconductor surfaces.

I

CHEMISTRY
AND PHYSICS
OF SURFACES

W. H. BRATTAIN

*Bell Telephone
Laboratories*

Introduction
to the Physics
and Chemistry of Surfaces

ABSTRACT

THE FUNDAMENTAL CONCEPTS of the physics and chemistry of surfaces are considered starting with Langmuir's work on thermionic emission and adsorption on metal surfaces and ending with the simple surface or phase boundary that occurs at a p-n junction in a semiconductor. Future progress depends on measuring both physical and chemical changes on the same surfaces at the same time.

1. INTRODUCTION

Knowledge of interest comes historically from two separate fields, thermionic emission and electrochemistry. The work on semiconductor surfaces comes later and, in a sense, bridges these older disciplines. The problem of giving a definite introduction to these vast fields is a broad task indeed and perhaps beyond the scope of this occasion. I will only try to sketch in what appear to me to be the high spots, and end with some tentative conclusions about semiconductors in simple electrolytes.

It may be said that electrochemistry begins with the work of Galvani in 1780 and Faraday's work on electrolysis in the first part of the 19th century. Volta's contact potential series (1800), Becquerel's discovery of a photo-emf at an electrolytic contact with an electrode (semiconductor) and Kelvin's elucidation of the essentials of contact potential were other high spots in this century. The application of thermodynamic reasoning to electrolytic problems led to great progress in the beginning of the 20th century. Richardson's work on thermionic emission followed by that of Langmuir led to a model surface of a clean metal in high vacuum. The relationship between contact potential and thermionic work function and the effects of adsorbed chemical species on the work function were all results basic to the understanding of surface phenomena. Langmuir's comments on the old controversy in regard to the role played by work function or contact potential in the potential of an electrolytic cell make interesting reading even today (1). One might say now that correlations between contact potentials in high vacuum and electrolytic potentials probably arise because both are essentially related to the work necessary to remove electrons from isolated atoms, i. e., ionization potentials.

Before proceeding further, it might be wise to define a surface. I will attempt this by suggesting that a surface is a boundary across which there is a difference in concentration of some essential chemical constituent and across which there is in general an electrostatic potential difference associated with some kind of charge double layer. It might even be said that a surface and a phase boundary are synonymous. The electrochemist properly likes to distinguish here between reversible surface reactions (thermodynamic equilibrium) and rate processes (nonequilibrium). No surface could exist in true thermodynamic equilibrium; a surface is at best a steady state condition to which thermodynamic reasoning applies. One should be careful about implying that another's steady state is not true equilibrium.

The relation between the charge distribution near a surface and the electrostatic potential change at the surface is given by Poisson's equation. Every person working with surfaces needs to become thoroughly familiar with this equation by performing the integrations involved. He need not, however, feel any compulsion to publish his particular integration. The literature is full of integrations of this equation differing little except in the symbols used. Unless the particular problem requires essentially new or different assumptions, the printed page might be put to better use. If the mathematical part must be redone it does save effort to measure potential in units of kT/e or RT/F. One generalization that all workers in the field should be thoroughly familiar with is how the distribution of the potential change depends on the extent of the charge double layer. If the charge distribution is symmetrical, half of the potential change occurs on the side of the positive charge and half on the other or negative side. If, however, the charge on one side, either positive or negative, is distributed in depth to a greater degree than on the other, i.e., the double layer is nonsymmetrical or lopsided to any extent (the magnitudes of the positive and negative charge must of course always be equal) then practically all the potential drop occurs on the side of the extended charge.

2. METAL SURFACES

At metal surfaces because of the high density of electrons (i.e., mobile charges free to move), the charge double layer necessary for any conceivable electrostatic potential change can occur in, at most, a few angstroms. The adsorption of almost any chemical species on a metal surface will change the magnitude of this double layer and thus the potential. The effects of adsorbing atoms such as oxygen or cesium on tungsten are too familiar to need comment here. About all one can do is measure the change in work function or potential jump and reason that it is consistent with the chemical nature of the species. Oxygen tends to attract negative charges increasing the work function and cesium gives up electrons to the surface. Any attempt to separate out the extra charge double layer from that already present on the surface is, to say the least, a difficult task.

In the case of a metal in a dilute electrolyte the charge on the electrolyte side extends further into the electrolyte because of the lower density of mobile charge; consequently, in cases of this kind an appreciable part of the potential change will occur in the electrolyte to a characteristic depth called the Debye length. The electrochemists call this the Gouy layer. This portion of the double layer is experimentally accessible and hence can be studied separately. As might be expected it can be described fairly simply in terms of ion concentrations in the electrolyte.

The subject of metal surfaces should not be left without a mention of the very important role that clean tungsten in high vacuum has played as a model for understanding surface phenomena. However many interesting surfaces are so complicated (dirty) and thus so far from this model, that the model is of little use for this type of surface. But it has contributed to the growth of the "clean surface school" who appear to believe that all one can hope to understand is a clean surface with at most a monolayer of a foreign species.

3. SEMICONDUCTOR SURFACES

The surfaces of semiconductors are radically different from the metal surfaces. Here the free carriers are orders of magnitude less concentrated than in metals; consequently the "space charge" layer inside the semiconductor surface plane extends to considerable depths. The characteristic or Debye length in germanium is 10^{-4} cm, 1,000 to 10,000 times greater than in a metal. Here also another phenomenon is found: some free electrons excited out of valence bonds and some free holes. Under equilibrium conditions in a given semiconductor, the densities of electrons (n) and of the holes (p) obey a simple mass action law. Their product at a given temperature is equal to a constant. This is analogous to the dissociation of water where the product of the concentrations of the H^+ and OH^- ions is a constant. Impurities in the lattice can increase or decrease the electron concentration without changing the concentration product, just as an acid or base changes the pH in water.

Probably the simplest surface or phase boundary known is that which exists inside an almost pure single crystal of a semiconductor (such as silicon or germanium) having on one

side electron donor impurities - say one part in a million or
less - and on the other side electron acceptor impurities; such
impurities could be arsenic and gallium, respectively, in sub-
stitutional solid solution. On one side n > p and the other p < n.
Since the products on both sides must be equal, it follows that
$n_I > n_{II}$ and $p_{II} > p_I$. For equilibrium to occur it is obvious that
electrons will diffuse to side II and holes to side I thus charging side II negatively and side I positively until the electrostatic
potential between side I and II (Ψ) is just sufficient to balance
the diffusion flow. The following relation then exists:

$$\Psi = \frac{kT}{e} \left(\ln \frac{n_I}{n_{II}} \text{ or } \ln \frac{p_{II}}{p_I} \right)$$

As usual in the equilibrium case one cannot measure this potential by attaching a voltmeter between sides I and II; in this case
one can calculate the distribution of both charge and potential
in the region of the surface and know its extent and size in great
detail. The situation is simpler than in an electrolyte in that
the donor and acceptor ions, being frozen in the lattice, are not
free to move. If the diffusion of the electrons and holes across
the interface could be sufficiently retarded so that there would
be time to measure the potential between I and II before the diffusion occurred, then there would be an electrochemical potential or Fermi level energy difference between I and II equal in
magnitude to eΨ. The corresponding potential difference could
be measured with a voltmeter. The potential measured across
a salt bridge between two reversible half cells seems quite analogous.

The above surface model is quite as useful in its way as
the clean tungsten model. Most of the phenomena occurring at
the "dirty" surface of a semiconductor in a gas, a liquid dielectric, or an electrolyte can be understood in terms of this
model. The semiconductor must come to equilibrium with its
surface. A charge layer on the surface and an equal and opposite space charge layer in the semiconductor is the result. The
surface can be changed all the way from very p-type to very n-
type, depending on the particular surface chemistry involved
regardless of whether the interior is n or p type.

Many types of measurement can be made on semiconductor surfaces. It is worthwhile to enumerate some of them: contact potential difference between the semiconductor and a reference electrode; change in this potential when the equilibrium density of electrons and holes is upset (for example, by injection or by creating electron-hole pairs by adsorption of light quanta); surface recombination of holes and electrons; change in lateral surface conductivity with surface potential (the surface potential can be changed by change in surface chemistry and/or a field applied to the surface); change in surface capacity. If several of these measurements are made simultaneously on the surface of a semiconductor whose body properties are not only well known but easily variable with respect to both equilibrium and nonequilibrium electron and hole density, then there are almost no adjustable parameters and therefore little guess work about the interpretation or meaning of the results. This is true at least in regard to the conditions on the semiconductor side of the surface.

We should not lose sight of the "clean surface school." All of the above measurements can be made on the clean surface; as the difficulties of obtaining the clean surface without radically altering the interior of the semiconductor are overcome, such work begins to result in important additions to our knowledge of surfaces.

4. SEMICONDUCTOR-ELECTROLYTE SYSTEMS

There is beginning to be a significant body of information in the case of a semiconductor in an electrolyte. Since the Debye length in the semiconductor is generally much greater than in the electrolyte (if the electrolyte is reasonably concentrated, one tenth normal or more), most of the changes in electrostatic potential occur in the semiconductor. Certain tentative predictions can be made, at least for electrolytes that are not very reactive, based on Dewald's (2) work on the capacity at the zinc oxide interface, Bohnenkamp and Engell's (3) work on the capacity of the germanium interface, and work done by Garrett and myself (4) using a germanium electrode. The systems in these cases consisted of a metallic (ohmic) connection to a semiconductor immersed in a given electrolyte with a salt bridge connecting to some standard reference half-cell, with means for measuring the open circuit potential of the system. Also included in the electrolyte solution was an inert counter-electrode such as platinum so that the potential between the semiconductor and the electrolyte could be changed. The changes could, of course, be measured in the open circuit potential between the semiconductor and the reference electrode or half-cell.

The generalizations from these experiments can be divided into two parts. First consider the cases where the current flow between the semiconductor and counter electrode is not large enough to upset significantly the equilibrium densities of electrons and holes near the semiconductor surface. The first general result is that the rest potential and/or equilibrium potential does not appear to depend on the concentration ratio of holes and electrons in the semiconductor; it does depend on the significant ion ratio in the electrolyte (metal ion ratio or pH). Thus for a given electrolyte with a given ion ratio the surface potential of the semiconductor appears to be fixed. As the electrochemical potential of the holes and electrons in the semiconductor is varied, the potential in the semiconductor has to rise or fall to adjust to quasi-equilibrium or steady state with respect to the electrolyte. An equation can be tentatively derived for the electrostatic potential between the electrolyte and the semiconductor ($\Delta\Psi_{ls}$) in terms of the activities of the pertinent ions and the electron or hole concentration in the semiconductor.

$$\Delta\Psi_{ls} = \frac{kT}{e} \ln \frac{(a_m{}^+)(p)}{(a_m{}^{++})} + \text{constant}$$

Because of the asymmetry of the charge distribution, nearly all this potential drop exists across the space charge layer. A change in p will change $\Delta\Psi_{ls}$ but since an equal and opposite change must occur at the metal semiconductor surface, no change in the measured potential with respect to the reversible reference electrode results. A change in the metal-ion ratio, however, changes the electrostatic potential at the semiconductor electrolyte interface without a corresponding change in electrostatic potential across the salt bridge. Therefore this change shows up in the measured potential - against the reference electrode.

In the case of zinc oxide, Dewald (2) found that by measuring the capacity he could find the bias on the counter electrode that would correspond to zero electrostatic potential across the space-charge layer (the flat band potential). He could, of course, measure the electrolytic potential for this condition. He found that at low electron density this electrolytic potential depended linearly on the logarithm of the ratio of the electron or hole density to the intrinsic density with the right slope, i. e., $(\frac{e}{kT})$. In other words, the potential with respect to the reference electrode changed in such a way that the changes were just equal to the corresponding changes in the electrochemical potential (expressed in volts) in the semiconductor.

Bohnenkamp and Engell (3) measured the capacity of a germanium electrode in KOH as a function of potential with respect to a reversible half-cell using a counter electrode to bias the germanium surface. Theory predicted that this capacity should go through a minimum and also how this minimum should depend on equilibrium electron hole density in the germanium. They measured how the electrolytic potential for the capacity minimum depended on electron-hole ratio. In this case the capacity is a function of frequency so the interpretation is not as simple as in the case of Dewald's results. The conclusion was that this potential behaved within experimental error as expected.

From the measurements that Garrett and I (4) made one can find the electrolytic potential for which the change in potential with light at constant electrolytic current goes to zero, and find how this potential depends on equilibrium hole electron density. One might expect this measurement to be equivalent to the flat-band condition, but the experimental facts are that the reference potential changes approximately twice as fast as the electrochemical potential in the semiconductor. From these results a plot can be tentatively made of the measured potential (E) for each of these conditions (flat-band, capacity-minimum, and light-effect-zero) as a function of the logarithm of the electron-hole ratio in the semiconductor (Fig. 1). Since one

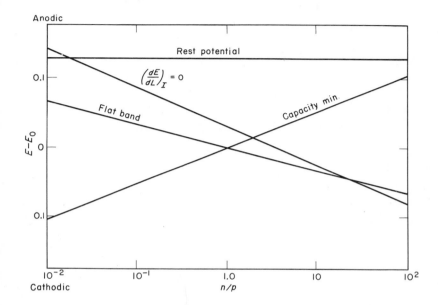

Fig. 1. Change in potential (vs. reference electrode) for
various conditions at the semiconductor-electrolyte
interface as a function of the equilibrium electron-
hole ratio.

would like to interpret changes in E in terms of changes in ψ,
the potential across the space charge layer, it would be interesting if we could make the same plot for ψ. We can at least
tentatively do this since we know that the flat-band line in Fig.1
will have zero slope in the ψ plot shown in Fig. 2. It should be
emphasized here that to go from Fig. 1 to Fig. 2 in the case of
a given semiconductor electrolyte system having determined
just one line or curve such as that for the capacity minimum is
dangerous; but if two or more of the curves in Fig. 1 are determined, especially the flat-band case, then the second figure
can be drawn with some confidence. Note also that we have
considered only the case where the semiconductor is not degen-

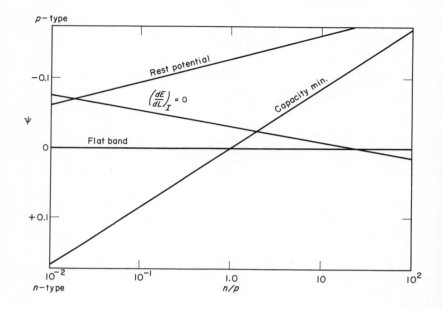

Fig. 2. Same as Fig. 1 except here the potential Ψ across the space charge layer in the semiconductor is used.

erate; in the chemist's language the electron or hole densities are dilute enough so that their "activities" are equal to their concentrations. As a result of all this we can write the equation

$$\frac{F\Delta E}{RT} = \frac{e\Delta E}{kT} = -\frac{e\Delta\Psi}{kT} + \ln \lambda$$

where $\lambda = \dfrac{p}{n_i} = \dfrac{n_i}{n} = (\dfrac{p}{n})^{1/2}$

and n_i is the square root of the equilibrium electron-hole concentration product.

There is still the interesting case where the electrolyt-

ic reaction or exchange at the electrolyte semiconductor surface
is fast enough to affect appreciably the electron or hole density.
One can then determine whether the reaction involved depends
primarily on electrons and/or holes. Garrett and I (4) found in
the case of germanium that in the anodic direction the hole density is controlling whereas in the cathodic direction the electron
density controls. In the anodic case, in other words, changing
the hole density from equilibrium changes the potential E so
that

$$\Delta E = \frac{kT}{e} \ln \frac{p_1}{p}$$

where p_1 is the actual hole density just inside the space layer
and p is the equilibrium density. The corresponding equation in
electron density holds in the cathodic case.

I would like to close with the suggestion that, while some
of my remarks are tentative, we are close to the description of
both the physical and chemical changes at a given surface. When
and if we succeed in doing this we will have reached a new level
of understanding of the "dirty" surface.

References

1. I. Langmuir, Trans. Am. Electrochem. Soc., 29, 125 (1916).
2. J. F. Dewald, Z. Physik (in press). See also this volume
    p. 205.
3. K. Bohnenkamp and H. J. Engell, Z. Elektrochem., 61, 1184
    (1957). See also this volume, p. 225.
4. W. H. Brattain and C. G. B. Garrett, Bell System Tech. J.,
    34, 129 (1955).

DISCUSSION

N. J. HARRICK (Philips Laboratory): Does the product
of the concentration of holes and electrons remain constant as
one goes through the space charge region to the surface?

W. H. BRATTAIN: Under equilibrium conditions and
to the approximation that one can solve Poisson's equation for
an average space potential the answer is yes. This solution,

however, has little or no meaning over very small distances of the order of an atom diameter of the surface.

A. J. ROSENBERG (M. I. T.) : Throughout your paper you treat the surface as a physical continuum, disregarding its atomistic structure. Chemically we know that we must consider the atomistic nature of the surface; I wonder if you might suggest how this aspect of the surface might be incorporated in your treatment.

W. H. BRATTAIN: I hope that chemistry will help to answer this question.

H. E. FARNSWORTH

Brown University

Clean Surfaces

ABSTRACT

METHODS OF OBTAINING atomically-clean surfaces of solids are listed with comments on their advantages and limitations. The method of argon-ion bombardment is reviewed with a discussion of the operating conditions and precautions necessary for successful results. The low-energy electron-diffraction method is used to determine the condition of the surface. Experimental results indicate that the relative positions of the atoms in the clean (100) surface planes of germanium and silicon are not the same as those of similar planes in the bulk crystals.

1. INTRODUCTION

The investigations of many surface properties of solids require a knowledge of the physical and chemical conditions of the surface. The presence of unknown contaminants in the form of stable chemical compounds or chemisorbed gases requires that the surface be made atomically clean before controlled surface conditions can be established. The following methods have been applied to this problem:

21

(1) Exposure of the contaminated surface to a suitable
gaseous ambient in the proper temperature range for
the promotion of a chemical reaction whose product can
be removed by heating. A simple example is the removal of oxygen from some metals by heating in a stream of
hydrogen. This method requires a knowledge of the contaminant and the existence of suitable reaction products
and is therefore limited in its application.
(2) Prolonged heating in an ultra-high vacuum. This
method is suitable for refractory materials of very high
purity which require the removal of adsorbed and absorbed gases. However small amounts of impurity such
as carbon may diffuse to and remain on the surface, thus
increasing the surface contamination density. This
method is obviously not suitable for solids having low
melting points of a few hundred degrees centigrade.
(3) Production of a fresh surface in an ultra-high vacuum
by cleaving a single crystal. This method is limited to
a relatively small number of cases.
(4) Removal of contamination by ion bombardment with
inert gas ions, followed by annealing. This method can
be applied to either single or poly-crystalline materials and has been found to be effective for the compound
indium antimonide having a melting point of $525^{\circ}C$ as
well as for more refractory materials. It has also
been found to be effective in removing a monolayer of
carbon from nickel and silicon crystals.

2. THE ION-BOMBARDMENT METHOD

Because of several recent applications, method (4) will
be discussed in some detail. Although the method of producing
films and of renewing the surface of a solid by the ion-bombardment or sputtering process has been used for many years, there
has been no direct information concerning the degree of clean-
liness of the resulting surface or the probability of removing
the resulting damage to a single-crystal lattice by annealing.
Is the resulting surface roughened or pitted by this procedure,
and are new crystal faces exposed during the cleaning process?

In recent years we have used the low-energy electron-diffraction technique to examine the surfaces of several crystals following bombardment by positive argon ions and annealing, and have obtained answers to the above questions.

2.1 The Low-Energy Electron-Diffraction Method

The low-energy electron-diffraction method is one of the most direct and sensitive means of examining a surface for small amounts of contamination. This is due to the extremely low penetrating power of low-energy electrons in the range 10 to 200 ev and to the fact that the wavelength in this energy range is suitable for diffraction from metal and semiconductor crystal lattices and from the monolayer plane gratings found on these surfaces.

A quantitative measurement of the depth of penetration of the diffracted electrons has been made previously by the author (1) by depositing silver vapor onto a gold crystal surface, using a calibrated silver source. Since the lattice structures are the same and the lattice constants differ by less than 0.4%, the silver was found to deposit as a thin crystal on the gold surface. Because of the different indices of refraction and certain fine-structure characteristics for the two metals, the diffraction beams from silver and gold were readily distinguished. The results show that the first monolayer of silver contributes at least 75% of the diffracted beam intensity at 50 ev primary energy, and the first two monolayers contribute more than 90%.

Although gases have a lower atomic number than silver and hence a lower scattering power, it is possible, nevertheless, to measure easily the diffraction pattern characteristic of a single gas monolayer (except hydrogen) on the surface of a solid if the gas atoms occupy a lattice somewhat different from that of the solid, as is usually the case (2). If the gas atoms in the surface monolayer occupy the same lattice as that of the supporting crystal, it is still possible to detect the presence of the gas atoms if the distance between the surface monolayer and the supporting atomic plane differs from that between two adjacent atomic planes (in the supporting solid) having the same Miller indices. This is true for chemisorbed oxygen and nitrogen on a {0001} titanium surface (3). The presence of surface gas may be detected in amounts as small as several percent of a single monolayer. When two or more monolayers of gas are absorbed, the outer ones are amorphous and may completely prevent the observation of a diffraction pattern from the underlying crystal. Hence it is generally necessary to partially clean the solid surface by heat treatment or other means in a high vacuum before any diffraction pattern can be detected.

The low penetrating power of the primary electrons results in an additional advantage of this method. The predominating effect of the surface monolayer of atoms causes the diffraction beams to grow and decay, as the wavelength is varied, in accord with the surface grating formula; thus a determination of the atomic plane forming the true surface can be made (4).

2.2 Experimental Diffraction Tube

The parts of a typical diffraction tube are shown in Fig. 1. Electrons are accelerated from a heated tungsten strip F_1 (1 mm wide) to circular anode A. A 2-mm circular aperture in A is covered with a fine nickel mesh having 120 lines per in. and 76% transmission to reduce field distortion and produce an intense transmitted electron beam. With a suitable retarding potential on deflector D, the electron beam is deflected to pass through a 2-mm circular hole in the disk A_2. Evaporated tungsten atoms are thus prevented from striking the crystal T. A_2' is a hollow cylinder attached to A_2 with the hole in A_2 centered on the axis of A_2'. The electrons passing through A_2 are decelerated by placing a suitable potential on the disk D and attached cylinder D'. Space charge is thereby reduced and higher current densities for the lower electron energies are achieved. Some of the decelerated electrons pass through the collimator C and strike the target T at near-normal incidence. The holes in the plugs at the ends of the collimator are 0.65 mm diameter and the collimator protrudes into the drum D so that the beam diameter remains small at the surface of the crystal (target T). All metal parts are constructed of non-magnetic chromel sheet and wire except for the small nickel mesh and the molybdenum collimator tube.

Four small holes are drilled symmetrically at 90° intervals near the periphery of all metal disks except A and D.

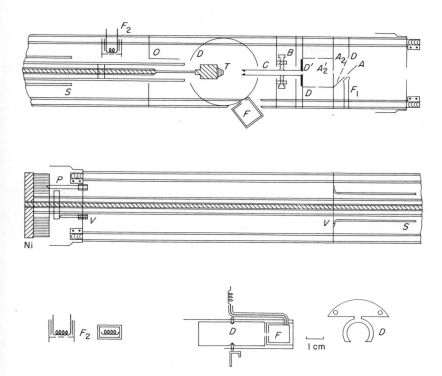

Fig. 1. Schematic diagram of a low-energy electron-diffraction tube.

The disks are held securely in place on a frame-work of four Pyrex glass rods, whose axes are parallel to the axis of the collimator, by glass-tube spacers which fit over the rods. The drum is mounted on the glass frame in such a way that it may be accurately positioned by adjusting screws. A metal disk B connected electrically to D prevents electrons from passing outside the collimator to the crystal T.

The crystal is mounted on one end of a solid molybdenum cylinder 1 cm in diameter and 1 cm long, which is supported at the back by a long, straight molybdenum rod. The rod is held by metal supports on the axis of a straight quartz tube 1 cm O. D. The tube rests in two metal V's positioned to support the quartz tube on the axis of the framework. A nickel rod is attached to the rear end of the quartz tube at right angles to the tube-axis so that a rotation of the tube or translation parallel to its axis may be produced by the action of an external magnet. A circular scale gives the azimuth angle. An adjustable stop locates the position of the crystal-face at the axis of the drum D when the crystal is in the forward position. The crystal may be withdrawn into the quartz shield S for cleaning by argon-ion bombardment or placed beneath the bombardment filament for outgassing by electron bombardment of the molybdenum cylinder.

The Faraday collector F is supported on chromel arms to which molybdenum points are attached for pivots. A small nickel rod, at the lower end of a 1-mm molybdenum wire attached to the lower chromel arm, serves as a magnetic control for rotation of the collector about an axis which lies in the face of the crystal and intersects the incident beam at an angle of 90°. A circular scale attached to the upper chromel arm gives the colatitude angle. Some of the diffracted electrons enter a 1-mm hole in the double-walled collector. The crystal can be rotated about an axis coinciding with that of the incident electron beam. Thus after proper adjustment of the crystal for a desired azimuth the diffraction pattern is explored by measuring the electron current to the inner Faraday box as a function of its angular position. This procedure must be repeated for a series of primary voltages separated by small intervals to obtain the complete diffraction pattern in a given voltage range. Only the elastically scattered electrons are measured, since a retarding potential is placed on the inner collector. Semi-automatic operation may be accomplished by rotating the shielded permanent magnet, which controls the Faraday collector, with a belt-and-pulley arrangement which is driven by an electric motor that also drives a recorder for the Faraday-collector current.

The bombarding filament F_2 is mounted as shown in Fig. 1a with an inner shield, outer shield and grid. The outer shield prevents evaporated tungsten from striking the crystal in both electron-bombardment and ion-bombardment positions. The grid and outer shield are maintained at about 50 volts positive with respect to the filament to furnish the necessary electron current. The inner shield is at filament potential to prevent excessive current to the outer shield.

A metal door O between the drum D and bombarding filament F_2 is operated by remote magnetic control located in a side tube. When closed, this door prevents evaporated or sputtered metal from entering the spherical bulb containing the drum.

The tube parts are enclosed in an all-Pyrex glass envelope sealed to the vacuum system with no wax or grease joints.

2.3 Experimental Conditions

Exhaustive tests have shown that an atomically clean surface may be obtained with the ion bombardment and heating procedure and that the damage to the crystal lattice caused by the ion bombardment can be removed by proper annealing (5). The resulting surfaces have also been found to be relatively free of roughening and pitting and were predominantly parallel to the atomic planes that formed the surfaces preceding the bombardment in all cases which have been tested ({100} and {111} surfaces of germanium and silicon, {0001} surfaces of titanium and silicon carbide, {100} surface of nickel, and {111} surface of InSb). However care must be taken to maintain certain conditions during the procedure to obtain these results and prevent contamination of the crystal. These conditions will now be discussed.

It is essential to use ultra-high vacuum techniques and first obtain residual pressures of less than 10^{-9} mm Hg with a partial pressure of oxygen much lower than this. This vacuum may be obtained in an all-glass envelope, with no wax or grease joints, after suitable outgassing with the combined use of diffusion pumps with cold traps and active getters. High purity argon in one-liter Pyrex flasks is passed through a molybdenum getter tube before entering the cleaning chamber. The argon pressure during the ion bombardment should be kept low to prevent return of contamination to the bombarded surface. Thus the pressure must be less than 1 micron and the discharge is not self-maintaining. An auxiliary filament and grid to furnish an ionizing current may be used. The filament should be shielded to prevent evaporated or sputtered tungsten from reaching the clean surface. No other surfaces should be ion bombarded. The grid, which is connected electrically to the anode used for the ion bombardment, should be spaced close to the filament so that a low grid voltage ($\lesssim 50V$) may be used to keep sputtering of the filament at a negligible value and to prevent charging of evaporated films on the walls to a negative voltage such that back sputtering on to the clean surface may occur. The bombarding voltage should be kept low (200 to 500V) to minimize damage to the crystal lattice. The bombarding current density should be kept low (100μ a /cm^2) to prevent roughening, pitting, or other deformation of the surface. Best results have been obtained by alternating periods of ion bombardment with periods of heating at the maximum safe temperature. It is also desirable to heat only the sample and its mounting with electron bombardment or induction; an oven heats the envelope and auxiliary components. The amount of annealing required to remove the lattice damage and argon after the last ion bombardment varies with the material and use for which the surface is prepared. For measurements of work function, 15 minutes has been found to be sufficient (6), while for recombination-velocity measurements many hours are required (7). The total out-gassing time should be such that the residual pressure with the sample hot is not more than a small multiple of the pressure at room temperature. This may vary from 50 to a few hundred hours. The total ion bombardment time may vary from one-half to several hours.

3. TESTS FOR CONTAMINATION

Independent tests have been made in a search for possible contamination of the (100) face of a germanium crystal from the ambient during the cleaning procedure, since half-integral-order diffraction beams were observed in the (110) azimuth.

In the first series of tests the germanium crystal was separated from a molybdenum supporting block by a thin slab of pile graphite and was held in place by molybdenum wires passing through quartz tubes, to prevent contact between ger-

manium and molybdenum. For these tests a tungsten flash filament and an omegatron mass spectrometer, in separate side
tubes, were attached to the experimental diffraction tube, and
a glass ball-and-socket valve was placed in the pumping line to
permit separation of the experimental tube from the pumps. A
ball-and-socket valve was also placed between the experimental
tube and the molybdenum-getter tube.

Using the gases N_2, CO, and O_2 in controlled experiments, it was found that only N_2 caused an appreciable pressure rise (8) (corresponding to desorption of one monolayer)
when the filament was flashed at $2000^{\circ}K$, thus indicating that
nitrogen was desorbed as a gas. Although O_2 was removed by
flashing at $2000^{\circ}K$, there was no detectable pressure increase
due to O_2 (less than that corresponding to 2% of one monolayer).
It is concluded that oxygen did not desorb as a gas but was removed from the surface in the form of a tungsten compound. It
was later observed that CO was removed with little pressure increase (less than that corresponding to 5% of a monolayer) only
if there was a relatively oxygen-free surface present, which
adsorbed CO, such as that in the ion gauge envelope under some
conditions. It was also observed that the presence of a monolayer of O_2 or CO on tungsten prevented adsorption of N_2. Thus
the determination of the amount of O_2 or CO adsorbed on the
tungsten flash filament was made by measuring the amount of
N_2 which the filament would adsorb and subsequently release
as N_2 when flashed. These tests showed that there was no
detectable amount (less that that corresponding to 2% of one
monolayer) of adsorbable gas present in the ambient during the
ion-bombardment process but that some gas was released during the subsequent annealing. The following evidence indicates
that O_2 was not present and that any adsorbable gas was predominantly CO. This evidence is based on the observation that
O_2 has never been found with an omegatron while the crystal
was being heated, and on the observation that, when the flash
filament was allowed to adsorb while the crystal was being
heated during the early stages of outgassing, the tube pressure
showed a time-dependent characteristic of CO, rather than O_2
or N_2. (The variation of pressure with time was a definite
characteristic of the particular gas present). Since rigorous

outgassing for several days did not decrease the rate of release of CO, it was presumed that it was liberated from the graphite in the crystal mounting.

In the second series of tests, the graphite and quartz were removed from the crystal mounting so that molybdenum made contact with the crystal. However the positions of the exposed molybdenum surfaces were such that no sputtered metal would strike the crystal face being tested. After the usual heat treatment, ion bombardment and annealing, diffraction beams from the (100) germanium face were similar in angle and wavelength to those previously observed before removing the graphite and quartz. Hence it was concluded that no contaminating effect from the molybdenum had occurred.

The following tests were then made to evaluate an upper limit to the amount of contamination which possibly could be adsorbed on the crystal face from the ambient during the annealing part of the cleaning process. These tests were of two types:

(1) Determination of the amount of gas which adsorbed on an auxiliary tungsten flash filament, and which produced a pressure rise on subsequent flashing of the filament. The flash filament was allowed to adsorb at room temperature during the last minute of ion bombardment and the following time interval until the necessary diffraction data had been obtained. The filament was then flashed and the pressure rise was observed on the ion gauge. The pressure rise corresponded to the preceding gas exposure (pressure x time). The exposure was determined from a calibration using nitrogen gas in the following manner. Nitrogen was allowed to flow through the tube at an equilibrium pressure of 10^{-8} to 10^{-7} mm Hg when the flash filament was hot (1800°-2000°C). The filament was then cooled for a short time, flashed, and the maximum pressure rise was recorded. The pressure during the time that the filament was cold was recorded, and the gas exposure was calculated. The procedure was repeated for different adsorption times and a curve showing maximum pressure rise on flashing versus exposure

to gas was obtained. From the exposure the total number of gas molecules that struck the surface of the crystal was calculated, using kinetic theory considerations. This number did not exceed that required to
form 0.1 of a monolayer on the germanium crystal
face, even if one assumes the maximum sticking coefficient of unity.

(2) Determination of the amount of gas which adsorbed
on the tungsten flash filament, but which did not produce a pressure increase on subsequent flashing of
the filament, e.g., oxygen which is removed as an
oxide (6). The procedure described above for test (1)
was followed until the necessary diffraction data had
been obtained. Then, without flashing the filament,
nitrogen was admitted to the tube at a pressure of
about 10^{-7} mm Hg until the filament was saturated.
The filament was then flashed and the pressure rise
was observed. (This has been done both with and
without removal of the nitrogen ambient). The filament
was then cooled to $25^{\circ}C$ and allowed to adsorb nitrogen until saturated; then it was flashed and the pressure
rise was again observed. This latter rise corresponded to one monolayer of nitrogen. The difference
between the two pressure rises was a measure of the
inhibition of nitrogen adsorption by any unknown gases.
It was assumed that the ratio of this difference in
pressure rise to the pressure rise from the nitrogen-
covered filament was the fraction of a monolayer on
the filament which was covered by these gases. A
particular ratio corresponded to a given exposure
(pressure x time) of the unknown gases. A calibration
of this ratio in terms of exposure was obtained in
the following manner. It was observed that one or
more of these gases were liberated when the electron-
bombarding filament was hot. Consequently the flash
filament was allowed to adsorb while the bombarding
filament was hot, and the exposure of the flash filament
was calculated after taking into account the residual
gas pressure in the tube. Nitrogen was then admitted

and the ratio was determined.

This test showed that the exposure of the germanium crystal was 10^{-9} mm Hg-min. If we allow for an error in the gauge calibration as great as a factor of two, this exposure might have become 2×10^{-9}. Assuming a maximum sticking coefficient of unity, a coverage on the germanium crystal of not more than 0.2 monolayer was obtained.

Even with the upper limits used in tests (1) and (2) in the foregoing, a coverage of much less than one-half monolayer was obtained. Since the probable values of sticking coefficients are much less than unity, the probable coverage was correspondingly smaller.

During the preceding tests, the following operating conditions applied:

Total time of heating the crystal was 400 hr at 600-650°C. Total argon-ion bombardments were 25 for 5 min each at 500 v, 100-150μ A. Each bombardment was followed by annealing at 600-650°C for 10 min. Total time of heating tungsten flash filament was 1000 hr at 2000°K. Total time of heating electron-gun filament was 1000 hr at 1500°K and 50 hr at 1700° K. Total time of heating bombarding filament was 400 hr at emitting temperature. Total time of outgassing ion gauge was 100 hr. Total time of operating ion gauge was 900 hr. Residual pressure in the experimental tube, after 400 hr of heating the crystal, with the crystal at 600-650°C, was 2 to 3×10^{-10} mm Hg. Residual pressure with the crystal at room temperature was 0.5 to 1×10^{-10} mm Hg.

The diffraction pattern and the relative intensities of the beams, including the half-integral-order beams in the (110) azimuth, near the end of the foregoing tests were the same as those obtained earlier and before graphite had been removed from the crystal mounting. Hence the CO liberated from the graphite had no observable effect on the diffraction pattern. This was probably due to the low value of the sticking coefficient of CO on a {100} face of germanium.

The above tests show that no observable oxygen contamination of the {100} germanium surfaces has occurred during the ion bombardment and subsequent annealing under the conditions used. The upper limit of the trace of CO which was observed is too small to be responsible for the half-integral-order beams. In fact, an exposure of CO of 10^{-2} mm Hg-min had little effect on the intensity of the diffraction beams from the clean surface. Greater exposures caused a decrease in the intensities of all beams but the effect was reversible at room temperature. The highest pressure used was 0.1 mm Hg.

Additional possible sources of contamination of the crystal are the diffusion of oxygen to the crystal surface from (1) the interior of the crystal and (2) from the molybdenum mounting. It has been observed that a clean surface becomes contaminated after ion bombardment and annealing unless there has been additional outgassing of the crystal and its mounting. However after a thorough outgassing for a few days, no evidence of diffusion during the annealing was found for any of the crystals which have been tested. Also there is no evidence for the diffusion of oxygen from the molybdenum to any of the crystal surfaces tested. Definite evidence against this possibility was obtained in the cases of titanium, silicon, and nickel for which chemisorbed oxygen was not removed from the crystal surface at the annealing temperature. In these cases a cleaned surface did not accumulate oxygen during heating at the annealing temperature as would be expected if oxygen diffused to the crystal face from the mounting during the annealing period. In the case of germanium, the adsorbed oxygen could be removed by heating at the annealing temperature.

Many investigations with surfaces have been carried out in this and other laboratories using the ion-bombardment method of cleaning. These include (1) structure investigations of the surface plane on clean surfaces, (2) work-function determinations, (3) adsorption measurements, (4) catalysis, (5) surface recombination velocity, (6) surface conductivity, and (7) field effect. One of the significant finds indicates that the relative positions of the atoms in the clean {100} surface planes of germanium and silicon are not the same as those of similar planes in the bulk crystals, but that these relative positions are the same when a monolayer of oxygen is adsorbed on these surfaces (9).

Acknowledgment

This paper includes results obtained by several present and former colleagues and students, and especially by Dr. R. E. Schlier. Support for this work has been obtained from a Joint Services Contract with the Massachusetts Institute of Technology and a subcontract with Brown University, and from a contract with the Air Force Cambridge Research Center, Air Research and Development Command.

References

1. H. E. Farnsworth, Phys. Rev., 49, 605 (1936).
2. H. E. Farnsworth and J. Tuul, J. Phys. Chem. Solids, 9, 48 (1959).
3. T. H. George, H. E. Farnsworth and R. E. Schlier, J. Chem. Phys., 31, 89 (1959).
4. H. E. Farnsworth, Phys. Rev., 49, 598 (1936); 44, 417 (1933).
5. H. E. Farnsworth, R. E. Schlier, T. H. George and R. M. Burger, J. Appl. Phys., 29, 1150 (1958).
6. J. A. Dillon, Jr. and H. E. Farnsworth, J. Appl. Phys., 28, 174 (1957).
7. H. H. Madden and H. E. Farnsworth, Phys. Rev., 112, 793 (1958).
8. R. E. Schlier, J. Appl. Phys., 29, 1162 (1958).
9. R. E. Schlier and H. E. Farnsworth, in R. H. Kingston, ed., Semiconductor Surface Physics, p. 3, University of Pennsylvania Press, 1957; J. Chem. Phys., 30, 917 (1959).

DISCUSSION

H. C. GATOS (M. I. T.): I would like to ask two questions: (1) Intermetallic compounds, such as InSb, have a <111> polar axis and consequently the {111} surfaces terminate with either In or Sb atoms. Have you examined both types of surfaces and if so, do you find any difference? (2) In some cases it is possible to deplete the surface of one constituent due to its volatility. Have you examined the structure of such a depleted surface?

H. E. FARNSWORTH: It was because of such questions that we started our work on InSb. We wanted to see if our low energy diffraction technique or our adsorption studies would show any difference on opposite {111} surfaces. We have examined a number of specimens and in every case except one, which we think was due to some uncontrolled difficulty, the results were the same. Furthermore, the adsorption characteristics have shown no differences to date. These results were unexpected. Work is still in progress, but perhaps the answer lies in a difference in surface spacing of the atoms. We have some evidence which indicates that the surface atoms are not in the expected positions for an idealized surface.

For your second question, we find that a more or less amorphous structure results when one component is driven from the surface. In other words, the diffraction pattern simply tends to be obliterated. Annealing at lower temperatures did not obliterate the diffraction pattern since presumably there is no loss by vaporization.

H. SELLO (Fairchild): Do the annealing conditions change with different bombarding ions? Also would you care to speculate on what kind of damage is done to the surface by the bombarding ions or what is relieved during annealing?

H. E. FARNSWORTH: I cannot answer that because we have only worked with argon. We were interested in finding a method of cleaning the surface rather than studying the parameters of the process. Certainly the annealing conditions vary with the material being bombarded. For example, InSb requires a very low temperature; Si requires a higher temperature than Ge, and so on. In metals it depends on the temperature necessary to make their atoms fairly mobile.

C. SAMPSON (Aerojet): Could you comment on the ion current density during bombardment?

H. E. FARNSWORTH: The current densities were kept low, the maximum being about 100 microamperes per square centimeter. With such low current densities longer bombardment times are necessary, but then the surface is not disturbed as badly. Wehner [in L. Marton, ed. , Advances in Electronics and Electron Physics, Vol. VII, p. 239, Academic Press, 1955] used high current densities in his sputtering with mercury ions and obtained hillocks on the surface. In some of our experiments we have used high current densities and have been able to duplicate his results even with argon ions. Our standard technique of sputtering with a low-current density with intermittent annealings does not produce any hillocks even when viewed with an electron microscope.

P. B. SEWELL (National Research Council of Canada): What techniques other than cleavage can be used to prepare surfaces that are parallel or atomically flat over relatively large areas? To what accuracy can lattice parameters be determined in surface layers by your low energy diffraction?

H. E. FARNSWORTH: The materials which I reported on have been prepared by mechanical methods. The samples were cut by a suitable method to less than half a degree of a given set of crystallographic planes. The surface was then ground, polished, and etched until it appeared to be smooth and parallel to the desired planes. Any gross surface irregularities, such as facets formed by etching, can be found by examination with oblique illumination. Any submicroscopic faceting can be found by the low-energy electron diffraction, itself. Because of the low penetrating power, one has a method of determining the predominant surface planes without removing the sample from the system. In other words, the surface planes determine some of the characteristics of the diffraction beams. The growth and decay of the beams follow the conventional plane grating equation. The resolving power is much lower than it is in the x-ray case, where the diffraction spots are sharp in angle and voltage. In this method, because of the low resolving power, the beam is present over a wide range of voltages and angles. By following the growth and decay over a range of angles, one can determine the predominant surface plane. An example is the work we did some years ago on a silver crystal cut parallel to the {110} planes. After etching, the surface appeared smooth and parallel to those planes. The crystal was placed in the tube and examined with low energy electron diffraction in the manner I have just described. These measurements showed that the surface was, indeed, parallel to {110} planes. The sample was then thermally etched. Reexamination of the surface showed that the {110} planes had been completely eliminated and replaced by $\{100\}$ and $\{111\}$ planes.

H. J. JURETSCHKE

Polytechnic Institute
of Brooklyn

Electronic Properties
of Metal Surfaces

ABSTRACT

THE CONCEPTS FOUND useful in the discussion of various electronic properties of metal surfaces are reviewed. Included are: a summary of theoretical work done in this area, predictions made by theory, a discussion of some recent experimental results, and what they tell about the relation of present-day theory to actual surfaces.

1. INTRODUCTION

The central problem of the atomic theory of metal surfaces is the proper determination of the surface energy of ideally flat and atomically smooth faces of a simple metal crystal. The methods of quantum mechanics permit the computation of energies with much less effort than is needed for a description in terms of correct wave functions; and, of course, the construction of a successful theory of surface energy must touch on most other aspects of the atomic nature of surfaces, such as the potential in the surface region and its associated double layer, or the atomic arrangement and the change in electronic configuration in the surface.

A discussion of the physical concepts useful in such
work and the detailed examination of various theoretical approaches are available in the literature (1, 2) and although there
have been few contributions since then, it is still worthwhile to
review the subject because of the recent advances in the experimental preparation and study of surfaces. With elaborate techniques it now appears possible to investigate surfaces approaching the perfection and purity of the idealized kind to which
present-day theory can hope to contribute a quantitative understanding. Theory and experiment are finally dealing with the
same kind of surface and it may be expected that in the near
future they will begin to interact more strongly than in the past.
In view of this it is useful to review the present state of surface
theory and how well its predictions have been borne out. The
following discussion will concentrate on the main concepts found
useful in the theoretical description of surfaces and will test
both their sufficiency and their implications against pertinent
experimental material.

2. THEORY OF SURFACE ENERGY

The surface region of a metal is extremely thin. Fig. 1
shows schematically two cross sections of the potential distribution for an electron in this region. The potential results partly from the electrostatic fields of the ionic cores and partly
from the interaction of the conduction electrons with each other.
Because of their high density the electrons are able to screen
out electric fields over all but the shortest distances; because
they are all of equal mass they stay out of each other's way,
with the consequence that any one electron is moving almost entirely in the field of the nearest ion. Thus the surface zone may
not be expected to extend into the crystal appreciably beyond the
first unit cell. Within the surface region, though, the electron
density is a rapidly varying function of position, and the one-
electron potential must be in self-consistent balance with this
electron distribution. Hence the surface exhibits neither the
long range translational symmetry of the interior, at least
along its normal, nor the rotational symmetry of atoms; therefore surface theory cannot count on the major computational

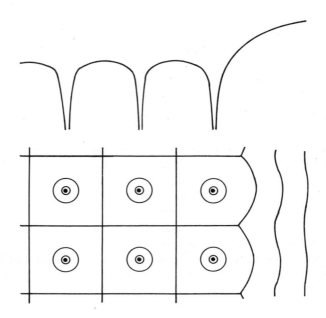

Fig. 1.　Schematic one-electron equipotentials in the surface of a simple metal.

simplifications introduced by such symmetry. The problem is more akin to that encountered in molecular theory and is in a similarly primitive stage of solution. Rather than work in detail on a particular face of a specific metal, the theory has concentrated on the study of simplified models in the hope of isolating the most important parameters in terms of which a surface can be characterized, and with the aim of estimating the relative importance of various contributions to the surface energy.

　　The simplest and most used model possible deals with non-interacting electrons in a potential box having a constant interior potential and plane-bounding surfaces of potential walls of finite height. Here the potential is only a function of distance along the surface normal and is of the form shown in Fig. 2. Because in this model the ionic charge is smeared out uniformly within each unit cell, its properties, and specifically its cohes-

ive energy, differ from those of a simple metal of corresponding electron density. To emphasize that one is dealing with an
artificial metal, Herring has given the model described here
the name "jellium" (3). The positive charge density and the
electron density for the surface region of jellium are also
shown in Fig. 2.

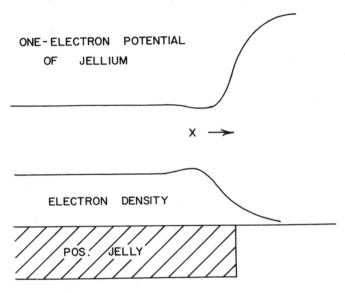

ONE-ELECTRON POTENTIAL
OF   JELLIUM

X ⟶

ELECTRON DENSITY

POS. JELLY

Fig. 2. Surface potential and charge density distributions of
the free-electron metal "jellium."

The surface energy of jellium is found by comparing the
energy of the bounded distribution of N^3 electrons confined by
potential walls with the energy of N^3 electrons in an infinite
medium of uniform electron density equal to the interior density
of electrons in the bounded metal. Such computations have been
carried out a number of times (4) and although differing in detail, they lead to the following general conclusions:
(a) There is a difference in energy between the two distributions which can be ascribed to the existence of the
surface. The energy difference is proportional to N^2,
and so leads to a specific surface energy independent of
the size of the solid.

(b) The most important contribution to the surface energy is the additional kinetic energy electrons acquire when confined to a finite volume. This part of the surface energy varies like the four-thirds power of the interior electron density.

(c) The electron density decays smoothly to zero outside the surface in a manner determined by the balance of considerations of potential energy, which tends to keep the electrons in the region of positive charge density, and of kinetic energy, which is minimized when the electrons occupy maximum volume. The net result is that electrons spill over the edge of the positive charge jelly, as shown in Fig. 2, and the surface acquires an electrostatic dipole layer of such direction as to increase the work needed to remove an electron from the metal.

Before comparing these results, and the magnitude of surface energies obtained, with experiment, it should be pointed out that the flat-surfaced jellium model is seriously deficient in the sense that it cannot predict any dependence of the surface energy or of the surface dipole layer on the crystal orientation of the surface. However using the above conclusions it is not difficult to extrapolate to the properties of jellium surfaces showing in their surface potential the periodicity of the atomic arrangement of a particular surface. If the important terms in the surface energy are of kinetic origin, it is at once clear that the electron density will make little effort to follow such potential contours exactly. Since usually only the highest energy electrons in the interior have wave functions of periodicity at all comparable to that of a low index surface, many more electrons would have to be promoted to high energy states for the density to exhibit pronounced periodic fluctuations within such a surface. We may conclude that the electron density in most crystal faces will reflect only weakly the bumpiness of the atomic arrangement; on atomically rough surfaces, in particular, one can expect many points at which the ionic charge is only partially screened, as well as points at which the electrons extend appreciably beyond the last ions. Detailed calculations on a simple model have borne out these predictions (5), schematically indicated in Fig. 3.

CLOSE PACKED   SURFACE

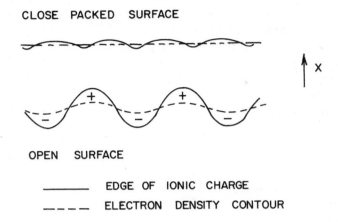

OPEN   SURFACE

_____   EDGE OF IONIC CHARGE

_ _ _ _   ELECTRON   DENSITY CONTOUR

Fig. 3. Approximate electron density variation on jellium surfaces with periodic positive charge boundaries. The
solid line gives the edge of the uniform ionic charge
density. The dashed line indicates the contour where
the electron density is equal to one-half its interior
value.

The important feature of such periodic surface potentials is that they lead to an additional dipole moment on each
surface. This moment is of differing strength for various crystal faces, and it is larger when the atomic roughness of the
face is more pronounced. Since this dipole moment is positive
towards the outside, the work function for electrons on different
faces should vary in inverse fashion, decreasing as the indices
of the surface become large. The dipole layer will also add to
the electrostatic energy of the surface. However it should make
only a small contribution to the total energy. The main increase
in energy occurs because on a low work function face the electron density decay is slower, leading to a larger transition region; since this region is populated mostly by high kinetic energy electrons, the total kinetic energy belonging to the surface
is increased (6). Another effect occurring on high index faces,
whose influence on the surface energy has not been studied in

detail, is the coupling of different and normally independent plane electron waves of the same energy due to diffraction by the periodic surface potential (7).

The metals most suited for comparison with the foregoing theory are the monovalent alkalis and noble metals. Values of their surface energy at absolute zero can be deduced from recent experimental data and are shown in Table I. For the alkalis the values are obtained from knowledge of the liquid surface tension and its temperature derivative near the melting point (8), corrected for a small contribution of the heat of fusion. The values for the noble metals are direct experimental surface energies of the solids in question (9). All the numbers have one common feature: They are much smaller than one would expect from the heat of sublimation of the solid, and from the number of neighbors lacked by the atoms in the surface. The theoretical approach is justified because the ability of the near-free electrons to adjust effectively to new boundary conditions is responsible for the lowering of the surface energy far below that of the broken bonds. Table I also lists the electron densities of the metals and shows that the nearly linear dependence of the surface energy on electron density found for jellium is approximately obeyed. The agreement with the four-thirds power of the density law is best for the two light alkalis but becomes poorer for potassium and the noble metals. A plausible cause for the disagreement in these solids is the relatively large size of their ionic cores. The suggestion here that the conduction electrons are now the only contributors to the surface energy has not been verified in detail.

The absolute value of the surface energy has been computed with some care only for the jellium metal of the electron density of sodium. The value obtained by various investigators (4) is somewhat larger than 200 ergs/cm^2, which taken at face value compares rather well with the experimental figure in Table I. Such an agreement is somewhat distressing because it means that all more refined theories in which the surface is allowed to stabilize by more detailed changes in the electronic configuration and also by atomic rearrangement would necessarily lead to surface energies considerably below the experimental result. However as pointed out by Herring, because of

TABLE I

Surface Energy (0° K) and Electron Density of Monovalent Metals

	K*	Na*	Li*	Ag**	Au**	Cu**
Surface Energy (ergs/cm^2)	146	240	510	1740	1960	2400
Electron Density (mol/cm^3)	0.022	0.042	0.077	0.097	0.098	0.14

* Ref. (8)
**Ref. (9)

the difference between jellium and a real metal, the surface energy of jellium should be compared to about two-thirds of that of the corresponding metal, or in our case to 160 ergs/cm^2. Thus the best computed values of the surface energy of jellium still lie above the experimental value although not excessively so. It should be noted, however, that only small changes in the approximation procedures used in most of the calculations could alter the computed value sufficiently to upset this conclusion. Nevertheless it is clear that theoretical surface energies based on free-electron considerations can, under the circumstances in which these apply, approximate quite closely the experimental values.

The further clear-cut theoretical prediction of the relation of the work function of a crystal face to its atomic roughness has also been confirmed experimentally. Table II reproduces a recent compilation by Müller (10) of work function data of various faces of tungsten, obtained by field emission. Tungsten is far from the simple metal for which the theory was designed, but the argument about the flatness of the electron density distribution on rough atomic faces should, in fact, hold more generally. It may lead to even larger dipole variations in metals having fewer conduction electrons. The data of Table II show that most high index faces have similarly low work functions but that those of the low index faces may be higher by more than 1 volt. The exact prediction of the order of the faces of increasing dipole moment, attempted seriously only by Smoluchowski (11), is still beyond present-day theory, even for the simplest metals.

This also applies to the relative surface energies of the higher index faces. Particularly for metal atoms with large ionic cores or solids with many overlapping bands - the most common case - both the direct interaction between ions and a transition of the electronic structure from that of the solid to that of the isolated atom have to be taken into account.

3. THE SURFACE POTENTIAL

A major obstacle in carrying out meaningful calculations for detailed surface effects is our lack of methods for dealing

TABLE II

Work Function of Various Faces of Tungsten, in ev (10).

(116)	(122)	(111)	(233)	(123)	(112)	(011)
4.30	4.35	4.39	4.46	4.52	4.65	5.70
					-4.88	-5.99

with the surface potential. As already pointed out, the surface potential is only partly electrostatic. A more important contribution is made by the interactions between electrons. The interactions derive from both the classical electrostatic repulsion of the electrons and the spin-dependent exchange repulsion of Fermi statistics; the interaction is a dynamic one since the motion of any one electron will be influenced by the position and motion of many other electrons, and its motion will in turn alter their paths. To cope with the many-body problem at all it has been found useful to separate it into two parts. First, the long range coulomb and exchange interactions of all electrons lead to a screening of the field of any one electron by leaving in its neighborhood a nearly spherical hole of such dimensions that the underlying ionic charge made bare in the hole amounts to that of the electron. The screening is very effective and results in hole dimensions of the order of the atomic size in the metal interior. Second, because the description of the collective interactions in terms of the potential applies only to the average state of affairs, there is another short-range interaction between the electron in question and all others so close that their screening radii overlap. This is a small contribution, in the nature of a correction to the picture of collective interaction. In this picture the one-electron potential we have referred to all along is largely the potential of the electron due to its associated hole.

Although understood in principle for many years, the detailed theory of collective screening has been worked out rather recently and only for a uniform distribution of electrons strictly in the limit of high density. The theory meets with new difficulties when applied to the problem of the surface potential.

First of all, the existence of the surface establishes a certain correlation between different electronic states, particularly between incident and reflected electrons. In addition there are electron density variations both within the surface and along the surface normal. Since the screening radius increases with decreasing electron density, it is obviously unrealistic to think of a spherical potential hole accompanying its electron in the immediate surface region, where the electron density drops very rapidly to zero. At the very lowest densities, in particular, the potential must somehow go over in continuous fashion into the classical image potential applying far away from the metal surface. Finally, from the dynamic nature of these interactions it follows that the problem must be dealt with self-consistently: each electron contributes to the holes of all the other electrons in a manner dependent on the detailed features of its own potential hole.

It is possible to discuss the problem more rigorously in spite of the absence of such a theory of coulomb interactions between electrons in the metal surface. As already mentioned part of the repulsion between electrons is a direct consequence of the exclusion principle, which is independent of the electron's charge. The mathematical theory of the exchange hole in a system of non-interacting electrons is straightforward and can be formulated without difficulty also for non-uniform electron distributions (12). Applied to surface problems, the theory formed the basis of the major attempt to construct a self-consistent surface potential in the work of Bardeen (13). Not surprisingly, the exchange hole has many features in common with the actual potential hole. Thus it accompanies the electron in its motion and its shape depends on the speed of the electron: faster electrons have shallower and more extensive exchange holes. It is therefore instructive to study the exchange hole of an electron in the surface region in order to gain more insight into the manner in which the surface potential arises.

The results of such a study (14) carried out for an average exchange hole in jellium are shown schematically in Fig. 4. The position of the electron for which the hole has been computed is given by the black circle and the cross section of the hole corresponds to the missing part of the electron density

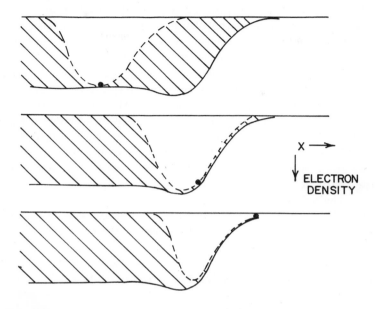

Fig. 4. Cross section of charge hole of an electron for various
         locations of the electron in the surface. The electron
         position is marked by the circle.

distribution. Far from the surface, the hole is spherical and
centered around the electron. As the electron moves into the
surface, its hole comes along, and displaces practically all
other electrons in this part of the surface. Furthermore the
electron is no longer at the center of the hole. As the electron
moves farther from the region of high charge density, the hole
becomes stationary at a point opposite the electron and starts
to flatten out laterally, as indicated by the smaller cross section of the hole in the lowest sketch in Fig. 4.

    The surface potential of the electron resulting from the
potential energy between the electron and its hole can be deduced qualitatively from the configurations depicted in Fig. 4.
As the electron moves out of the center of its hole the potential
begins to rise, until it is of value e^2/r when the electron is at

the edge of the hole of radius r. For larger distances the potential depends on the shape of the hole. If as indicated, the
hole flattens out in the surface, the potential starts to approach
the classical image potential which is due to a similarly distributed induced surface charge. In this explicit calculation the
exchange hole shows in the surface the major characteristics
to be expected from the screened interaction of an electron
with a metal surface; although there are some obvious differences between the two, in the absence of a more complete theory
the exchange hole and potential approach should be a useful
means for constructing self-consistent surface potentials in
more realistic surface models.

Undoubtedly one of the reasons why detailed surface potential calculations have not been pursued very actively is that
predictions of the fine structure of the surface potential are
not easy to follow up experimentally. Apart from its averaged
effect on the surface dipole layer, the surface potential shape
helps determine the reflection and transmission coefficients of
electrons passing through the surface; the information gained
by measuring the scattering cross sections for different electrons can therefore be used in reconstructing the potential. The
effects to be expected are largest for very low energy electrons;
for a long time the best source of such electrons has been the
electrons in the metal itself, barely able to escape from it by
thermal excitation. This is the thermionic emission of electrons from metals, in which theory long ago predicted the
Richardson equation for the current density J as a function of
temperature

$$J = (1 - R) A e^{-\phi/kT}$$

Here A is a universal constant, ϕ is the work function of the
surface, and R is the average reflection coefficient for electrons in the range of energies of interest. The experimental
situation to which the Richardson equation applies is difficult
to realize. Only recently has it been possible to work under
experimental conditions sufficiently controlled to allow an unambiguous determination of all the parameters appearing in it
(15). At last it is now clear that the Richardson equation truly

applies and that the constant A has its theoretical value. The reflection coefficient R is then of the order of magnitude of 0.1, a value in good agreement with the reflectivity predicted for most surface barriers of reasonable shape. Similar information, but potentially much more detailed, is coming out of new experiments measuring the reflection of very low energy monochromatic electron beams (16). Very low energy electron diffraction studies of surfaces will soon throw considerable light on the fine structure of the surface potential.

The most direct evidence for surface potential variations in the plane of the surface has come from new surface investigations by field ion microscopy (17); however detailed maps of the potentials observed have not yet been worked out.

So far only one specific characteristic of computed surface potentials seems to have an important effect on experimental results. For thermionic emission of surfaces subject to an electric field, the Richardson equation must be modified in two ways. First the potential barrier is lowered by the electric field to give a new work function ϕ'. In addition the reflection coefficient is altered. The relative current J/J_0 as a function of applied field E becomes

$$\log J/J_0 = -\frac{\phi'(E)-\phi}{kT} + C\frac{E^{0.8}}{T}\cos\left(\frac{a}{E^{0.25}}+\Theta\right)$$

The resulting periodic deviations from the usual Schottky plot (18) come about because of resonances in the reflection of electrons from the surface potential and from the Schottky hump of the barrier. The constants C, a, and Θ depend on the shape of the surface potential barrier. Although the experimentally found oscillations were of predictable frequency and magnitude the phase Θ could not be explained using any reasonable, monotonically increasing surface potentials until Cutler and Gibbons (19) took seriously the dip in the potential just below the surface. The dip is shown in the theoretically derived curves in Fig. 2. It should be emphasized that the agreement may be partly fortuitous; similar changes in the phase Θ may result from a consideration of a general three-

H. J. JURETSCHKE

dimensional, rather than a very detailed one-dimensional, surface potential. At any rate, experimental results on surfaces are now reaching the stage where more refined theoretical models than those discussed here will have to be applied to obtain reasonable agreement.

Traditionally in this field experimental results could at most be discussed qualitatively because they were not obtained under conditions well enough defined to allow a unique interpretation. The number of experiments having an immediate bearing on our fundamental understanding of surfaces is still small but increasing rapidly. Pressure is now shifting towards the development of better theories.

Acknowledgment

This work was supported by the U. S. Office of Naval Research.

References

1. C. Herring, in Metal Interfaces, p. 1, American Society for Metals, 1952.
2. P. P. Ewald and H. J. Juretschke, in R. Gomer and C. S. Smith, eds., Structure and Properties of Solid Surfaces, p. 82, Univ. of Chicago Press, 1953.
3. C. Herring, in Metal Interfaces, p. 117, American Society for Metals, 1952.
4. Most earlier work is mentioned in Ref. 1) and 2). More recent calculations are given by R. Stratton, Phil. Mag., 44, 1236 (1953); 2, 702 (1957); A. B. Scott, ibid., 45, 1173 (1954).
5. C. H. Kelley, The Kinetic Energy of Electrons Associated with the Line Boundary of a Two-Dimensional Crystal, (thesis), Polytechnic Institute of Brooklyn, 1954.
6. H. A. Bethe and R. F. Bacher, Revs. Modern Phys., 8, 83 (1936).
7. H. A. Müser, Phil. Mag., 45, 1237 (1954).
8. J. W. Taylor, Phil. Mag., 46, 867 (1955).

9. H. Udin, A. J. Shaler and J. Wulff, J. Metals, 1, 186 (1949); H. Udin, ibid., 3, 63 (1951); F. H. Buttner, H. Udin and J. Wulff, ibid., 3, 1206 (1951); E. R. Funk, H. Udin and J. Wulff, ibid., 3, 1209 (1951).
10. E. W. Müller, J. Appl. Phys., 26, 732 (1955).
11. R. Smoluchowski, Phys. Rev., 60, 661 (1941).
12. J. C. Slater, Phys. Rev., 81, 385 (1951).
13. J. Bardeen, Phys. Rev., 49, 653 (1936).
14. H. J. Juretschke, Phys. Rev., 92, 1140 (1953).
15. H. Shelton, Phys. Rev., 107, 1553 (1957).
16. H. A. Fowler and H. E. Farnsowrth, Phys. Rev., 111, 103 (1958).
17. E. W. Müller, J. Appl. Phys., 28, 1 (1957).
18. For a recent discussion and introduction to the literature see R. H. Good, Jr., J. Appl. Phys., 28, 1405 (1957); D. Juenker, ibid., 28, 1398 (1957).
19. P. H. Cutler and J. J. Gibbons, Phys. Rev., 111, 394 (1958).

DISCUSSION

J. J. GILMAN (General Electric): In tungsten, $\{110\}$ planes are the most close-packed, and according to theory these planes should have the lowest surface energy. Thus one would expect tungsten to cleave along $\{110\}$ planes because the cleavage plane is the one of lowest surface energy. However, it is observed to cleave along $\{100\}$ planes. Please comment on this discrepancy.

H. J. JURETSCHKE: Cleavage does not always take place along planes of lowest surface energy. Furthermore, $\{100\}$ planes are still relatively densely packed and should, for tungsten, also be planes of low surface energy. This is supported by the fact that the work function of the $\{100\}$ planes is high, so that it is measured reliably only with difficulty, and has, in fact, not been determined accurately by field emission experiments. Theory cannot yet establish the exact ordering in energy of the low surface energy faces.

P. HANDLER

University of Illinois

Electrical Properties
of the Surfaces
# of Semiconductors

ABSTRACT

A BRIEF REVIEW of the research in semiconductor surface physics is presented. Emphasis
is placed on the limits of present theory and the importance of knowing the composition and structure of
the surface of interest. The feasibility of new experimental approaches to the study of surfaces such
as nuclear magnetic resonance and quadrupole resonance is discussed. A review of recent develop-
ments in an understanding of the energy level diagram of the cleaned germanium surface is reviewed.

1. INTRODUCTION

During the past decade our understanding of the volume
properties of semiconductors has been greatly augmented by a
vast amount of research on single crystals. This research has
made it possible to attempt a study of single crystal surfaces
by means of their electrical properties. The complex surface
of a semiconductor must be considered in three dimensions
rather than two. In the third dimension the semiconductor surface may be roughly divided into the surface region and the
space charge region beneath it. The surface region may consist of only the first layer of atoms or perhaps the first few
layers of atoms. If there is an oxide present it may be consid-

54

ered part of the surface region. Just beneath the surface region there is usually a region of space charge which may vary in thickness from less than 100 Å to half the width of the crystal. The energy level diagram for the region of space charge is very similar to that found for the volume. It can be represented by an almost empty conduction band and an almost filled valence band separated by a forbidden band of energies, i. e., the energy gap of the semiconductor. In contrast to the region of space charge, the energy level diagram of the surface region is almost wholly unknown.

The region of space charge arises from the trapping of excess charge in the surface region. If the net excess charge trapped in the surface region is positive, the electrostatic potential energy in the region of space charge will be lowered for electrons and raised for holes. Thus for an n-type semiconductor, electrons would accumulate in the space charge region and make the surface more conductive, while for a p-type semiconductor the positive charge in the surface region would repel holes. A depletion layer, a region which is less conductive than the volume, would be formed. Correspondingly, if the net excess charge in the surface region is negative, the electrostatic potential energy in the space charge region will be raised for electrons and lowered for holes. Holes will accumulate in the space charge region of a p-type semiconductor while electrons will be repelled in an n-type semiconductor. In semiconductors, where both hole and electron conduction are possible, the carrier type in the region of space charge may be either n or p. For example in germanium an n-type crystal may have a p-type region of space charge due to a large amount of negative charge trapped in the surface region. This type of space charge region is called an inversion layer. If the net excess charge in the surface region is zero, there will be no region of space charge and the volume properties will extend right up to the surface region. Fig. 1 shows four possible states of an n-type semiconductor as the sign of the charge in the surface region changes from positive to negative:

(a) An n-type accumulation layer: an n-type space charge region on an n-type semiconductor;

(b) The flat band condition: zero excess charge in the

surface region and no region of space charge;
(c) A depletion layer: the negative charge in the surface region is compensated by fixed donor atoms in the
region of space charge;
(d) An inversion layer: a p-type region of space charge
on an n-type semiconductor.

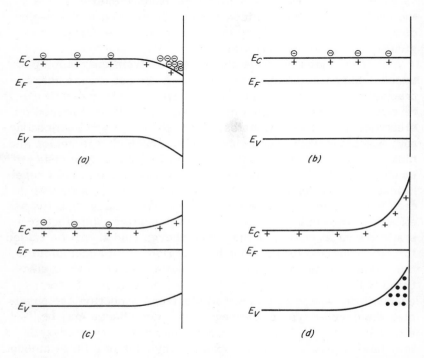

Fig. 1. Four possible states of an n-type semiconductor as the
        sign of the charge in the surface region changes from
        positive to negative: (a) an n-type accumulation layer,
        (b) the flat band condition, (c) a depletion layer, (d)
        an inversion layer. E_C and E_V represent the edge of
        the conduction band and valence band respectively. E_F
        represents the Fermi energy or chemical potential of
        electrons in the solid. + represents ionized donor
        atoms, $\ominus$ mobile electrons and $\oplus$ mobile holes.

E_c and E_v represent the edge of the conduction band and valence band respectively. E_F represents the Fermi energy or the chemical potential of electrons in the solid. A measurement of the conductivity of the region of space charge would show a large value for the n-type accumulation layer shown in Fig. 1 (a). In Figs. 1 (b) and 1 (c) the conductivity is reduced as the electrons leave the region of space charge. A minimum would be reached when the surface is in a state shown in Fig. 1(c). Here all the negative charge in the surface region is compensated for by the fixed charge of ionized donor atoms. In Fig. 1 (d), the conductivity is large again due to the presence of the holes.

A great part of semiconductor surface research today is concerned with the characterization of the properties of the region of space charge; thus the properties of the surface region may be deduced via the relations which connect them. The most important of these relations is that of electrical neutrality: the charge in the region of space charge must be equal and opposite to the charge in the surface region. The remainder of the paper will review some aspects of what is known about the electrical properties of various semiconductor surfaces and will point out some of the unsolved problems in the field.

2. THE CLEANED GERMANIUM SURFACE

It has been shown by Farnsworth (1) that a clean germanium surface could be produced and maintained in ultra high vacuum. He cleaned his surfaces by means of ion sputtering and then annealing at about 600° C. The surfaces investigated by means of low energy electron diffraction methods, to a very good first approximation, show the diffraction maxima expected from the germanium surface lattice. In silicon this ion sputtering technique, and another which requires only heating to just below the melting point, have been shown to produce clean surfaces (2). The work function and photoelectric threshold of cleaned germanium surface have been measured by Dillon and Farnsworth (3). They found that the two quantities are approximately equal. While normal for a metal, this equality does not hold for a semiconductor such as germanium, with its surface in the condition shown in Fig. 1(b). The photoelectric threshold is the difference in energy between the first occupied states and the vacuum level. In a semiconductor such as shown in Fig. 1(b) the first occupied level of any consequence is the valence band. The work function is defined as the difference between the Fermi level and the vacuum level. Thus for a semi-conductor in the flat band condition the difference between the photoelectric threshold and the work function should be $E_F - E_V$. For germanium this would be of the order of 0.3 ev; however the experimental result was almost zero. To explain this re-sult it must be assumed that either the valence band edge has been raised at the surface so that it is coincident with the Fermi level or the conduction band has been lowered so that it is coin-cident with the Fermi level. In the first case a p-type region of space charge would occur while in the second an n-type re-gion of space charge would occur. The problem was resolved by the data of field induced surface conductivity measurements (4) of the cleaned germanium surface. These measurements showed that the dominant carriers in the region of space charge are holes. Therefore the valence band, rather than the con-duction band, is degenerate near the surface. Measurements of the conductivity and Hall coefficient (5) of these holes show-ed that their number was large and that the valence band had to be close to degenerate at the surface to accommodate them. Thus two different types of experiments, the photoelectric threshold experiment where an electron is ejected through the surface region, and the surface conductivity experiments where the transport properties of electrons moving parallel to the surface are measured, give a similar picture of the germanium surface. The surface conductivity data indicate that there are approximately 10^{12} holes per cm^2 in the region of space charge. Since the surface is electrically neutral there must be an equal number of electrons in the surface region. It is assumed that these electrons are in localized surface states with energies in the forbidden band. The exact nature of these states is unknown at present; but a band model which correlates some of the ex-perimental data will be presented in Section 6. From an atomic viewpoint, it can be shown that these acceptor-like surface states are probably associated with the unfilled orbitals of the germanium surface atoms. Fig. 2 shows a line of atoms on a (111) germanium surface. The distance between surface neighbors is 1.63 times the distance to nearest neighbors. Therefore to a first approximation the surface atoms can be considered as atoms at the end of a large molecule. They have three covalent bonds to the crystal below it and one free orbital above the surface plane. The free orbital has one electron in it and may accept a second from the bulk. In accepting an electron from the bulk the surface atom achieves a stable octet of eight electrons and becomes negatively charged. A hole is generated nearby and is free to move, as is observed experimentally.

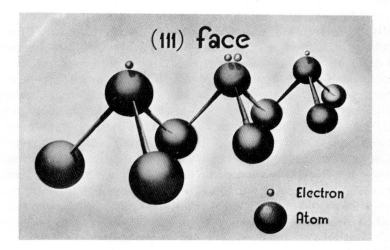

Fig. 2. Surface atoms on a (111) face of germanium.

3. THE EFFECT OF GASES ON SEMICONDUCTOR SURFACES

The effect of gases on the oxide-covered germanium surface has been extensively studied over the past few years. The oxide-covered surface is usually produced by means of an aqueous etch. It is not stable in air, but changes rapidly during the first day and somewhat more slowly thereafter. Its structure and chemical composition are unknown and its thickness may vary from a few angstroms to as many as a hundred.

Also, its properties are somewhat different from an atomically
clean surface which has been exposed to pure oxygen. None-
theless these results have added greatly to our understanding of
surfaces. For example it has been shown that by the addition
of water vapor, or other electron donor-type molecules to the
surface, the region of space charge can be made more n-type,
while the addition of oxygen or other electron acceptor type
molecules to the surface can make the region of space charge
more p-type. Using these techniques Bardeen and Brattain (6)
showed clearly the existence of the space charge region. Since
that time the various properties of the space charge region
which may be derived from a solution of a classical one-dimensional Poisson's equation have been substantiated experimentally (7). From these experiments, the surface region of the
etched germanium surface has been shown to exhibit a number
of discrete surface states in the vicinity of the energy gap. The
states have densities of the order of 10^{11} per cm^2. Some are
effective recombination centers while others are not. Capture
cross sections for some of them are estimated to be as high as
10^{-14} cm^2 (8). The states are in fast equilibrium with the region of space charge, their relaxation times being the order
of microseconds or less at room temperatures. At the present
time no particular structure or defect has been associated with
them, but they are assumed to lie at or very near the semiconductor oxide layer interface. Similar states are found on an
etched silicon surface (9).

There is a second group of states observed on etched
germanium and silicon surfaces which are differentiated from
the fast states mentioned in the preceding paragraph: these are
the slow states. Their densities are much larger and their relaxation times are of the order of seconds to hours. Their origin is not clear. One hypothesis suggests that they are associated with adsorbed gases, while another suggests that they are
intrinsic to the oxide. If a thick oxide layer is grown on the
surface of silicon or germanium, the relaxation effects associated with the slow states seem to disappear, indicating that
either the relaxation times of the states have increased by orders of magnitude, or that they have been removed (10). The
addition of water vapor will reduce the relaxation times of

thick oxide layers somewhat but will not return them to the values observed for the etched surface. In addition to the methods mentioned above, a region of space charge may be induced in compound semiconductors, such as zinc oxide, by departures from stoichiometry in the surface region. Thomas and Lander (11) have shown that adsorbed zinc atoms act as donors at the surface, giving up electrons to the crystal to form an n-type region of space charge. Introduction of oxygen to the surface removes the n-type region of space charge and may be made to induce a depletion layer. Heiland (12) has shown that atomic hydrogen will produce an n-type region of space charge on zinc oxide which may be removed by the introduction of oxygen. Thus we see that the state of a zinc oxide surface depends strongly on the partial pressures of the gases above it. Collins and Thomas (13) have shown that an n-type space charge region may be introduced in zinc oxide by the illumination with light of energies equal to the fundamental optical adsorption edge. In this process either neutral oxygen atoms are formed at the surface or oxygen is desorbed.

4. THE MOBILITY OF CHARGE CARRIERS IN THE REGION OF SPACE CHARGE

Electrons and holes moving in the region of space charge are constrained to move in a narrow potential well. A characteristic of these potential wells is that they become narrower in width as they become deeper in energy. Thus with increasing depth, the carriers will have a greater probability of colliding with the surface. If the mechanism of collision with the surface is to scatter the charge carriers non-specularly, then the mobility will be reduced below the value it has in the volume. The theory of this effect has been worked out by Schrieffer (14) and has been experimentally verified for shallow potential wells by Zemel and Petritz (15). For very deep wells, most of the carriers are moving in a channel which is less than 100 Å wide. In this case the assumption that the region of space charge has an energy level diagram similar to the bulk is no longer valid. Problems arising from narrow regions of space charge will be discussed in the next section.

5. NARROW REGIONS OF SPACE CHARGE

For small deviations from the flat band condition of
Fig. 1(b) the charge carriers in the valence or conduction band
can be considered as free. The normal volume density of
states at the edge of the bands is assumed to be valid throughout the region of space charge. In this case the number of
carriers in the region of space charge may be simply related
to the depth of the well. Since the carriers are distributed according to Maxwell-Boltzmann statistics, most of them are in
states which are within 2 or 3 kT of the bottom of the well. The
width of the well at these energies determines not only how
much the mobility of the carriers will be reduced, but also
whether the carriers can be considered as free. A simple electron in a box type of calculation shows that quantum effects
will begin to be important when the width of the well is less
than 100 Å. At this width the electrons and holes can no longer
be considered as free. The distribution of states at the band
edge must change and a new relationship between their number
and the depth of the well must be derived. However the derivation of the new density of states is very difficult because it is
doubtful whether a one-dimensional Poisson's equation can be
used. These problems may be understood by examining the
properties of the cleaned germanium surface.

As mentioned in Section 2 the cleaned germanium surface is degenerate. The space charge potential well is 0.3 ev
deep and is estimated to have a width of about 50 Å. The transport data indicate that there are of the order of 10^{12} holes per
cm^2 in the region of space charge and 10^{12} electrons per cm^2
in the surface region. Thus both the holes and the electrons
are spaced 100 Å apart parallel to the surface and are separated by a distance of only 50 Å. The potential well in which the
holes move is no longer one-dimensional, but three-dimensional and hemispherical. The density of states and mobility of
carriers moving in such a potential well have not been treated.

One other problem which arises in dealing with deep
space charge region is the part played by the barrier in limiting the recombination of minority carriers at the surface. In
the papers of Bardeen and Brattain (6), Stevenson and Keyes (16),

Many (17), and Wang and Wallis (18), it is explicitly assumed
that in adapting the Shockley-Read model (19) of recombination
via traps to the surface the volume and surface portions of the
conduction bands are in good thermodynamic equilibrium.
Garrett (20) has shown, however, that in the case where the
region of space charge is much wider than the mean free path
of the carriers, the barrier may become the limiting factor.
The barrier for electrons on a cleaned germanium surface is
0. 3 ev; according to the criterion of Garrett it may become rate
limiting. The data of Law and Garrett (21) on the surface recombination velocity of a cleaned germanium surface seems to
support this view. They find that the surface recombination
velocity is low as long as the barrier is of the order of 0. 3 ev.
As soon as the barrier begins to fall below this value the surface recombination velocity begins to increase quite rapidly.
Their results indicate that the Shockley-Read model of recombination may not be correct when large space charge barriers
are present.

6. SURFACE STATES

The existence of localized states at the surface of a one-
dimensional lattice was first shown by Tamm in 1932 and by
Shockley in 1939 (22). These states have wave functions with
maxima at the surface and are damped exponentially into and
out of the lattice. They have energies in the forbidden band
and their number is equal to the number of surface atoms.
Recently Koutecky (23) has shown that localized subsurface states may also occur if the perturbing potential due to the
existence of the surface is large enough. These states would
have wave functions localized about subsurface atoms and their
energy in the forbidden zone would be between the surface states
and the band out of which the states had been perturbed. These
treatments have all assumed that the potential depends only on
the direction into the crystal: a one-dimensional potential. The
discussion above of the cleaned germanium surface has shown
that a three-dimensional potential may be necessary. A second
failing of these treatments is their lack of consistency: the
effect on the potential of the filling of the surface states with

electrons must be taken into account. However much more experimental work will be needed before a self-consistent calculation can be undertaken.

Recently a model of the cleaned germanium surface, derived from the experimental data, has been presented by the author (24). In qualitative terms it can be described as follows. The germanium atom in the solid has 8 electron states which are split up into 4 bonding and 4 antibonding states. The 4 bonding states are used in the valence band to form the tetrahedral bonds and the antibonding states are used to make up the conduction band. A germanium atom at the surface does not have 4 bonds to the crystal. It has 3 bonds at best. One or more orbitals or dangling bonds are thus left free at the surface. The free orbital has room for a second electron in a state which normally would have been in the conduction band. However it is experimentally observed that this state takes an electron from the valence band, which indicates that these states have an energy coincident with or less than the valence band edge. From the energy band picture of solids one describes the germanium surface as follows: it is assumed that due to the presence of the surface, states are perturbed out of the conduction band into a surface band many electron volts wide. This surface band overlaps in energy both the conduction band and the valence band. Since some of these states lie below the edge of the valence band, the number of states at the surface will exceed the number of electrons in the surface region and a large number of holes will be formed in the valence band. Fig. 3 shows a schematic energy level diagram of the clean germanium surface. E_0 represents the bottom of the surface band.

Since these surface states are spread out in a very wide band, it is only possible to determine the density of states per electron volt in the vicinity of the Fermi energy. It is no longer experimentally possible to determine the total number. One criterion which has always been applied in the past is that in order for the observed states to be true surface states their number must be equal to the number of surface atoms. If the present model is correct this criterion may never be proved.

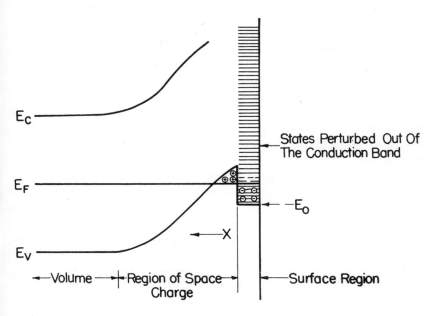

Fig. 3. A schematic representation of the energy level diagram of the cleaned germanium surface.

7. THE SURFACE REGION

The brief review of surface research in the first portion of this paper shows that our knowledge of the properties of the region of space charge has increased considerably. However our knowledge of the surface region is still poor. The crux of the problem is that it has not been possible in general to investigate this region directly. Our information has come from indirect measurements of the properties of the region of space charge or from the gas above the solid surface. The state of the surface region can only be inferred from such measurements. For example there are many states in which the surface region can exist which will give rise to identical regions of space charge. The advantage of semiconductor surface studies is that the data resulting from the region of space charge may be correlated with the data of the gas phase to de-

lineate the actual state of the surface region. Experimental
techniques are now needed which are capable of measuring the
properties of atoms in the surface region. One such method,
the infrared adsorption of chemisorbed molecules, has recently been developed by Eischens (25) and promises to yield new
insight into our understanding of the surface region. Other
methods capable of giving information about the surface atoms
themselves are the application of electron paramagnetic resonance and nuclear magnetic and quadrupole resonances. Unfortunately there are great difficulties in applying these techniques to the measurement of the properties of surface atoms.
In the case of electron paramagnetic resonance, a system must
be found which has not only a large density of unpaired electrons
at the surface, but also a suitable relaxation time. In the nuclear magnetic and quadrupole resonance techniques, the relaxation problems are not as great, but the sensitivity is poorer.
While the electron paramagnetic resonance technique is capable
of sensing 10^{11} unpaired electron spins for a line width of one
gauss, the nuclear techniques would require 10^{18} or more surface nuclei. Very fine powders would be required: they would
have to be produced from single crystals so that each grain
could be considered a single crystal. The nuclear quadrupole
resonance technique can give the value of the electric field
gradient about the surface nuclei and therefore something about
the electron density directly at the surface. The methods mentioned here hold great promise for surface physics and it is
hoped that we will see increased activity in these fields during
the next few years.

Acknowledgment

This work was supported by the U. S. Office of Naval
Research.

References

1. R. E. Schlier and H. E. Farnsworth, J. Appl. Phys., 30,
917 (1959); H. E. Farnsworth, R. E. Schlier, T. H. George
and R. M. Burger, ibid., 29, 1150 (1958).

2. F. G. Allen, J. Eisinger, H. D. Hagstrum and J. T. Law, to be published.
3. J. Dillon and H. E. Farnsworth, J. Appl. Phys., 28, 174 (1957).
4. P. Handler, in R. H. Kingston, ed., Semiconductor Surface Physics, p. 120, University of Pennsylvania Press, 1957.
5. R. Missman and P. Handler, J. Phys. Chem. Solids, 8, 109 (1959).
6. J. Bardeen and W. H. Brattain, Bell System Tech. J., 32, 1 (1953).
7. For a review of this subject see:
   C. G. B. Garrett and W. H. Brattain, Phys. Rev., 99, 376 (1955); R. H. Kingston, J. Appl. Phys., 27, 101 (1956); R. H. Kingston, ed., Semiconductor Surface Physics, University of Pennsylvania Press, 1957.
8. G. Rupprecht, Phys. Rev., 111, 75 (1958).
9. H. Statz, G. deMars, L. Davis, Jr. and A. Adams, Phys. Rev., 106, 455 (1957).
10. M. Lasser, C. Wysocki and B. Bernstein, Phys. Rev., 105, 491 (1957).
11. D. G. Thomas and J. J. Lander, J. Phys. Chem. Solids, 2, 318 (1957).
12. G. Heiland, Z. Physik, 148, 15 (1957); 148, 28 (1957).
13. R. J. Collins and D. G. Thomas, Phys. Rev., 112, 388 (1958).
14. J. R. Schrieffer, Phys. Rev., 97, 641 (1955).
15. J. Zemel and R. Petritz, Phys. Rev., 110, 1263 (1958).
16. D. T. Stevenson and R. J. Keyes, Physica, 20, 1041 (1955).
17. A. Many and D. Gerlich, Phys. Rev., 107, 404 (1957).
18. S. Wang and G. Wallis, J. Appl. Phys., 30, 285 (1959).
19. W. Shockley and W. T. Read, Phys. Rev., 87, 835 (1952).
20. W. H. Brattain and C. G. B. Garrett, Bell System Tech. J. 35, 1019 (1955).
21. J. T. Law and C. G. B. Garrett, J. Appl. Phys., 27, 656 (1956).
22. See discussion by F. Seitz, Modern Theory of Solids, p. 320, McGraw-Hill Book Co., 1940.
23. J. Koutecky, Phys. Rev., 108, 13 (1957).
24. P. Handler and W. Portnoy, to be published.
25. R. P. Eischens, J. Chem. Educ., 35, 385 (1958).

DISCUSSION

N. CABRERA (University of Virginia): You have discussed a model only for {111} surfaces. Have you tried to use a similar model on other surfaces; is there much difference?

P. HANDLER: I have discussed the model for {111} surfaces because it is the simplest. The model is qualitative. I believe that eventually I will be able to show that there is quite a difference between various surfaces.

S. L. MATLOW (Hoffman Electronics): You mentioned eight atomic orbitals, 4 anti-bonding and 4 bonding. Strictly speaking atomic orbitals are not considered as bonding or anti-bonding; only molecular orbitals resulting from the interaction of atomic orbitals are so designated. Now assuming that the valence band is composed of sigma molecular orbitals, what is the justification for assuming that the conduction band is made up of anti-bonding sigma orbitals rather than pi orbitals resulting from the overlap of the d orbitals? There are reasons for believing that the latter is the case.

P. HANDLER: The only point I want to get across is that states in the conduction band or higher energies are brought down so that their energy is coincident with the valence band states. I will be interested in seeing your reasons for believing that the d orbitals are important.

II

IMPERFECTIONS
AND
SURFACE BEHAVIOR

N. CABRERA
University of Virginia

On the Role of Dislocations
in the Reactivity of Solids

ABSTRACT

THE FORMATION OF dislocation etch pits and in particular the nucleation of steps at dislocations and the motion of steps are briefly discussed. The role of dislocations in oxidation processes is summarized.

1. INTRODUCTION

The heterogeneous nature of the reactivity of crystal surfaces has been known for a very long time. It is only recently, however, that the existence of an interrelation between these heterogeneities and the dislocations in the crystal was suggested by Shockley and Read (1), particularly in the case of etch pits. There is no doubt that this suggestion is correct, but the detailed understanding of the kinetics involved, leading to a prediction of the optimum conditions required for experimental observations, are still matters of controversy. In fact, the present discussion was organized in the hope of clarifying some of the underlying principles.

There is one point on which there seems to be general agreement: The process of formation of an etch pit consists of

71

two parts: (a) nucleation of monomolecular steps at the dislocation (source); (b) motion of the steps away from the source. These two parts are not really independent of each other; the presence of diffusion fields makes the treatment of this dependence a rather complicated problem which has not as yet been satisfactorily solved.

In accordance with this point of view, some comments will be made on the nucleation of steps at dislocations, the motion of steps, and the application of the same ideas to the process of oxidation.

2. NUCLEATION OF STEPS

There is ample evidence that the initiation of an etch pit is a nucleation process. Indeed pitting occurs only under sufficiently high undersaturations and is very sensitive to small changes of this variable. This behavior would be difficult to understand if a nucleation process were not involved.

A phenomenological treatment of this nucleation process was developed several years ago by N. Cabrera and M. Levine (2, 3). According to this treatment the activation energy for nucleation at a dislocation ΔF_d is smaller than that on a perfect surface because of the extra energy localized around the dislocation. This difference is only significant at high undersaturations, at which ΔF_d decreases and becomes ultimately zero.

A quantitative theory can only be developed if one assumes an expression for the extra energy around the dislocation. There is one case for which such an expression can be written with sufficient certainty; namely, the case of a "fresh" dislocation free of impurities in its core. Then the extra energy per unit length $w(r)$ contained in a cylinder of radius r around the dislocation is

$$w(r) = \frac{\tau b^2}{2\pi} \ln (r/r_0) = \frac{\tau b^2}{2\pi} \ln (r/a) + w_c \qquad (1)$$

In this expression τ is some combination of elastic constants ($\sim 10^{11}$ erg/cm^3), b the magnitude of the Burger's vector of the dislocation, a the nearest neighbor distance in the crystal and

r_0 a length ($\sim 10^{-8}$ cm) chosen so that w_c represents the core energy (non-elastic energy) of the dislocation. Huntington, Dickey, and Thomson (4) have shown that Eq. (1) represents very satisfactorily their atomic calculations in the case of an edge dislocation in a NaCl crystal, with a Burger's vector $b = \sqrt{2}a$ <110> and lying in a (110) plane. Then $\tau b^2/2\pi = 2.9 \times 10^{-5}$ erg/cm, and $r_0 = 1.31$ Å compared to $a = 2.81$Å; also $w_c = 2.2 \times 10^{-5}$ erg/cm.

Assuming Eq. (1), it is then a simple matter to show that there is indeed a critical undersaturation beyond which no nucleation barrier exists at the dislocation. Considering in particular a crystal in contact with a dilute solution, with a saturation concentration c_e, this critical undersaturation c_0/c_e is determined by

$$kT \ln (c_e/c_0) = \pi^2 \gamma^2 \Omega /\tau b^2 \tag{2}$$

where γ is the surface energy of the edge of the step and Ω the molecular volume. In the etching experiments of Gilman, Johnston, and Sears (5) and others (6, 7) with LiF crystals in aqueous solutions, it was found experimentally that $c_e/c_0 = 5$ at room temperature. If the same value is assumed to occur for NaCl, Eq. (2) gives the value $\gamma = 170$ erg/cm^2 for the surface energy of NaCl. Furthermore, the radius of the critical nucleus corresponding to Eq. (2) is found to be

$$\rho = \tau b^2 /2\pi^2 \gamma \tag{3}$$

which in our case $\rho = 2.0a$, and implies that according to Eq. (1) the extra energy involved in the nucleation process appears to be approximately half elastic and half core energy.

The foregoing appears to be as satisfactory as can be expected from a phenomenological theory, and seems to indicate that more etching experiments with ionic crystals in aqueous solutions (or other media for which the thermodynamic data are known) should be made in order to see whether or not the correlation between critical undersaturation for etching and surface energy is confirmed. In spite of its success, this simple approach has been criticized to a surprising extent (see for

instance Gilman's paper in this volume). The criticism is
based on the fact that strain energy appears to play a fundamental role. This is misleading, however, because the use of
Eq. (1) does not imply that only the strain (elastic) energy is
being taken into account, as emphasized above. Nevertheless,
Eq. (1) will not be justified if the value ρ given by Eq. (3) turns
out to be smaller than a, or at any rate, smaller than r_0. This
appears to be the case in metals when γ is so large that "fresh"
dislocations cannot be etched unless the medium is capable of
reducing γ substantially.

   Another criticism of the use of Eq. (1) is the fact that
the equation refers to the interior of the crystal and not to the
surface layers, where the elastic strain energy decreases and
even becomes zero for the particular case of a pure screw dislocation normal to the surface. The statement is certainly correct, but the criticism is clearly irrelevant to the problem in
hand. Indeed, all that the theory assumes is that during the
time a two-dimensional nucleus of critical size ρ is created in
the surface layer, the crystal around this nucleus relaxes and
recreates the surface configuration one molecular layer down-
ward. Accepting this, it is clear that the total change in strain
energy of the crystal is exactly a w (ρ), where a is the height
of the molecular layer. This assumption is indeed correct since
the relaxation occurs in a time interval a/c (c being the velocity
of sound) which is very small compared to the time required for
the nucleation of the two-dimensional nucleus.

3. MOTION OF STEPS

   The argument of the preceding paragraph applies only to
the initiation of the pit when the undersaturation at the dislocation is the observed one. As soon as a step is created, it moves
away by dissolving material into the solution, consequently reducing the undersaturation at the dislocation itself and making
the nucleation of the next step more difficult.

   This "back stress" effect has not been considered
theoretically in any detail although it is clearly the reason why
steps must be poisoned in order to observe etch pits, as has
been pointed out in the work of Gilman, Johnston, and Sears (5).

The argument can perhaps be put forward in the following way:
    A step of radius r centered on the dislocation maintains
in its neighborhood a concentration c(r) determined by the curvature of the step. Under steady state conditions the concentration in the solution decreases in all directions approaching
the value c maintained at a macroscopic distance from the
crystal surface. It follows then that the concentration at the
dislocation c(0) must obey the condition c(r) > c(0) > c. In
fact, a brief calculation shows that the relation among these
three quantities is

$$\frac{c(0) - c}{c(r) - c} = \frac{\pi}{\ln(r/a)} < 1 \tag{4}$$

provided r is sufficiently larger than the height a of a step (say
r > 40 a).
    Consider first the case of clean steps. The curvature
of the step is then entirely determined by its macroscopic radius r. Consequently, c(r) increases continuously with r reaching rather rapidly the saturation concentration c_e. If it is now
assumed that for a new step to be nucleated $c(0)/c_e$ has to be
equal to the critical value c_0/c_e given by Eq. (2), it is clear
that r/a has to become macroscopically large whatever the
value given to c; in other words, the first step has to make
room for the following one to be nucleated. In particular, if
c_0/c_e = 0. 20 as appears to be the case for LiF in water solutions considered above, one deduces from Eq. (4) that r/a =
10^6 even for c = 0. Needless to say, such a large value of r/a
corresponds to an extremely flat crystal surface and no visible
pit.
    Let us now turn to the case where the steps are locally
poisoned in the presence of low concentration of adsorbable impurities in such a way that between the adsorbed impurities the
step becomes festooned and is consequently able to carry along
the adsorbed impurities during the course of its motion. Then
a step of macroscopic radius r will have a much smaller local
radius of curvature, in fact, it will be of the order of the average distance between adsorbed impurities along the step. Thus
it follows that c(r) will remain small and the "back stress"

effect will be practically eliminated.

This point of view regarding the role of adsorbed impurities at the steps follows closely the idea first suggested by Price, Webb, and Vermilyea (8) to explain the growth of whiskers. The production of a high local curvature is believed to be the important point rather than the fact that the impurities will be adsorbed preferably at the kink sites; in fact, this will clearly not reduce the number of kink sites because new ones will be produced.

It has also been proposed (6, 7) that the impurities might be very effective in reducing the nucleation rate by decreasing the surface energy γ. This might be so in some cases, but certainly the same kind of impurity cannot do both things; decrease the nucleation rate and retard the motion of steps. Indeed, in order to be effective in a nucleation process, the impurities have to be extremely mobile so that they can be adsorbed during the time the critical nucleus is being formed; on the other hand, this high mobility would destroy their ability to produce a high local curvature in a moving step required for the argument developed above.

4. OXIDATION

The process of oxidation of metals will now be considered very briefly. The same heterogeneity observed in the chemical reactivity of crystals in liquid media appears to occur also when a solid film is produced during the reaction. In the particular case of oxidation, and on top of a thin more or less uniform oxide film, a structure of nuclei of oxide appears, indicating a pronounced difference of reactivity between different points on the crystal surface. The author suggested several years ago (3) that the oxide nuclei might be connected with the dislocations in the metal. This suggestion has been proved wrong by the work of F. W. Young (9) and Coleman and Laukonis (10). Young has shown that boundaries resulting from polygonization in Cu do not form rows of oxide nuclei when the oxidation is carried out unless the dislocations contain impurities (namely Te) in their core. On the other hand, he observed a high concentration of random oxide nuclei independently of the polygonization boundaries. Similarly Coleman and Laukonis observed a high density of oxide nuclei during the oxidation of large iron whiskers which clearly did not contain that many dislocations.

It is quite clear, of course, that the dislocations in the metal and those much more numerous in the oxide crystals composing the oxide layer   play a role in the growth of the oxide, but because of the "back stress" effect mentioned earlier, they should produce a very nearly uniform film. The formation of these oxide nuclei remains, therefore, unexplained. It might be that they correspond simply to those oxide crystals with a high degree of perfection, able to grow further when many other more imperfect crystals cannot. Alternatively the nuclei formation might be connected with an instability of the uniform oxide film due to a buildup of high stresses in these films.

Acknowledgment

This work was supported by the U. S. Office of Naval Research.

References

1. W. T. Read and W. Shockley, Phys. Rev. , 78, 275 (1950).
2. N. Cabrera and M. M. Levine, Phil. Mag. , 1, 450 (1956).
3. N. Cabrera, in R. H. Kingston, ed. , Semiconductor Surface Physics, p. 327, Univ. of Pennsylvania Press, 1957.
4. H. B. Huntington, J. E. Dickey, and R. Thomson, Phys. Rev. , 100, 1117 (1955).
5. J. J. Gilman, W. G. Johnston, and G. W. Sears, J. Appl. Phys. , 29, 747 (1958).
6. G. W. Sears, to be published.
7. M. B. Ives and J. P. Hirth, to be published.
8. P. B. Price, D. A. Vermilyea, and M. B. Webb, Acta Met. , 6, 524 (1958).
9. F. W. Young, J. Appl. Phys. , 29, 760 (1958).
10. R. V. Coleman and J. V. Laukonis, J. Appl. Phys., 30, 1364 (1959).

DISCUSSION

P. H. KECK (Sylvania): What variation could one expect in the thickness of an oxide layer formed on germanium or silicon by thermal oxidation?

N. CABRERA: For metals, at least, there is no standard variation. Soon after oxidation has started the thickness of the nuclei may be in the neighborhood of twice that of the underlying film; however, further oxidation can increase this variation. In the case of oxide whisker or platelet growth, the variation can be quite large.

J. W. FAUST, JR. (Westinghouse): With the exception of whisker and platelet growth which I have not observed on germanium, the statement made by Prof. Cabrera is true for germanium. Concerning the question of whether oxide nuclei form at dislocations, we studied the oxidation of germanium by nitric acid and by oxygen at both high and very low partial pressures. Germanium has the advantage in that one can observe dislocations and oxide particles at the same time. Initial studies showed that oxidation by these methods attacked the same planes, namely $\{111\}$. For both types of oxidation, we found many more oxide particles than dislocations, and furthermore that very few oxide particles were at dislocation sites. This is illustrated in Fig. 1; the oxidation was carried out at a pressure of approximately 10^{-3} mm and at 900°C, at this temperature the oxide is volatile thus a pit is formed. Fig. 2 shows oxidation at a similar pressure on $\{111\}$ material; although there are fewer oxidation pits in this picture, they are not found at dislocation sites. Oxidation in concentrated nitric acid had the advantage that the oxide layer left by the CP4 etch that was used to remove the damaged layer could be removed by HF. Many more oxide particles were formed on surfaces that did not have this oxide layer removed prior to oxidation. Thus we can say, at least for germanium, that the dislocations do not act as preferential sites for the nucleation of oxidation.

H. C. GATOS (M. I. T.): In connection with the role of impurities in maintaining undersaturation at a source, some recent work that we have performed may be of interest. For indium antimonide, and other III-V intermetallic compounds, a

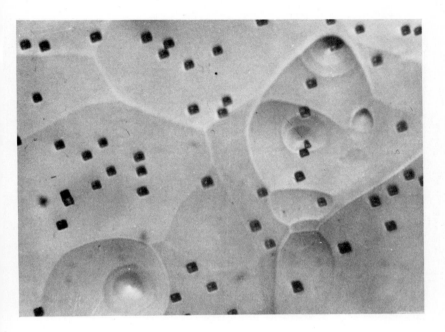

Fig. 1.   Dislocation sites and sites of oxide nucleation on a {100}
          surface of germanium.   Etched in CP4 and oxidized in
          poor vacuum.

number of etchants produce pits at dislocations on only the
{111} surfaces that terminate with group III atoms.   We have
found that by doping the InSb with group IV elements which may
concentrate at dislocations, pits can be produced on the other
{111} surfaces also.   [J. Appl. Phys. 31, 743 (1960)].   Furthermore, by adding to the etchants surface active agents, such as
stearic acid which can presumably adsorb and act as an impurity,
pits can be produced at dislocations on any {111} surface.

        J. J. GILMAN (General Electric): Prof. Davis and one
of his students at Harvard has recently shown that during rapid
cooling from high temperatures, vacancy clusters precipitate
at the surfaces of metals.   Could such vacancy clusters be the
nucleation centers for oxidation?

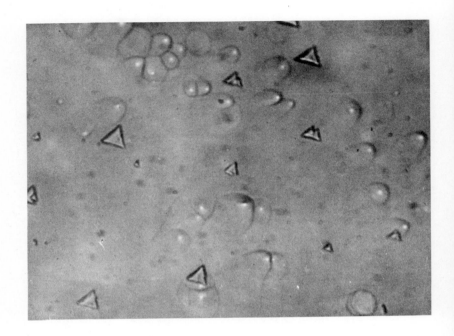

Fig. 2. Dislocation sites and sites of oxide nucleation on a
{111} surface of germanium. Etched in CP4 and
oxidized in poor vacuum.

N. CABRERA: Vacancy clusters could conceivably be
nucleation sites for oxidation; however, the number of such
clusters at the surface must be very high, in the order of 10^{10}
per cm^2, to account for the observed nuclei density. Furthermore, at the high temperatures of oxidation that I have been
discussing, one could question the existence of vacancy clusters
at the surface.
　　　　P. B. SEWELL (National Research Council of Canada):
We have some information on the oxidation of iron which supports
some of the ideas on oxidation presented by Professor Cabrera.
Reflection electron diffraction photographs were made on (100)
surfaces of single crystal iron that had a thin oxide layer. The
mean thickness of these oxide layers, as measured by electro-

chemical methods, was 25Å. Examination of the diffraction patterns and the spots of the pattern show that the layer: (a) is very highly oriented, (b) is composed of particles approximately 20 to 25Å in diameter, and (c) has a fairly smooth surface. These observations would suggest that the initial oxidation process is not associated with dislocations in the iron.

N. CABRERA: I certainly agree with you. Initially a thin oxide layer is formed at the natural surface. After this, however, nuclei of larger size begin to form at various sites.

L. E. SAMUELS
Defense Standards
Laboratories

Damaged Surface Layers:

Metals

ABSTRACT

TWO SEPARATE ALTERED or damaged layers classically have been recognized on metal surfaces formed by cutting- or polishing-type processes; namely, an amorphous-like "Beilby" layer and a plastically deformed layer. Modern work indicates that the Beilby layer is not, in fact, formed by the common important methods of surface preparation but that a deformed layer always is. The detailed structure of this layer is reviewed. Some consideration is also given to residual elastic stresses, surface topography, and embedded abrasive.

1. INTRODUCTION

In many laboratory experiments, and in many more industrial applications, the metal surface to be dealt with is a "technical" surface that has been formed by some mechanical process. It is recognized that such a surface inevitably is both chemically contaminated and physically altered, or "damaged. " The purpose of the present paper is to review existing knowledge on the nature of the physically altered layer.

The subject is complicated by the very wide diversity of processes that may conceivably be used for surface preparation. Attention will be confined here to processes in which the new surface is machined by cutting, particularly by operations such as grinding and abrading which involve the use of abrasives, or is polished by methods in which the surface is worked against a fine abrasive. It has been accepted in the past that the possibility of the presence of two physically distinct layers must be recognized on surfaces produced by these processes; namely, an outer layer known as the "Beilby Layer" and a layer of material which differs from the unaffected substrate only in that it has been plastically deformed. It will be necessary to consider these two layers separately.

2. THE BEILBY LAYER

The existence of this layer was originally proposed by Beilby (1) as an integral part of his theory that polishing occurs by surface flow; until recently, a considerable weight of expert opinion (2, 3, 4) supported his hypothesis, even though it has always been a subject of dispute. The Beilby layer is taken to be a smear, about 50Å thick on metallographically polished surfaces (5, 6), which covers the surface and which fills minor depressions; the material of the layer is thought to have lost its obvious crystalline properties and in this sense to be "amorphous-like. " Because there is some confusion on the point, it is worth noting that, even in this view, the formation of the Beilby layer is regarded as being a special characteristic of polishing; it is not proposed that it forms during machining, grinding or abrading.

The existence of the Beilby layer has been reconsidered in a recent series of investigations (7-10) and it has been established with reasonable certainty that it is not formed during polishing by the standard metallographic and industrial methods which are under consideration here. The new view, the evidence for which has been reviewed fully elsewhere (11-13), will be accepted as the basis for the present discussion. It is not suggested that flow, particularly flow of the type proposed by Bowden and his colleagues (3,14), could not be a feature of other mechanical brightening methods. The burnishing processes investigated by Raether (15) are a case in point, but they will not be discussed further.

The new concept is that polishing occurs primarily by cutting and, in this respect, differs essentially only in degree from abrasion and machining. It is possible on this basis to discuss all the processes under consideration together. It must be recognized, however, that the difference in degree between polishing and abrasion is a very considerable one. Most abrasion and machining processes can simply be considered as being part of a progressive series, but some special consideration usually must be given to polishing.

3. SURFACE PLASTIC DEFORMATION

The most satisfactory general description of the plastically deformed layer has been obtained from the examination of metallographic taper sections of the surfaces concerned. Investigations of 70:30 brass surfaces (16,7,10) have been particularly informative because etching techniques are available to develop in the taper sections indications of prior plastic deformation that can be interpreted in some detail (17-21). The present description will be based on the metallographic approach, the more quantitative data obtained by x-ray and electron diffraction techniques being used to supplement it.

Two distinct zones can be recognized in the plastically deformed layer; namely, an outer fragmented layer of severer deformation, and a subcutaneous layer of general and more minor deformation.

3.1 The Outer Fragmented Layer

This layer invariably can be sharply distinguished from the substrate in a metallographic section. For example, it is seen in 70:30 brass as a dark-etching unresolvable layer (Fig. 1(a)); in α-iron, as a layer in which the substrate crystals appear to have fragmented into many sub-grains (Fig. 1(b)); in the pearlitic areas of steels, as a layer in which the carbide plates are distorted and even broken into fragments. Clearly, it is a

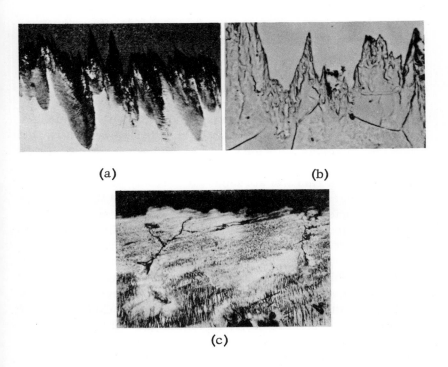

(a)   (b)

(c)

Fig. 1. Taper sections of abraded surfaces showing the outer fragmented layer. (a) Brass. The zone is dark-etching and unresolvable. Taper ratio: 7.7. X1000, before reduction for publication. (b) Iron. The zone appears to be broken up into many sub-grains. Taper ratio: 10. X1500, before reduction for publication. (c) Bronze. Shrinkage cavities exposed in the fragmented zone have completely collapsed, indicating the high order of compressive stresses in this region. Taper ratio: 11.6. X500, before reduction for publication.

layer which is highly distorted. The layer closely contours the surface topography, and usually extends beneath the root of a surface scratch for about the same depth as the depth of the scratch itself.

The structure at various levels in this fragmented layer has been investigated by both x-ray (22-26) and electron diffraction techniques (9, 10, 27-31). The structure varies so rapidly with depth, however, that adequately detailed information usually can be obtained only by the electron diffraction method.

Work using the latter technique (9, 10) indicates that, with the exception of fine metallographic polishes, the extreme outer layer is broken up into comparatively small but coherent fragments which are randomly oriented (Fig. 4(a)). A light metallographic etch exposes material which is still fragmented but much less severely misoriented (cf. Figs. 4(a) and 4(b)), and hence less severely deformed. The deformation texture in this region has been investigated in detail by Scott and Wilman (27), who examined a range of abraded and coarsely polished surfaces of magnesium and beryllium. They showed that a normal [001] fibre orientation is developed as a compression texture in the outermost regions, and an oblique [001] fibre orientation at greater depths, the fibre axis being inclined against the direction of cutting. This is followed by a zone of transition between the oblique fibre texture and the base structure. These conclusions are in general agreement with the earlier, but less precise, results of Lees (6) on copper and gold, Courtel (28, 29) on iron and an austenitic steel, Agarwala and Wilman (30) on iron, and Takahashi (31) on copper, silver and a number of copper alloys. It is not certain that the layer referred to in these investigations corresponds fully with the fragmented layer observed by metallographic methods, but it would appear that the results apply mostly to it.

The clear implication from these results is that the deformation of the outer layers during fine cutting operations employing abrasives is principally compressive in nature. Metallographic observations (10) indicate that some shear displacement parallel to the surface does also occur, but confirm that this tends to be a minor phenomenon compared with the

compressive one. * This conclusion is of considerable importance in assessing the type of damage to be expected in the surface. For example, it has been observed (32, 33) that abrasion
results in extensive plastic deformation in the surface layers
of ionic crystals, such as rock salt, calcite, and fluorite,
which are quite brittle by ordinary standards. King and Tabor
(32) have explained this by pointing out that Bridgman (34) has
established that such materials can deform in a highly ductile
manner if they are subjected to a superimposed hydrostatic
pressure. Although it has not been established that the compressive stresses developed during abrasion are of sufficient
magnitude to support fully this explanation, it is undoubtedly
true that a small volume of material is deformed under the
special conditions of constraint in all directions.

An indication that these compressive effects are of a
significant magnitude is obtained from a recent observation
(10) that internal cavities collapse completely when they are
exposed in the fragmented layer (Fig. 1(c)). Mulhearn (35) has
also measured compressive strains greater than 60% immediately beneath indentation hardness impressions, and they are
a static analogue.

A layer of somewhat similar metallographic characteristics to those already discussed is also present on polished
surfaces (cf. Figs. 1(a) and 3(a)) but its structure has not been
investigated in such detail. In this case, the layer can be very
much less severely fragmented, the degree of fragmentation
decreasing with increasing fineness of polish (8, 9). The surface misorientations are only about ± 5° (Fig. 4(c)) for the finest polish so far investigated (9), but the deformation texture
is still of the same general type as that found immediately beneath abraded surfaces. Light etching of such a surface exposes highly perfect material (Fig. 4(d)). An important corollary to the latter observation is that surfaces polished by means
of a fine abrasive suspended in a mild etching reagent (the so-
called "polish-attack" technique) may be similarly perfect.
Indeed, there is reason to believe that completely strain-free

*Plastic flow parallel to the surface may be more significant
in gross machining operations, such as turning or drilling.

surfaces can be prepared by this technique (7, 8).

3.2 The Subcutaneous Layer of Minor Deformation

This zone, characterized by the fact that it differs from the substrate only in being subjected to comparatively mild deformation of a simple type, constitutes the bulk of the deformed layer. It can be recognized metallographically only in those special cases where indications of prior plastic deformation can be developed by etching, or a similar technique.

In the outer regions (i. e., immediately beneath the fragmented layer), the plastic strains are very inhomogeneously distributed, being concentrated in rays extending beneath individual surface scratches (7, 10, 36). This is indicated in the taper section of an abraded brass surface shown in Fig. 2(a) by the areas containing the systems of parallel dark lines. The latter represent the traces of lamellar slip bands (18), an incidental feature of the deformation of brass from the known characteristics of which (18, 21) several qualitative deductions can be made. Firstly, the density of development of the slip bands indicates that the plastic strains in the rays are not particularly high; the boundary of the region containing the slip bands probably represents a strain contour of about 5% compression. Secondly, the slip bands are mostly aligned parallel* to the mean surface in those grains suitably oriented for the best etching effect; this may be a function of the compressive nature of the strains in this region.

Also visible in Fig. 2(a) are diffusely etched bands coincident with and extending beyond the rays containing the slip bands. This etching effect represents a type of kink band (20), i. e., an area at the edges of which the orientation changes abruptly. Similar kink bands have also been observed in abraded surfaces of zinc (37), and can be expected to be general.

The regions between these rays of slip bands, and a layer extending considerably beyond them, are also plastically deformed, although to a considerably lesser extent. This can

---

*In the original paper (7), these features were erroneously interpreted as being parallel to the mean surface.

(a)   (b)

Fig. 2. Taper sections of a brass surface abraded on 1/0-
grade emery paper. Taper ratio: 8.2. (a) Etched
in ferric chloride reagent and showing the inhomo-
geneous distribution of the deformation close to the
surface. X 1000, before reduction for publication. (b)
Etched to develop slip-line traces, showing the full
extent of the plastically deformed layer. X 250, before
reduction for publication. The fragmented layer,
which is more clearly shown in Fig. 1, is also discern-
able in these micrographs.

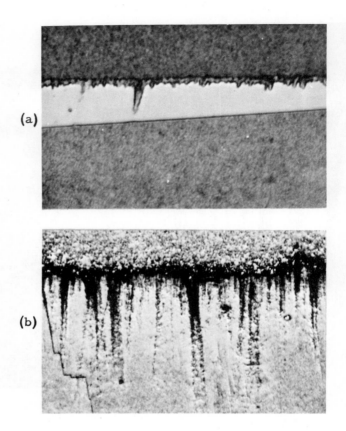

Fig. 3. Taper section of a metallographically polished brass
surface. Taper ratio: 10.9. X 2000, before reduction
for publication. (a) Etched in ferric chloride reagent
to show the fragmented layer (cf. with Figs.1(a)and 2(a)).
(b) Etched to develop slip-line traces; showing the full
extent of the plastically-deformed layer. (cf. with
Fig. 2(b)).

be shown in taper sections of abraded brass surfaces (16, 7) by
using etching techniques which develop the traces of virtually
all the planes on which slip has occurred (17, 18, 19) . The full
extent of the plastically-deformed layer is then delineated

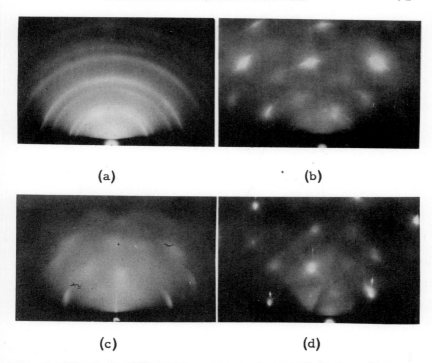

(a)   (b)

(c)   (d)

Fig. 4.   Electron diffraction patterns from polished surfaces
of a silver single crystal. (a) As polished by indus-
trail methods. Surface consists of randomly oriented
coherent fragments. (b) As for Fig.4(a), but given a
very light etch. Fragments now show misorientations
of only ± 8° about the base crystal orientations. (c)
As polished metallographically on magnesium oxide.
A grating pattern from a single crystal containing
misorientations of ± 5°. (d) As for Fig.4(b), but given
a very light etch. Kikuchi lines are visible indicating
that material of high perfection has been exposed.

(Fig.2(b), and this may be as much as 50 times the depth of the
surface scratches (7). Experiments with etching techniques of
varying sensitivies (7) indicate that the strain gradient throughout this zone is of the general form shown in Fig. 5.
      In distinction to abraded surfaces, virtually all of the

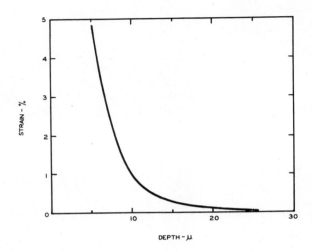

Fig. 5.   Estimate of the strain gradient in a brass surface
abraded on 600-grade silicon carbide paper.

minor deformation in surfaces finely polished by either metallographic or industrial methods is concentrated in rays extending
beneath individual surface scratches (Fig.3(b)). The strains in
these rays are also of a much lower order of magnitude. In
brass, for example, they nowhere exceed the threshold value
of about 5% compression necessary for the development of
lamellar slip bands (7).

The phenomena so far described apply only to the effects
produced by any one particular operation. It is often necessary
in practice to use a sequence of different operations; the deforma
tion in the final surface will then be that characteristic of the
final operation only if the pre-existing deformed layer is removed completely at each stage of the sequence. This can be
achieved in metallographic practice if suitable precautions are
taken (7, 36, 37), but often would not be achieved in an industrial sequence. The final surface would then contain the residuals of one or more of the deformed layers produced by the
earlier stages of preparation, and these could be much more
extensive than the deformed layer produced by the final stage itself.

3. 3 Special Features of the Deformed Layer

The above is a description of the general distribution of the plastic strains in the surface. The plastic deformation may have secondary effects in some cases, or be modified in others, and a number of common examples of such effects will now be discussed.

3. 31 Twinning in Non-Cubic Metals. Mechanical twins form in non-cubic metals after comparatively small strains and twinning is then to be expected in the deformed layer. The twins developed in abraded and machined surfaces (37, 38) are, in fact, of the type to be expected (Fig. 6), the profusion of twinning at any level being related reasonably to the expected compressive strain at that level and the depth of the layer affected to the threshold strain for twinning. Generally, gross twinning is not found, however, in polished surfaces (37); instead, small discrete twins are produced at the sites of some, but not necessarily all, of the surface scratches (Fig. 8). The number of these twins, their width, and the depth to which they extend all decrease with increasing fineness of polish (37).

3. 32 Recrystallization and Strain Relief. The strains in the outer portions of the deformed layer in machined and abraded surfaces are large enough to cause spontaneous re-crystallization in metals of low melting point, e. g. , lead, tin, and zinc (Fig. 6). The proportion of the deformed layer which recrystallizes and the grain size of the recrystallized layer both vary considerably with the method of preparation (37), presumably because of slight differences in the surface temperature attained. Similar recrystallization, and polygonization in the less highly strained regions, occurs in other metals if the specimen is heated subsequently to an appropriate elevated temperature (39).

Recrystallization does not generally occur during fine polishing, but strain relief does. Strain relief may be complete immediately after polishing in the case of metals such as tin and zinc (8, 37), or after a delay of several days in metals such as high-purity aluminum (26). This suggests that it might be possible to obtain highly strain-free polished surfaces of other

Fig. 6. Taper section of a ground zinc surface. A recrystallized surface layer and a zone containing deformation
twins are present. Taper ratio: 16.2. X 100.

metals by a post-heat treatment at comparatively modest temperatures.

3. 33 Phase Transformations. Deformation at room temperature may initiate a phase transformation in a metastable alloy, the most thoroughly investigated case being that of the 18/8-type austenitic stainless steels. The classic view is that deformation carried out below a critical temperature causes a martensitic-type transformation in this material to form a ferritic phase, the transformation occurring in lamellae along slip bands (40, 41). It has recently been suggested, however, that the phenomenon is not strictly a phase transformation but rather one involving stacking faults (42). The older terms will be used here for ease in description.

The phenomenon has been investigated in a number of finely machined and abraded surfaces by electron diffraction (43, 44), x-ray diffraction (45) and metallographic (36) methods, the results supplementing one another well. The heavily distorted or fragmented surface layer can be recognized clearly in metallographic taper sections (Fig. 7), and electron diffraction evidence indicates that this layer is composed entirely of deformed ferritic phase. Transformation is confined to the slip bands in the subcutaneous layer of more minor deformation, the slip bands again tending to be concentrated in rays extending beneath the surface scratches (Fig. 7). Transformations of a similar nature should occur in the surface layers of other metastable alloys. Takahashi (31) has found evidence of it in a β-brass, and Barrett (46) in a copper-silicon alloy.

All of this work has been done on abraded or machined surfaces. It has not been established unequivocally whether or not similar transformations are induced by fine polishing operations.

3. 34 Modifications due to Surface Heating. Bowden and Hughes (14) recognized that even if surface melting does not occur as a general phenomenon, quite appreciable temperatures may be reached in the surface layers during abrasion and polishing. There is now a good deal of reasonably direct experimental evidence to support this suggestion (29-31, 44, 47-49), but the circumstances under which surface heating becomes

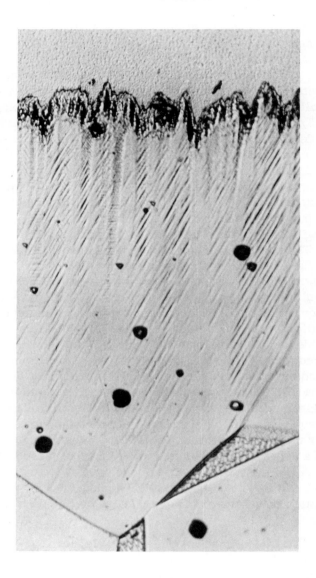

Fig. 7.　Taper section of an abraded surface of an austenitic
stainless steel.　Note the distorted surface zone and
the rays containing lamallae of ferritic phase.　Taper
ratio: 10.1.　X 1000.

Fig. 8.   Taper sections of a metallographically polished zinc
surface. Isolated twins are associated with some of
the surface scratches. (Arrows indicate the section
line). Taper ratio: 10. 5. X 1500.

significant are not clear. A rough generalization appears to
be that high surface temperatures are likely to be attained only
in severe machining operations, particularly operations such
as grinding and linishing; more minor heating is possible during abrasion and industrial polishing, but even this is unlikely
during metallographic polishing. In any event, very high temperatures are likely to be attained only in a very thin surface
layer.

Observations to date indicate that the following effects
can result, but in view of the uncertainites just discussed, this
information can be used only as a guide to what might happen
if the surface heating is severe enough:

(a) Strain relief and recrystallization of the plastically-
deformed layer in metals where this would not occur spontane-
ously. (b) Tempering of hardened steels (48-50), and presumably similar softening in other cases such as age-hardening
alloys. (c) The introduction of a phase, or a product of a
phase, normally stable only at elevated temperatures; known

examples are the development of martensitic structures in
steels (48, 50, 51) and the retention of the f. c. c. allotrope of
cobalt (29). (d) The transformation of a metastable phase; for
example, the transformation of retained austenite in steel (51).
(e) The suppression of the deformation-induced transformation
of a metastable phase; this has been observed in ground austenitic
steels (44, 36). (f) The spreading of a thin layer of a phase of
low melting point across the surface; this is probably a rare
event, occurring only with phases of very low melting point, but
evidence of it has been observed in a copper-lead alloy (31).

3. 4 The Depth of the Plastically-Deformed Layer

Most of the measurements that have been made of the
depth of the deformed layer produced by various preparation
procedures are of doubtful significance for one or both of two
reasons. Firstly, it is not certain that the layer investigated
is representative of the procedure concerned and free from the
residuals of layers produced at early stages of preparation.
Secondly, no information is available on the sensitivity of the
method used to detect deformation; this can have a considerable
influence on the depth value determined (see Fig. 5), although
the results of any one investigation may still be comparative
within themselves.

Perhaps the most informative work has been that of
Jacquet (16), Samuels (7, 10), and Thomassen and McCutcheon
(52) on 70:30 brass; Wulff (44), and Samuels and Wallwork (36)
on austenitic steels; Samuels and Wallwork (37) on zinc; and
Vacher (23) on steel, copper and aluminum. Most of the measurements in the references quoted pertain to metallographic
abrasion processes, but they also include standard machining
operations (35, 36, 41, 51), metallographic polishing (7, 16, 23,
36), and industrial abrasion and polishing (10). All refer to
polycrystalline specimens. A number of measurements have
been made on single crystals (22, 24, 53, 54), but probably none
of these is of absolute significance for the reasons already discussed. However, the results of Boas and Schmid (22) at least
indicate that the depth of the deformed layer varies considerably
with the orientation of the crystal face treated, and those of

Benard et al. (24) that the layer is much deeper, perhaps two
or three times deeper, in single crystals than in polycrystals.
    The measurements have also so far been confined to
soft metals and alloys in the annealed condition and it is difficult at present to predict from these results the likely depths
in harder alloys; it can only be assumed as a rough approximation that the depth will be inversely proportional to hardness
(36, 37). It may even be doubted by some whether there can be
such a thing as a plastically-deformed layer in very hard
metals, but there is good reason to believe that this can be so.
An extensive zone of this nature has, in fact, been identified
beneath indentation hardness impressions in fully-hardened high-
carbon steels (35, 55). It is again necessary to remember that
the surface deformation occurs under very special conditions.

4. RESIDUAL ELASTIC STRESSES

    The presence of residual elastic stresses is inevitable
in a surface which contains a plastically deformed zone whose
thickness is limited compared with that of the bulk s pecimen.
Alternatively, the relief of these stresses may cause distortion
of the specimens in cases where the thickness of the two is
comparable. Very little work has been done on this important
subject and, so far as can be ascertained, none that can be
related to the complexities of the plastically-deformed layer.
Considerable complications are introduced because the residual
stresses may be of thermal as well as mechanical origin and
because those of mechanical origin may be altered by the thermal effects.
    Work to date has largely been confined to machined
surfaces (56-61), particularly ground surfaces (57-60), of
steel but exploratory investigations have also been carried out
on lapped (58) and abraded (61) steel surfaces. All measurements indicate that the residual stresses are high, often ex-
ceeding the yield point of the original material (but not, of
course, that of the material of the plastically-deformed layer),
and are of a biaxial nature at least (56, 58-60). They progressively decrease in magnitude throughout a layer of appreciable
thickness (57-60), presumably that of the plastically deformed

layer, sometimes in a complex manner and sometimes even changing　sign (58-60). The stresses usually are of a tensile nature at the surface in machined and ground steels, although they may be compressive under some grinding conditions (59). In lapped and abraded surfaces, on the other hand, they appear to be compressive in nature (58, 59, 61). The magnitude of the stresses and the depth to which they extend vary considerably, depending upon the exact machining conditions (56-60).

5. MECHANICAL DAMAGE

The discussion to this stage has been confined to deformation effects in the surface layers. There are several mechanical effects that are worthy of consideration.

5.1 Surface Topography

All of the surfaces under consideration are composed of a system of grooves or scratches. As a rough approximation, each groove is shaped as an obtuse-angled vee, the width of the open end of the vee varying from visible dimensions for machined surfaces down to the order of 1000Å for the finest metallographic polishes (9, 62). The ratio of the width to depth of the vee is about 10 for machined and abraded surfaces but is probably considerably more than this for finely polished surfaces, the ratio increasing with increasing fineness of polish (9). It also depends on the polishing pressure and the type of abrasive used (62).

There is reason to believe from the study of taper sections (7, 10) and other evidence (62) that the scratches in polished surfaces do have a reasonably smooth vee-shaped form. Those in abraded and machined surfaces, however, certainly do not, particularly where abrasive particles are used for cutting. The vee is often truncated (see Fig.1(b)for example), and prominent second order irregularities are superimposed on the primary vee. Therefore, although the average inclination of the scratch flanks may be only about 10°, this value can be exceeded considerably at local perturbations. Fine folds may be present (10), apparently as a result of the crests of adjoining scratches being crushed against one another. Pinner (63) has also observed slivers of metal torn out of the surface but still attached to it at one end.

The yielding backing usually employed in polishing per- mits level differences to develop between areas which have different polishing rates; the areas concerned may be constitu- ents of a second phase, segregates, or even individual grains (7, 64). The relief may become marked enough to be detectable by the unaided eye.

5. 2 Surface Cracking

Since the surface strains are largely compressive in nature, the tendency to the development of cracking in the sur- face should be small. However, some surface cracking or shattering does occur in materials which are brittle in bulk, particularly if they cleave easily. The final surface may then be composed, in part or in whole, of systems of cleavage facets (15, 33). This phenomenon has been observed in a number of ionic crystals, such as rock salt and fluorspar, but not so far in metals.

Comparison with the static analogue of indentation hardness impressions and with observations made on polished glass surfaces (65) suggest that there could be a scale factor involved in the phenomenon. That is, the degree of surface shattering might decrease with increasing fineness of the scratch and eventually might be eliminated. The compressive forces in the surface layers decrease with increasing fineness of finish and apparently the forces responsible for surface shattering do so also.

5. 3 Embedded Abrasive

Whenever abrasive particles are used for surface prep- aration, whether loose or bonded, it is almost inevitable that some will become embedded in the surface. The density of embedded particles presumably depends upon factors such as the availability of loose or fractured abrasive particles, the nature and shape of these particles, the pressure used and the hardness of the base metal.

Williams (66) has recently established conclusively by a radiometric technique that such particles are present in lapped steel surfaces. They have also been observed directly in taper sections of abraded and polished surfaces (10), these sections showing that the particles are so well entrapped that they would not be readily removed short of the dissolution of the surface layers; this is in agreement with Williams' experiments. It has been recognized for a considerable time that large numbers of abrasive particles may be forced into the surface of soft metals during industrial polishing (67), and this also occurs during metallographic polishing (68, 69, 9).

The influence of these particles on both the mechanical and chemical behavior of the surface appears to have been largely overlooked in the past, but clearly could be of considerable importance in many instances.

6. REMARKS

In spite of the fact that only a comparatively modest amount of systematic work has been carried out on what is undoubtedly a complicated subject, it is now possible to assemble a reasonably complete and basically sound description of the damaged layer produced during the machining and polishing of metal surfaces. It is immediately apparent that some caution must be exercised in applying the term "damage" in a strictly literal sense. The surface is certainly altered, and often is drastically altered, but this does not always constitute damage. The likely influence of the alterations in the surface layers must be appraised in any particular set of circumstances.

The major change in the surface is that due to plastic deformation. An outer fragmented zone can be distinguished in this deformed layer and it is this zone that mostly would be of greatest interest; not only because it is the outer layer, but also because it is much more drastically altered than the immediately underlying regions. An important feature of the fragmented layer is that the degree of fragmentation varies markedly with the method of finishing; this is very considerable in machined and abraded surfaces but can be comparatively small in finely polished surfaces. Sufficient information is not yet available, however, to define these relationships with any exactness.

Information obtained from the study of metal surfaces, particularly when it is related to similar studies of ionic crystalline solids, provides some guide to the effects to be expected in semiconductors, which are considered in the complimentary paper of this volume (70). An extensive plastically-deformed layer should be present, in spite of the extreme brittleness of these materials in bulk, but some surface shattering, particularly the development of cleavage facets, could also occur.

Acknowledgements

This paper is published by permission of the Chief Scientist, Department of Supply, Australia.

References

1. G. Beilby, Aggregation and Flow of Solids, Macmillan Co., 1921.
2. G. I. Finch and A. G. Quarrell, Nature, 137, 516 (1936).
3. F. P. Bowden and D. Tabor, The Friction and Lubrication of Solids, Clarendon Press, 1950.
4. G. P. Thomson, in R. Gomer and C. S. Smith, eds., Structure and Properties of Solid Surfaces, p. 185, University of Chicago Press, 1953.
5. H. G. Hopkins, Trans. Faraday Soc., 31, 1095 (1935).
6. C. S. Lees, Trans. Faraday Soc., 31, 1102 (1935).
7. L. E. Samuels, J. Inst. Metals, 85, 51 (1956).
8. L. E. Samuels, J. Inst. Metals, 85, 177 (1956).
9. L. E. Samuels and J. V. Sanders, J. Inst. Metals, 87, 129 (1958).
10. L. E. Samuels, J. Australian Inst. Metals, 4, 1 (1959).
11. L. E. Samuels, Australian J. Sci., 21, 163 (1959).
12. L. E. Samuels, Electroplating and Met. Finishing, 12, 130 (1959).

13. L. E. Samuels, in Advanced Metallographic Techniques, American Society for Metals, in press.
14. F. P. Bowden and T. P. Hughes, Proc. Roy. Soc., A, 160, 575 (1937).
15. H. Raether, Métaux & corrosion, 22, 2 (1947); Z. Physik, 124, 286 (1948).
16. P. A. Jacquet, Rev. mét., 47, 355 (1950).
17. P. A. Jacquet, Compt. rend., 228, 1027 (1949); 237, 1248 (1953).
18. L. E. Samuels, J. Inst. Metals, 83, 359 (1954).
19. L. E. Samuels and M. Hatherly, J. Inst. Metals, 84, 84 (1955).
20. M. Hatherly and L. E. Samuels, J. Inst. Metals, 85, 437 (1956).
21. L. E. Samuels and M. Hatherly, J. Inst. Metals, 86, 442 (1957).
22. W. Boas and E. Schmid, Naturwissenschaften, 20, 416 (1932).
23. H. C. Vacher, J. Research Nat. Bur. Standards, 29, 177 (1942).
24. J. Benard, P. Lacombe and G. Chaudron, J. Etats de Surfaces, 1945, 73.
25. C. Legrand, Rev. mét, 46, 147 (1949).
26. E. A. Owen and Y. H. Liu, J. Inst. Metals, 78, 93 (1950).
27. V. D. Scott and H. Wilman, Proc. Roy. Soc., A, 247, 353 (1958).
28. R. Courtel, Rev. mét., 46, 24 (1949).
29. R. Courtel, Métaux & corrosion, 25, 145 (1950).
30. R. P. Agarwala and H. Wilman, Proc. Phys. Soc., B, 66, 717 (1953); J. Iron Steel Inst., 179, 124 (1955).
31. N. Takahashi, Métaux Corrosion-Inds., 26, 189 (1951).
32. R. F. King and D. Tabor, Proc. Roy. Soc., A, 223, 225 (1954).
33. P. Gay, P. B. Hirsch and J. N. Kellar, Acta Cryst., 5, 7 (1952).
34. P. W. Bridgman, Studies in Large Plastic Flow and Fracture, McGraw-Hill Book Co., Inc., 1952.
35. T. O. Mulhearn, J. Mech. and Phys. Solids, 7, 85 (1959).
36. L. E. Samuels and G. R. Wallwork, J. Iron Steel Inst., 186, 211 (1957).

37. L. E. Samuels and G. R. Wallwork, J. Inst. Metals, 86, 43 (1957).
38. P. A. Jacquet, Métaux corrosion usure, 19, 71 (1944).
39. P. A. Jacquet, Rev. mét., 52, 307 (1955).
40. B. Cina, J. Iron Steel Inst., 177, 406 (1954); 179, 230 (1955).
41. H. C. Fiedler, B. L. Averbach and M. Cohen, Trans. Am. Soc. Metals, 47, 267 (1955).
42. H. M. Otte, Acta Met., 5, 614 (1957).
43. J. T. Burwell and J. Wulff, Trans. Am. Inst. Mining Met. Engrs., 135, 486 (1939).
44. J. Wulff, Trans. Am. Inst. Mining Met. Engrs., 145, 295 (1941).
45. E. F. Erbin, E. R. Marshall and W. A. Backofen, Trans. Am. Soc. Metals, 49, 686 (1957).
46. C. S. Barrett, Trans. Am. Inst. Mining Met. Engrs., 188, 123 (1950).
47. R. Courtel, Rev. mét., 47, 700 (1950); Métaux & corrosion, 25, 188 (1950).
48. W. E. Littmann and J. Wulff, Trans. Am. Soc. Metals, 47, 692 (1955).
49. A. Kochanovská, Acta Tech. Acad. Sci. Hung., 13, 421 (1955).
50. L. P. Tarasov and C. O. Lundberg, Trans. Am. Soc. Metals, 41, 893 (1949).
51. K. E. Beu and D. P. Koistinen, Trans. Am. Soc. Metals, 48, 213 (1956).
52. L. Thomassen and D. M. McCutcheon, Mech. Eng., 56, 155 (1934).
53. R. Maddin and W. R. Hibbard, Trans. Am. Inst. Mining Met. Engrs., 185, 700 (1949).
54. D. M. Evans, D. N. Layton and H. Wilman, Proc. Roy. Soc., A, 205, 17 (1951).
55. D. V. Wilson, J. Iron Steel Inst., 176, 28 (1954).
56. E. K. Henriksen, Trans. Am. Soc. Mech. Engrs., 73, 69 (1951).
57. J. Frisch and E. G. Thomsen, Trans. Am. Soc. Mech. Engrs., 73, 337 (1951).
58. H. R. Letner and H. J. Snyder, Trans. Am. Soc. Mech. Engrs., 75, 873 (1953).

59. H. R. Letner, Trans. Am. Soc. Mech. Engrs., 77, 1089 (1955).
60. H. R. Letner, Trans. Am. Soc. Mech. Engrs., 79, 149 (1957).
61. R. G. Martindale, J. Inst. Elec. Engrs., 95, pt. 2, 620 (1948).
62. I-Ming Feng, J. Appl. Phys., 22, 820 (1951).
63. W. L. Pinner, Proc. Am. Electroplaters' Soc., 40, 83 (1953).
64. L. E. Samuels, J. Inst. Metals, 81, 471 (1952).
65. E. Brüche, K. Peter and H. Poppa, Glastech. Ber., 31, 341 (1958).
66. K. J. Williams, in Proceedings of the Conference on Lubrication and Wear, Inst. Mech. Engrs., 1959.
67. A. Jefferson, J. Inst. Metals, 28, 447 (1922).
68. L. H. Callender, Proc. Roy. Soc., A, 115, 349 (1927).
69. R. C. French, Proc. Roy. Soc., A, 140, 637 (1933).
70. T. M. Buck, this volume, p. 107.

T. M. BUCK
Bell Telephone
Laboratories

Damaged Surface Layers:
Semiconductors

ABSTRACT

THE PREPARATION OF semiconductor surfaces usually involves cutting and lapping or polishing. Owing to the brittleness of germanium and silicon these operations cause conchoidal fracture and cracking. The damage produced causes changes in surface recombination velocity, field effect mobility, conductivity, etching rate, x-ray rocking curves and other properties. These effects provide methods of estimating the depth of the damaged layer. The nature of the damage, which extends somewhat beneath the apparent roughness of the surface, is not yet well understood. Dislocations and vacancies might account for most of the effects. No direct evidence has been reported for dislocations produced by such abrasive action, although dislocations produced by other means at room temperature have been reported.

1. INTRODUCTION

The preparation of semiconductor specimens in research and in device technology usually involves cutting small samples from large single crystals, and further lapping or polishing to approach required dimensions. The damage caused by these operations often has drastic effects on the electrical properties; the damaged layer is therefore removed by etching. It is important to know the extent of the damage since dimensions before and after etching are usually quite small and critical.

The literature on damaged surface layers on semiconductors is less extensive than for metals. There is little to compare with the metallographic studies on metals described in the preceding paper (1). The brittleness of germanium and silicon leads one to expect chipping, cracking and conchoidal fracture rather than the approximately V-shaped grooves found in metals. Examples of this behavior are shown in Fig. 1; scratches were made on an etched germanium surface by one stroke on a few SiC particles (600 mesh) in water on a glass plate. Branching cracks may be seen extending out from the scratch. There is a rather large conchoidal fracture pit.

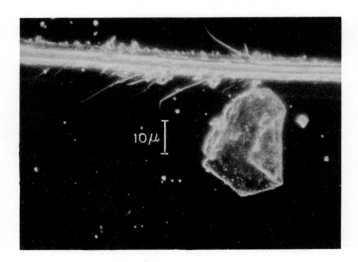

Fig. 1 (a) Scratch in etched germanium surface produced by 600 mesh SiC. One of the abrasive particles is shown.

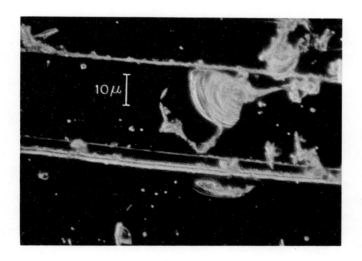

Fig. 1 (b)   Conchoidal fracture in etched germanium surface
produced by 600 mesh SiC.   Dark field illumination.

Fig. 2 shows profiles of germanium surfaces which had been
thoroughly lapped with 600 mesh SiC or No. 305 alumina whose
nominal particle sizes are 25μ and 5μ, respectively. The profiles were exposed by cleavage on $\{111\}$ planes normal to the
lapped surfaces. The maximum peak to valley depth is about
10μ for the 600 mesh lap and 3μ for the 305 lap. The depth of
the roughness is not as great as the nominal particle size of
the abrasive; there may be cracks, of the type shown in Fig. 1,
which go deeper although none were revealed in this brief study.
Wolff et al (2) have shown that a large proportion of cleavage
facets $\{111\}$ are developed by lapping germanium and silicon.
       Although metallographic information on abraded semi-
conductor surfaces is limited, phenomena such as X-ray line
broadening, etching rate, recombination of excess holes and
electrons, and conductivity are influenced by surface damage;
these offer means of determining the depth of the disturbance
and insight into the nature of it. The use of these phenomena
and others in studies of surface damage will be reviewed.

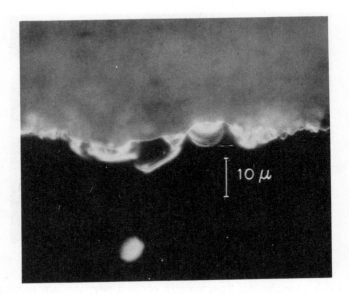

Fig. 2 (a) Profile of germanium surface lapped with 600 mesh
            SiC.

Considerable attention will be given to the depth of damage (in
germanium and silicon) detectable by the various methods,
since depth of damage is important in practical applications as
well as in arriving, eventually, at a better description of the
nature of the damage. At present such a detailed description
cannot be given and one can only suggest certain possibilities.

2. X-RAY METHODS

The disturbance by abrasive action of the orderly arrangement of atoms in a crystal may be detected by x-ray diffraction; early experiments demonstrated such phenomena (3).
Armstrong (4) has described a number of x-ray techniques which
have been used on inorganic materials such as quartz. Surface
abrasion damage was a major problem in the technology of

quartz crystal oscillator plates (5) before semiconductor devices became important.

Fig. 2 (b) Profile of germanium surface lapped with No. 305 alumina. Profiles obtained by cleaving perpendicular to lapped surface. Cleaved surface in lower half of picture. The radial lines are "tear marks" (31) which originated at a deep flaw to the right. They are steps, not cracks. Dark field illumination.

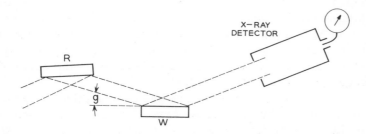

Fig. 3 (a) Schematic diagram of double-crystal x-ray rocking-curve technique (6).

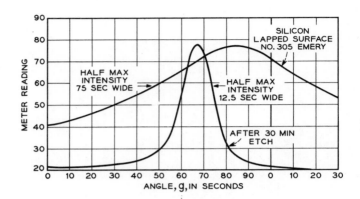

Fig. 3 (b) Rocking curves produced by lapped surface and same
surface after etching to remove 3μ (9).

One method used frequently is the double-crystal
rocking-curve method (6, 7); a schematic diagram is shown in
Fig. 3 (a). X-rays are reflected from the reference crystal R
to the work crystal W and into the detector. If W is rotated
only a few seconds, the reflection intensity will drop sharply to
background level. However if the surface of W is damaged the
drop in intensity with rotation will be less rapid since misoriented material will present atomic planes at the Bragg angle as the
crystal is rotated slightly. Curves of detector response versus
rocking-angle for lapped and etched surfaces on silicon are
shown in Fig. 3 (b). Progressive etching decreases the width
of the rocking-curve at half-maximum intensity until finally a
constant value is reached; this depth is taken as the depth of
damage detectable by this method.

The rocking-curve method has been applied to semiconductor materials by several workers. Weissmann (8) estimated
5μ as the depth of damage on germanium lapped with No. 305
abrasive (3200 mesh alundum, having nominal particle size of
5μ). On silicon Andrus and Bond (9) found $1/2\mu$ depth for a fine
polish, 3μ for No. 305 lap, and 10μ for a diamond saw-cut; the
widths at half-maximum intensity before any etching were 13,
75, and 98 seconds, respectively, and thus gave some indication

of the relative depths of damage. Andrus and Fillingham (10) have found that extremely large widths at half-maximum are sometimes obtained on very thin (6 mil) polished specimens and that this is related to bending of the specimen which is apparent after removal from the backing plate used in polishing, before the x-ray measurement.

3. ETCHING RATE METHOD

A mechanically damaged semiconductor surface etches more rapidly than a thoroughly etched surface. This familiar effect is sometimes exaggerated by a temperature increase due to the heat of reaction. Even when the temperature is held constant the rate of etching is initially high and decreases as the damaged layer is removed, finally reaching a constant value (Fig. 4). This provides a means of determining the depth of the damaged layer.

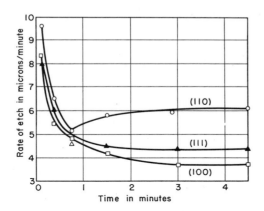

Fig. 4. Rate of etching as a function of time of etching and crystal orientation. Germanium surfaces had been finely ground with No. 305 abrasive (11).

Camp (11) attributed the increase in etching rate to increased surface area. Gas adsorption studies (12) indicate that sandblasting causes a three-fold increase in surface area on

germanium. Etching rate increases found by both Camp (11) and
Faust (13) were of this order of magnitude. However Faust
suggested the rate increase was due at least in part to increased
dislocation density in the damaged surface; this would help to
explain different depths of damage obtained sometimes with the
same abrasive material but different methods of application.

Camp (11) determined depths of damage of 7, 5, and 3μ
on (100), (111), and (110) faces of germanium lapped with No. 305
abrasive, and discussed the shapes of the curves for different
faces in terms of the relative etching rates on different faces.

Faust (13) used the etching rate method on both germanium and silicon and covered a wide range of abrasive particle
sizes. Some of his data are shown in Fig. 5 (14). He found
that for a given abrasive treatment the depth of damage on silicon was about one fourth that on germanium.

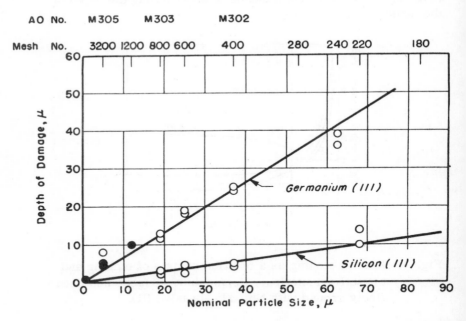

Fig. 5. Depth of damage on germanium and silicon as a function
of abrasive particle size. ○ Etching rate method
(14). ● Data from references 11 and 15 (After Faust
(14)).

4. RECOMBINATION OF EXCESS CARRIERS AT DAMAGED SURFACES

Recombination rates of excess minority carriers are very high near a damaged semiconductor surface. A high density of recombination centers is thus implied. The increase in surface area is inadequate to account for the observed increases in recombination rate of a factor of 10^3 or more. Conceivably a freshly fractured surface might have an abnormally high concentration of recombination states right at the surface; but these should be wiped out by very light etching. Such light etching, or other chemical treatment which does not remove sufficient material, does not reduce recombination rates. The recombination centers are evidently distributed through an appreciable depth near the surface.

Methods that determine filament lifetime, diffusion length, or photomagnetoelectric voltages or currents have been used to study damaged surfaces. All of these are related quantitatively or qualitatively to surface recombination velocity, S. As a damaged surface is etched progressively, S decreases from a very high value, perhaps 10^4-10^5 cm/sec on germanium and silicon, to a value of about 50-100 cm/sec, depending on the chemical condition of the surface determined by details of the etching procedure and ambient atmosphere.

Two modifications of the photomagnetoelectric (PME) effect were used by Buck and McKim (15). In one, illustrated in Fig. 6 (a), the PME voltage increases as S at the illuminated surface of the specimen decreases. Progressive etching of the illuminated surface, after an abrasive treatment, causes the PME voltage to increase and level off eventually, giving curves of the type shown in Fig. 6 (b). This method is simple and convenient for comparing depths of damage by different treatments, although it does not provide quantitative values of S. Another PME method (15, 16, 17) did give quantitative values of S and indicated the same depths of damage as the first method for treatments tested. Progressive etching of large germanium diodes after abrasive treatments caused the reverse characteristics to recover at depths which agreed closely with the PME results.

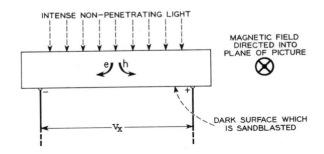

Fig. 6 (a) Photomagnetoelectric method. Open circuit voltage
measurements. Abrasive treatment to be studied is
given to illuminated surface.

A few tests by the PME method on silicon surfaces (18)
indicated depth values about half those for the same abrasive
on germanium. Measurements on silicon are more difficult because of its tendency to have very high S values even on thoroughly etched surfaces unless special chemical treatments are used
(19).

Measurements of filament lifetime by the photoconduc-
tivity decay (PCD) method (20) have been made on germanium by
Buck and McKim (18) more recently than the PME measurements.
Typical data are shown in Figs. 7, 8, 9, and 10. This method
is more sensitive to changes in S at low values which accounts
for the random fluctuations in lifetime values after the curves
level off. These fluctuations occur in spite of careful control
of etching and atmospheric conditions. In general, however,
depth values obtained by the PCD method agreed with those by
the PME method. An exception was found in diamond saw-cut
damage, 40-70μ by PCD as compared with 12-13μ by PME. Differences in sawing technique may have caused the discrepancy.

Fig. 8 shows lifetime values together with results of
field-effect measurements made by the Aigrain method (21, 22).

The field-effect measurements detected damage to the same depth as the lifetime test.

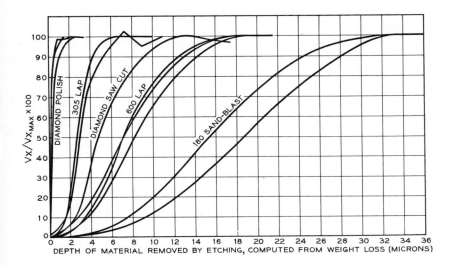

Fig. 6 (b)   Change of PME voltage with etching after various abrasive treatments on germanium. Normalized curves.

Baker and Yemm (23), measuring diffusion length by the traveling light spot method (24) to detect changes in S, and also by measuring etching rate in one case, found much greater depths of damage than those discussed above. Values ranged from 36μ for a fine polish to 60μ for a 600 mesh lap. This disagreement will be descussed below.

5.   ABRASION DAMAGE AND CONDUCTIVITY

In one of the earliest studies of abrasion damage Clarke and Hopkins (25, 26) found that sandblasting germanium produced a surface layer of relatively high p-type conductivity. The thickness of the layer was estimated at about 0.7μ. It should be noted that 3μ silica particles were used, much smaller than the 125μ silicon carbide used in the sandblasting treatment tested by the PME method (15), which gave a $32-34\mu$ depth. The average resistivity in the surface layer was about 0.2 ohm-cm at room temperature as compared with 47 in the bulk. Annealing in helium at $488°C$ for 21 minutes increased the surface layer resistivity to 10 ohm-cm. Measurements of resistivity as a function of temperature indicated two acceptor levels at 0.022 and 0.4 ev above the valence band. The latter (a tentative value) was suggested as a recombination level.

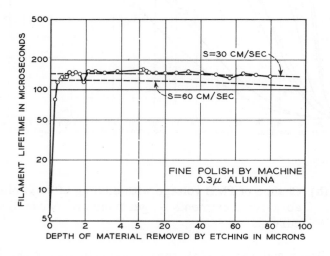

Fig. 7. Photoconductivity-decay lifetime, as a function of depth removed by etching, after fine polish. Note change in scale at 5μ.
N-type germanium; $\rho = 2.5$ ohm-cm; $\tau_B = 180\mu$ sec.
Dimensions before etching: 2.35 x 0.775 x 0.0584 cm.

6. OTHER PHENOMENA

Other phenomena which have been observed on damaged semiconductor surfaces include the following. Ahearn and Law (27) have studied the Russel effect, the darkening of a photo-

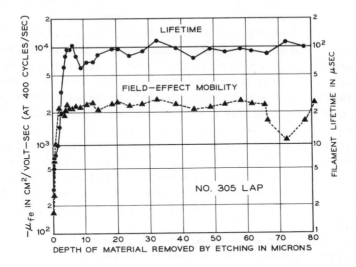

Fig. 8.   PCD lifetime and field-effect mobility.   No. 305 lap.
n-type germanium; $\rho = 2.5$ ohm-cm; $\tau_B = 180\mu$ sec.
Dimensions before etching: 2.28 x 0.633 x 0.0496 cm.

graphic plate by hydrogen peroxide generated at freshly abraded
silicon and germanium surfaces.   Electron spin resonance lines
due to surface damage will be discussed below.   Hopkins (28)
and Dash (29) have studied the elastic bending of thin slabs of
germanium (28) and silicon (29).   Dash found that removal of
0.7μ from a lapped (600 mesh) surface allowed the specimen to
unbend to its original form, within experimental error.   Uhlir
(30), measuring the reverse characteristics of electrolyte-
germanium barriers, found that for typical abrasive sawing and
lapping 20 to 50 microns had to be removed before further etching produced no change in the characteristics.   Removal of this
amount was necessary even if the lapping was followed by polishing to a mirror finish.

7. COMPARISON OF RESULTS BY VARIOUS METHODS

Values of depth of damage obtained by the various methods discussed are compiled in Table I for comparison. Fig. 5 shows values for a wider range of particle size for one method, etching rate. Even though the method of abrasion is an important factor which will be discussed further below, it may be seen that x-ray, etching rate, and surface recombination methods as employed by a number of different workers agree fairly well on certain depths of damage characteristic of certain abrasive particle sizes used in lapping. A useful rule of thumb appears to be that on germanium the depth is approximately equal to the diameter of the abrasive material in lapping treatments while on silicon the damage is about one fourth to one half as deep.

There are some apparent disagreements, however. Uhlir (30) suggested that the electrolyte-Ge barrier method showed much larger depths for fine polishes, because that method is more sensitive to isolated spots of damage than are other methods which measure an average property over a large surface area. This suggests the need for extreme care to avoid scratches by large foreign particles, in order to realize the benefits of fine polishes. The large values of Baker and Yemm (23) obtained by diffusion length and, in one case, by etching rate, do not seem explainable on this basis, however. It is believed that much deeper damage was caused by their method of lapping by machine between steel plates, than is caused in gentle hand lapping on glass in a water slurry or in polishing on a cloth wheel with gentle pressure.

It is felt, therefore, that the depth of damage values for germanium approximately equal to the abrasive particle size are minimum values which can be obtained by gentle application of the abrasive material. The manner of treatment is important. A fine lap or polish must of course go far enough to remove damage left by any previous coarse treatment (Fig. 9). Incomplete lapping with No. 305 abrasive on a saw-cut surface resulted in a curve which has a first maximum at 4-5μ and finally levels off at 15-20μ. Hand lapping with 600 mesh silicon carbide usually produces damage 15-20μ deep but Fig. 10 shows

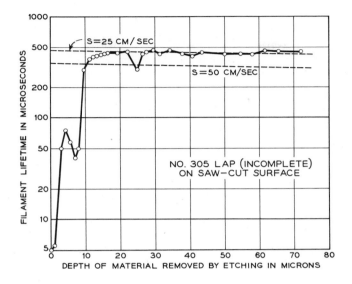

Fig. 9. PCD lifetime as a function of depth removed by etching,
after No. 305 lap (incomplete) on saw-cut surface.
P-type germanium; ρ = 4 ohm-cm; τ_B = 700μ sec.
Dimensions before etching: 2.40 x 0.637 x 0.077 cm.

the result of applying the same abrasive with an ultrasonically
driven tool using rather excessive drive amplitudes. There is
an upward trend in lifetime to a depth of about 60μ. On the
other hand a dilute suspension of this abrasive in ultrasonically
agitated water caused damage only 1-2μ deep (15).

Faust (13) has found deeper damage caused by lapping in
boiling water, lapping with dry abrasive, and lapping with irregular SiC particles rather than the more spherical alundum.

It is certainly conceivable that some ultra-sensitive
method might detect damage which does not show up in any of
the methods discussed. In device technology a device itself may
be the best indicator of the extent of damage and the depth of
etching required.

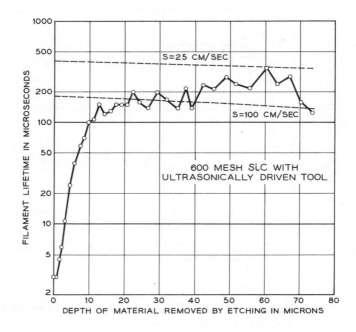

Fig. 10.   PCD lifetime as a function of depth removed by etching, after abrasion with 600 mesh SiC using ultrasonically driven tool.   P-type germanium; ρ = 4 ohm-cm;
τ_B = 700μ sec.   Dimensions before etching: 2. 30 x
0. 623 x 0. 0529 cm.

8.   NATURE OF ABRASION DAMAGE

The available data do not provide a detailed picture of
the nature of abrasion damage on germanium and silicon.   A
complete description would have to explain the effects on various phenomena such as x-ray rocking curves, etching rates,
lifetime of minority carriers and conductivity.   The measurable
effects on the first three of these are felt to about the same
depth.   (The conductivity data are not directly comparable).
The effects are felt below the apparent roughness revealed in

TABLE I

Abrasion Damage
Measurements on Germanium and Silicon

Abrasive and Nominal Particle Size in Microns	Method of Treatment	Method of Measurement	Depth of Damage in Microns	Ref.
		Germanium		
		Fine Polish		
Linde A; 0.3	Machine, Nylon Lap	PCD	1	18
Linde B; 0.1	Machine, Cloth Lap	PME	1	15
Diamond Dust; 0.5	Machine Cloth Lap	PME	1-2	15
Diamond Dust; 0.5	Machine Cloth Lap	Diode Characteristic	1	15
-	-	Electrolyte-Ge	30-50	30
0.5	Steel Plates	Diffusion Length	36	23
		Coarse Lap		
No. 305 (3200 Mesh)	Water Slurry on Glass	PCD	5-6	18
" 5	"	PME	6-7	15

Abrasive and Nominal Particle Size in Microns	Method of Treatment	Method of Measurement	Depth of Damage in Microns	Ref.
		Germanium		
	Coarse Lap			
No. 305 (3200 Mesh)	Water Slurry on Glass	Diode Characteristic	7-9	15
" 5	"	Etch-Rate	5-7	11
" 5	"	"	8-10	14
- 5	-	X-ray	5	8
- 5	Steel Plates	Diffusion Length	43	23
600 Mesh SiC; 25	Water Slurry on Glass	PCD	15	18
" 25	"	PME	17-18	15
'' 25	"	Diode Characteristic	16-18	15
" 25	"	Etch-Rate	18-19	14
- 25	Steel Plates	Diffusion Length	60	23
	Sawing			
220 Mesh; 68μ Diamond Particles		PME	12-13	15

Abrasive and Nominal Particle Size in Microns	Method of Treatment	Method of Measurement	Depth of Damage in Microns	Ref.
		Germanium		
	Sawing			
		PCD	40-70	18
		Etch-Rate	50-80	13
	Sand-Blasting			
180 Mesh SiC; 125		PME	32-34	15
Silica Powder; 3		Conductivity	0.7	25
		Silicon		
305 lap; 5	Water Slurry on Glass	X-ray	3	9
	"	PME	3-4	18
600 Mesh lap; 25	"	Etch-Rate	7-8	13
	"	PME	8-10	18
		Elastic Bending	0.7	29

the profiles of Fig. 2, by about 10-15μ in the case of the 600 mesh lap, and the effects can go deeper than this for more severe methods of application. There may be deep cracks not revealed in the profiles which would correspond to the long branching cracks of Fig. 1. Thus there may be a rough top layer and a second layer containing deep cracks, with the effects on properties extending only as deep as the cracks. In any case it seems worthwhile to try to account for changes in conductivity and lifetime in terms of defects on an atomic scale, such as dislocations and vacancies.

The presence of high dislocation densities in damaged semiconductor surfaces has been suggested (13, 28, 29, 23) but no direct evidence has been reported. Faust (13) has pointed out a difficulty in considering dislocations, which is that they are ordinarily produced by deformation at elevated temperatures. It is only recently that dislocations produced by any means in germanium at room temperature have been reported, and these were rather special circumstances. Johnston, Stokes, and Li (31) found it was possible to generate dislocations by fracturing germanium at room temperature under an etching solution. In this situation the fracture stress was much higher than it is in air. Kuczynski and Hochman (32) found that fracture that occurred under strong illumination was preceded by some plastic flow; dislocation densities increased from less than 10^2/cm^2 to 10^5-10^6/cm^2. Gilman et al. (33) have studied crack nucleation of dislocations in a number of brittle inorganic oxides and salts, especially lithium fluoride. These results all suggest that dislocations may be generated by the fracturing involved in abrasive action. Faust (13) has suggested that local heating during abrasion may raise the temperature in small areas to the plastic range, which begins at about 350 and 600°C respectively for Ge and Si (34). This difference in temperature for the plastic ranges might account for the difference in depth of damage on germanium and silicon with a given abrasive material. Samuels (1) has pointed out that plastic deformation occurs during abrasion of ionic salt crystals which are ordinarily considered brittle and that this has been attributed to a hydrostatic pressure effect.

Dash (35) has shown that a scratch made on silicon at

room temperature serves as a source of dislocation loops which move into the bulk on subsequent heating. He does not interpret this as proving necessarily that dislocations were present near the scratch at room temperature; they may very well be there, but if so they are evidently too dense to be resolved by conventional techniques.

We have made a few attempts to detect dislocations by etching into a cleaved surface which was normal to a lapped surface as in Fig. 2 (a). Etch pit density was not significantly higher near the rough profile. Possibly dislocations were there but were too dense to be resolved by this method. We have also considered the possibility that elastic strain in the damaged surface might cause the observed low lifetime. A thin, etched specimen of germanium was bent slowly, at room temperature, until it finally fractured. The lifetime in the region where fracture finally occurred was measured continuously during the bending, but it did not change from its initial value of 150μ sec. The measurement merely ceased when fracture occurred.

If high densities of dislocations are introduced by some undetermined mechanism during abrasion they could account for the high recombination rates since lifetime is strongly affected by dislocations at room temperature (36). Vacancies associated with the dislocations might explain large increases in conductivity at room temperature. Acceptor type behavior is expected from either dislocations or vacancies, but coulombic repulsion causes low occupation of sites in a line imperfection (dislocation) as compared with point imperfections (vacancies). Clarke and Hopkins (25) found that a sandblasted germanium surface had high p-type conductivity. The low annealing temperature, $488^{\circ}C$, and the energy level of 0.022 ev (above the valence band) correspond to behavior which has been suggested as being characteristic of single vacancies while the tentative 0.4 ev level coincides with a level which has been suggested for dislocations (37). However there are as yet no firmly established energy level schemes for vacancies and dislocations.

Electron spin resonance lines associated with mechanical surface damage have been observed by Fletcher et al (38) and Feher (39) in silicon, and by Walters (40) in germanium. Feher found that removal of 10^{-4}cm of silicon by etching was required to eliminate the line and that the density of paramagnetic centers was about 3×10^{14}/cm^2 after sandblasting with 600 mesh SiC. Walters (40) suggests that these centers are the holes that account for the p-type conductivity observed in damaged surfaces. In regard to the type of defect which might be responsible for these paramagnetic centers which appear to be holes, Feher (41) has found that samples which have high densities of dislocations in the bulk do not give such lines. So the defects detected in damaged surfaces by the paramagnetic resonance method are evidently not dislocations, although there may be dislocations present which are not detected.

Etching rate increases may be due to a combination of increased area and dislocation density. The x-ray rocking-curve effects do not require the presence of dislocations, only misoriented material, but they might be caused by dislocations (42).

Further experimentation will be required to obtain more direct evidence of high dislocation densities and to show quantitative correlation with electrical and other properties. If such evidence cannot be found then another explanation must be sought to account for the properties of damaged surface layers on semiconductors.

Acknowledgments

The author wishes to thank F. S. McKim for his collaboration in the experiments reported from this laboratory, and also J. Andrus, W. L. Bond, J. W. Faust, Jr., P. J. Fillingham, D. F. Gibbons, G. W. Gobeli and Mrs. E. A. Wood for helpful discussions and the use of unpublished data.

References

1. L. E. Samuels, this volume, p. 82.
2. G. A. Wolff, J. M. Wilbur, Jr., and J. C. Clark, Z. Elektrochem., 61, 101 (1957).
3. A. H. Compton, Phys. Rev., 10, 95 (1917).
4. E. J. Armstrong, Bell System Tech. J., 25, 136 (1946).

5. G. M. Thurston, in R. A. Heising, ed., Quartz Crystals for Electrical Circuits, p. 321, D. Van Nostrand Co., 1946.
6. W. L. Bond, Proc. I. R. E., 38, 886 (1950).
7. W. L. Bond and J. Andrus, Am. Mineralogist, 37, 622 (1952).
8. S. Weissmann, private communication; J. Intrater and S. Weissmann, Acta Cryst., 7, 729 (1954).
9. J. Andrus and W. L. Bond, private communication.
10. J. Andrus and P. J. Fillingham, private communication.
11. P. R. Camp, J. Electrochem. Soc., 102, 586 (1955).
12. J. T. Law and E. E. Francois, Ann. N. Y. Acad. Sci., 58, 925 (1954).
13. J. W. Faust, Jr., Electrochemical Society Meeting, Buffalo, N. Y., Oct. 1957, to be published.
14. J. W. Faust, Jr., Am. Soc. Testing Materials, Symposium on Cleaning of Electronic Device Components and Materials, Special Tech. Publ. 246.
15. T. M. Buck and F. S. McKim, J. Electrochem. Soc., 103, 593 (1956).
16. W. van Roosbroeck, Phys. Rev., 101, 1713 (1956).
17. T. M. Buck and F. S. McKim, Phys. Rev., 106, 904 (1957).
18. T. M. Buck and F. S. McKim, unpublished work.
19. T. M. Buck and F. S. McKim, J. Electrochem. Soc., 105, 709 (1958).
20. J. R. Haynes and J. A. Hornbeck, Phys. Rev., 90, 152 (1953).
21. P. Aigrain, J. Lagrenaudi, and G. Liandrat, J. phys. radium, 13, 587 (1952).
22. H. C. Montgomery, Phys. Rev., 106, 441 (1957).
23. D. Baker and H. Yemm, Brit. J. Appl. Phys., 8, 302 (1957).
24. L. B. Valdes, Proc. I. R. E., 40, 1420 (1952).
25. E. N. Clarke and R. L. Hopkins, Phys. Rev., 91, 1566 (1953).
26. E. N. Clarke, Ann. N. Y. Acad. Sci., 58, 937 (1954).
27. A. J. Ahearn and J. T. Law, J. Chem. Phys., 24, 633 (1956).
28. R. L. Hopkins, Phys. Rev., 98, 1567 (1955).
29. W. C. Dash, J. Appl. Phys., 29, 228 (1958).
30. A. Uhlir, Bell System Tech. J., 35, 333 (1956).

31. T. L. Johnston, R. J. Stokes, and C. H. Li, Acta Met., 6, 713 (1958).
32. G. C. Kuczynski and R. H. Hochman, J. Appl. Phys., 30, 267 (1959).
33. J. J. Gilman, C. Knudsen, and W. P. Walsh, J. Appl. Phys., 29, 601 (1958); J. J. Gilman, Trans. Met. Soc. AIME, 212, 310 (1958).
34. G. L. Pearson, W. T. Read, Jr., and W. L. Feldmann, Acta Met., 5, 181 (1957).
35. W. C. Dash, J. Appl. Phys., 30, 459 (1959); in H. C. Gatos, ed., Properties of Elemental and Compound Semiconductors, Interscience Publishers, 1960.
36. J. N. Hobstetter, in N. B. Hannay, ed., Semiconductors, p. 508, Reinhold Publishing Co., 1959.
37. P. Haasen and A. Seeger, in W. Schottky, ed., Halbleiter- probleme, Vol. IV, p. 68, Friedr. Vieweg & Sohn, 1958. See also discussion by Penning, Hornstra, and Vink.
38. R. C. Fletcher, W. A. Yager, G. L. Pearson, A. N. Holden, W. T. Read, and F. R. Merritt, Phys. Rev., 94, 1392 (1954).
39. G. Feher, Phys. Rev., 114, 1219 (1959).
40. G. K. Walters, preprints of Second Conference on Semi- conductor Surfaces, U. S. Naval Ordnance Lab, White Oak, Md., December 2-4, 1959.
41. G. Feher, private communication.
42. P. Gay, P. B. Hirsch, and A. Kelly, Acta Met., 1, 315 (1953).

DISCUSSION

J. W. FAUST, JR. (Westinghouse): As Dr. Buck men- tioned, I have postulated that part of the damaged layer is caused by plastic deformation. Although this conclusion was based on convincing experimental evidence, the evidence was none-the- less indirect. I would like to mention some preliminary results of an investigation that we undertook to supply direct evidence.

Lapped surfaces were successively etched in CP4 for 10 sec. and examined microscopically after each etch. The etching and examination were carried on until the damaged layer had been removed as evidenced by a smooth surface showing no structure except the characteristic pits at dislocations. We have found no evidence of microcracks extending into the damaged layer but have been able to reveal a high density of tiny pits. These pits have the characteristic shape of the larger type that have been shown to be associated with dislocations and they disappear when the damaged layer has been removed. Fig. 1 shows such pits on a sample that had been abraded in a manner that would produce a damaged layer deeper than the minimum. The density of these pits is approximately $10^8/cm^2$; this value must be considered a minimum for this level in the damaged layer. It must be remembered that the density of mechanically induced dislocations undoubtedly decreases from the surface being zero at the extent of the damaged layer. Dr. McKelvey, of our Laboratory, has roughly calculated the average density of dislocations necessary in the damaged layer to account for the high surface recombination velocity; in these calculations, he assumed that the recombination cross section of the mechanically induced dislocations was the same as the value he calculated for edge dislocations [Phys. Rev., 106, 910 (1957)]. He found that 10^8 dislocations/cm^2 in the damaged layer would account for the observed surface recombination velocity.

You mentioned Dash's work [in H. C. Gatos, ed. , Properties of Elemental and Compound Semiconductors, p. 195, Interscience Publishers, 1960] on dislocation loops found to extend from a scratch on silicon after heating. We found that the strain introduced by a scratch on germanium was relieved in the form of arrays of dislocations along slip lines by heating at approximately 500°C for a few minutes. [ASTM Symposium on Cleaning of Electronic Device Components and Materials, Special Tech. Pub. No. 246] . If, however, the strain of the scratch is first removed by etching, no dislocation arrays are observed upon heating.

G. W. CULLEN (RCA): You mentioned that the results of Baker and Yemm [Brit. J. Appl. Phys., 8, 302 (1957)] were in disagreement with most of the other data and suggested that the reason for this may be that their abrasion was performed between steel plates rather than glass or cloth. Could not the reason for their more deeply damaged layers be that they failed to abrade long enough to remove the damage caused by sawing? In their short communication, they gave no assurance that they had removed the saw damage.

Fig. 1.   Imperfections in the damaged layer on germanium.

          T. M. BUCK: This is certainly another possible explanation. The method of abrasion affects the depth of damage as I showed in Table I; thus it is important to point out the use of steel plates. One might expect that machine grinding with steel plates could produce relatively high temperatures by local heating as discussed by Bowden and Tabor [The Friction and

Lubrication of Solids, Clarendon Press, 1950]; this would then give a more deeply damaged layer than the minima reported in my paper.

H. C. GATOS (M. I. T.): You mentioned that one of the objections in accepting that dislocations are introduced during abrasion   relates to the low temperature of abrasion. Could not local heating raise the temperature to a degree that disloca- tions could be introduced?

T. M. BUCK: It is certainly conceivable that local heat- ing of the type that Bowden and Tabor have measured on metals could raise the temperature at the surface high enough to do this. No one has, as yet, demonstrated this possibility for germanium or silicon.

J. W. FAUST, JR. : I would like to comment on this question. I believe that the damaged layer consists of two parts: (1) a thin layer at the surface consisting of highly fragmented material or possibly microcracks and (2) a deeper layer of plastically deformed material containing mechanically induced dislocations. I feel that local heating plays a role in the forma- tion of the plastically deformed part of the damaged layer; how- ever, it may be possible that hydrostatic pressure under the abrasive particles, as suggested by King and Tabor [Proc. Roy Soc., 223A, 225 (1954)] may be high enough to contribute also. Thus any condition or set of conditions by which the dissipation of heat away from the sample is retarded, or more heat is gen- erated, will give a damaged layer deeper than the minima re- ported by Dr. Buck. Such conditions develop relatively easily in abrasion by machines. Thus it is possible, as Dr. Buck has pointed out, for excess local heating to account for the deeper damaged layers reported by Baker and Yemm. I find it difficult, however, to explain on this basis the knee in their curves that roughly corresponds to our minimum values. One can easily explain how such a knee could occur if the damaged layer caused by cutting were not completely removed. Without further information, we can only say that either explanation could be correct or possibly a combination of the two.

R. G. OLSSON (General Electric): Would it not be pos- sible to have plastic deformation in the thin damaged layer that was much greater than you were able to produce in your bending experiments?

T. M. BUCK: I do not feel that the bending experiments proved anything about plastic deformation. They did demonstrate, however, that elastic strains up to the breaking point did not affect the lifetime. Thus we were able to rule out elastic strains as a cause of the high surface recombination velocity found on abraded surfaces.

B. ROSS (Wesson Metal): I wonder if a standardized experiment has not been carried out, or could not be carried out, in which the lapping or polishing variables were all held constant except the pressure. Then by varying the pressure, perhaps one could tell something about the role of local heating.

J. W. FAUST: Samuels has done this for some metals [J. Inst. Metals, 85, 51 (1956)]. In our studies of the damaged layer on germanium, we varied the pressure over a very moderate range and found no observable change in the depth of the damaged layer. We did find an increase in the depth, however, when we carried out the abrasion at 100°C.

J. J. GILMAN (General Electric): Chang [J. Appl. Phys., 28, 385 (1957)] reported an etching effect due to radiation damage in germanium and silicon. Since he found that no additional dislocations were introduced as a result of irradiation, the etching effects presumably show the presence of point defects. Does etching give any indication that point defects exist in the damaged layers that you discussed?

T. M. BUCK: We did not find any such evidence in the rather brief etching studies we made. The only evidence of any kind that I know of was reported by Clarke and Hopkins [Phys. Rev., 91, 1566 (1953)].They found an energy level of 0.022 ev. for their damage: this value is now regarded as a possible energy level for vacancies. Furthermore, they were able to anneal out the conductivity change caused by sandblasting, which also suggests vacancies. In our studies, we have not been able to anneal out the damage responsible for the surface lifetime effects.

In regard to the question of whether dislocations are present in the damaged layer and, if so, how they are produced, I would like to add two points: (1) We tried lapping germanium under liquid nitrogen (Dr. Faust suggested this once) with the thought that if there is some plastic deformation at room temperature, or at the higher temperatures which may prevail in spots, then these effects should be greatly reduced at liquid nitrogen temperature. But the depth of damage was even greater than it would normally be for room temperature lapping. This makes it difficult to believe that there is any ordinary plastic deformation involved which depends on temperature. (2) Recently Allen [Phil. Mag., 4, No. 45, 1046 (1949)] has proposed "Dislocation Cracks" to explain phenomena produced by local impact on InSb. He suggests that cracks open and reseal quickly, leaving a wall of dislocations. We did not see evidence of such dislocation cracks in our etching studies on profiles of lap surfaces, but it is an interesting suggestion which should be tested further as a possible mechanism of abrasion damage.

J. J. GILMAN

General Electric
Research Laboratories

Effect of Imperfections
on Dissolution

ABSTRACT

EXPERIMENTAL EVIDENCE INDICATES
that it is the very core of a dislocation that is
most important in nucleating the dissolution process.
In contrast, some theories consider the elastic
strain energy field to be important. Dissolution inhibitors appear to slow down dissolution by adsorbing at special surface sites; namely, kinks in crystallographic steps.

1. INTRODUCTION

When the rate of dissolution of a solid is rapid, the
process is controlled by the rates of chemical and thermal diffusion in the solvent. As the dissolution rate (or the undersaturation of the solvent) becomes smaller, surface imperfections
of the solid play a role of increasing importance in dissolution
until they completely dominate the process. These general
features of the behavior are well known (1). However there is
some controversy about the mechanisms by which imperfections
affect the dissolution process. This paper attempts a better
definition of some of the mechanisms on the basis of simple
cause-and-effect arguments derived directly from experiments.

136

Refer to Fig. 1 for a definition of the various imperfections that will concern us.

The unit process in dissolution is the removal of a molecule from the corner of a kink in a surface step (Fig. 1). However the process can occur only if: (a) a step exists on the surface, (b) the step contains kinks, (c) the solvent is undersaturated at the particular kink corner in question. Any one or a combination of these factors can control the rate of dissolution. We shall not consider factor (c) because it can usually be minimized by an agitation that causes rapid flow of the solvent over the crystal surface.

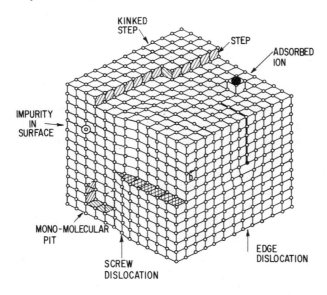

Fig. 1.   Surface imperfections on a crystal.

The edges of a crystal are good sources of steps and kinks during dissolution, so in practical cases the rate of dissolution is never limited by the need for these defects. However if a crystal is large, the rate of dissolution of the centers of its faces may be quite small if its edges are the only sources of steps and kinks. The first step in dissolution at the center of

a crystal face is the creation of a mono-molecular pit (Fig. 1).
If the bond energy in a simple cubic structure is ϕ then an energy of about 5ϕ is required to remove the first atom from a
perfect surface. This may be compared with about 3ϕ to remove an atom from a kink corner, and about 4ϕ to remove an
atom from a step edge. For an atom at the center of an edge
dislocation we can see that the energy is also roughly 4ϕ and is
therefore appreciably less than for a perfect surface. At very
low undersaturations, these energies are but part of the problem because a pit that is only one molecule in size may not be
stable. At moderate undersaturations, however, the slowest
stage in the process will be the formation of mono-molecular
pits, and this is the case that will be discussed here.

2. NUCLEATION OF STEPS

2.1 Vacancies and Impurities

Single lattice vacancies that happen to be situated at a
surface are, of course, small monomolecular pits. Therefore
they may influence dissolution under some conditions. However they and the steps that they might produce are difficult to
see, and the author is not aware of any attempts to study their
effects. The same is true of isolated impurity atoms. On the
other hand, clusters of lattice vacancies or impurity atoms can
sometimes be detected quite readily (2). They produce small
flat-bottomed etch pits during dissolution (Fig. 2); but the pits
stop growing deeper as soon as the cluster has dissolved away.

2.2 Dislocations

Dislocation lines are quite effective in acting as nucleation centers for dissolution steps. Fig. 3 demonstrates that
an etch pit that formed at a dislocation line in calcite stopped
getting deeper when the dislocation was moved away (3).
The effect of a dislocation line on dissolution nucleation
has been attributed to the effect of their elastic strain energies
on the chemical potential of the material nearby them (4). However this is a doubtful idea in both theory and practice. In
theory the elastic energy of a screw dislocation line does not

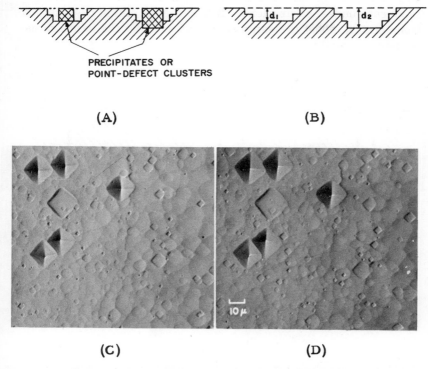

PRECIPITATES OR
POINT-DEFECT CLUSTERS

(A)   (B)

(C)   (D)

Fig. 2. Etch pits produced by point-defect clusters. (A) pits
         beginning to form at small precipitates; (B) pits be-
         come flat-bottomed when precipitates are gone; (C)
         small pits caused by precipitates in LiF; (D) same as
         (C) after more etching (large pits are at dislocations).

exist at the end of the dislocation that intersects a free surface.
A screw dislocation has a pure shear stress field that must
drop to zero at a free surface in order to satisfy elastic equilibrium (5).   Thus the surface layer around a screw dislocation
that lies normal to a free surface is stress free except at the
very core of the dislocation.   For an edge dislocation that intersects a free surface most of the strain energy remains, but
. this is not the case treated by the theory.
        It might be thought that the surface steps associated

with screw dislocations would be important for dissolution at moderate under-saturations. But both edge and screw dislocations etch in about the same way, and at about the same rates in many crystals.

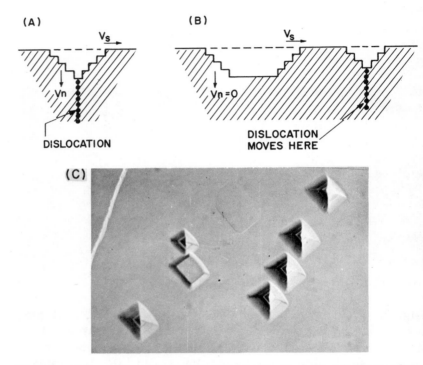

Fig. 3. Effect of motion of a dislocation line in calcite on dissolution. The crystal was etched in conc. formic acid (15 sec) then stressed at 500°C for 5 min, and finally etched again (15 sec). During the stressing one of the dislocations moved. X500, before reduction for publication.

Since neither the elastic strain-energy of dislocations nor the steps of their screw components seems of prime importance in dissolution, we are left with the large chemical energies of their cores. The energy has been calculated in the case of NaCl crystals (6), and it is found that the energy of the

NaCl ions at the center of an edge dislocation is about 0.3 ev, as compared with 0.1 ev for a pair of ions in the perfect sur- face. Much experimental evidence supports this as the most important feature of dislocations during dissolution:

(1) It is well-known that it is more difficult to etch dis- locations in metal crystals than in ionic and covalent ones. The cause might be poor techniques, but a relatively low energy in- crement for metal atoms near a dislocation core could also be a cause. It certainly cannot be attributed to a difference in el- astic strain energy because metal crystals have just as large, if not larger, Burgers vectors and elastic moduli as ionic and covalent crystals.

(2) When two dislocations get close together, much of their stress fields cancel out, especially if they are arrayed in a tilt-type grain boundary, or if they are the two ends of a small loop. Therefore if their strain energy fields were im- portant in dissolution, isolated dislocations would etch more rapidly than those in boundaries. In fact they etch at almost identical rates (7), so again it may be concluded that the stress fields of dislocations have little effect on dissolution at moder- ate undersaturations.

(3) Perhaps the best evidence of the importance of the core structures of dislocations in dissolution is the behavior of crystals that have the zinc blende structure, such as InSb (8). In these crystals the structure parallel to the {111} glide planes consists of pairs of planes separated by gaps that are wider than the spacing within each pair (Fig. 4). Each pair consists of one layer of one atom type and one layer of the other type. Therefore if positive edge dislocations are centered on In atoms, then negative ones are centered on Sb atoms. The core struc- tures are thus quite different chemically, and indeed it is found that they etch differently (8). The strain energy fields around positive and negative edge dislocations are identical, so their different etching behaviors can only be attributed to differences in their core structures.

3. MOVEMENT OF SURFACE STEPS

The rate of dissolution of a crystal can be markedly influenced by the presence of "inhibitors" in the solvent. For example, in pure water LiF crystals dissolve at a rate of about 900 Å/sec, but if 2×10^{-6} mole fraction of Fe^{+3} is added to the water the rate drops to about 90 Å/sec (9). Also Si crystals dissolve very rapidly in mixed HF and HNO_3, but if acetic acid is added to the solution the rate drops to a low value. The question arises: Does inhibition occur by the formation of a protective surface film? Does it occur by means of adsorption on surface steps or on kinks in steps? A general answer cannot be given at present but in particular cases the answers are known. For LiF crystals dissolving in water, the evidence strongly indicates that inhibition occurs by adsorption at kinks in surface steps (9).

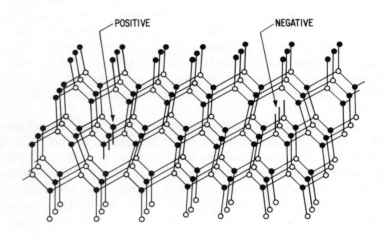

Fig. 4. Edge dislocations in the zinc blende crystal structure.

        The effect of inhibitor ions on etch pit formation in LiF is shown in Fig. 5. As the concentration of inhibitor in the solvent is increased, the sides of the etch pits become increasingly steep. It has also been found that the rate of deepening of the etch pits is almost independent of the inhibitor concentration. Therefore the rate at which steps move away from the place where they are nucleated must be strongly influenced by inhibitor ions. Since the rate of nucleation is unaffected by

the inhibitor, it may be concluded that no continuous protective
film is formed by the inhibitor.

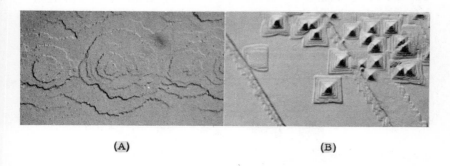

(A)   (B)

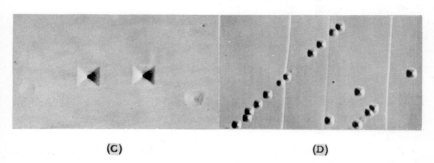

(C)   (D)

Fig. 5. Effect of Fe^{+3} concentration on etch pit formation in
         LiF. All specimens etched for two minutes in water
         plus FeF_3. X1000, before reduction for publication.
         (A) No Fe^{+3}; (B) 0.5 x 10^{-6} mole frac. Fe^{+3}; (C)
         2.0 x 10^{-6} mole frac. Fe^{+3}; (D) 8.0 x 10^{-6} mole frac.
         Fe^{+3}.

    Having established that the inhibitor for LiF dissolution
acts by slowing down the motion of steps, it is of interest to
know whether general adsorption of inhibitor ions along the
steps stops the nucleation of kinks, or whether the inhibitor acts
by adsorbing at kinks and thereby slows down their motion.
Present evidence shows the latter process to be the important
one because only very specific ions act as inhibitors. Out of
some 30 ions tried as inhibitors for LiF, only Fe^{+3} and Al^{+3}

were effective (9). The effective ions are ones that are known
to form strong complexes with fluorine. Kinks in surface steps
appear to be especially favorable sites for complex formation
because they have three anions arranged properly to receive
and form coordination bonds with a cation (Fig. 6).

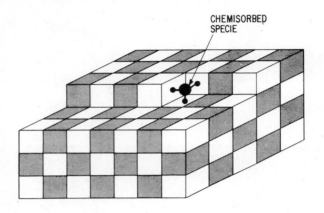

Fig. 6. Kink in < 100 > step on {100} surface of rocksalt structure as chemisorption site.

      Furthermore it is the rate of kink motion that controls
the process. In Fig. 5 the steps around a pit are square at a
certain concentration of Fe^{+3}, so they are composed almost entirely of steps lying in < 001 > directions. When the concentration of Fe^{+3} is increased the corners of the pits become rounded and the overall rate of motion of the steps is reduced. Since
the rounded steps do not lie parallel to a low index direction in
the surface, they necessarily contain high concentrations of
kinks. The rate of kink nucleation is therefore not limiting the
motion of the steps; rather it is the rate of kink motion that does
so.
      The adsorption of inhibitor ions at kinks does not appear
to be simple physical adsorption, but a chemisorption process,
because the shapes of etch pits are very sensitive to the adsorbed
specie. Thus Fe^{+3} adsorbs strongly on kinks in < 001 > steps
in a neutral solution, but in an acid solution it prefers kinks on
< 110 > steps (Fig. 7).

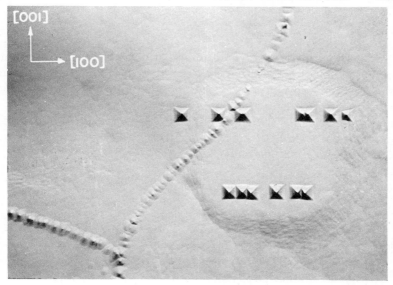

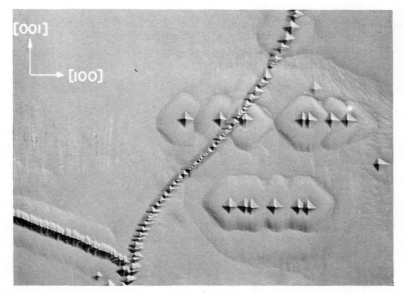

Fig. 7. Effect of solvent on inhibitor action. The same field
is shown for two solvents, both using Fe^{+3} as the inhibitor. X500, before reduction for publication. (A)
Water solvent, (B) mixed HF and HAc as solvent.

4. SUMMARY

The core structures of dislocations are more important during ordinary dissolution than the elastic stress fields. While this conclusion might not be true for very low undersaturations, experimental evidence indicates that it is true for moderate undersaturations. Evidence indicates that dissolution inhibitors act by chemisorbing at specific surface sites; namely, at kinks in crystallographic surface steps.

References

1. W. K. Burtom, N. Cabrera and F. C. Frank, Phil. Trans. Roy. Soc. London, Ser. A, 243, 299 (1951).
2. J. J. Gilman and W. G. Johnston, J. Appl. Phys., 29, 877 (1958).
3. R. E. Keith and J. J. Gilman, Acta Met., in press.
4. N. Cabrera and M. M. Levine, Phil. Mag., 1, 450 (1956).
5. A. H. Cottrell, Dislocations and Plastic Flow in Crystals, p. 36, Clarendon Press, 1953.
6. H. B. Huntington, J. E. Dickey and R. Thomson, Phys. Rev., 100, 1117 (1955).
7. J. J. Gilman and W. G. Johnston, in J. C. Fisher, W. G. Johnston, R. Thomson, and T. Vreeland, Jr., eds., Dislocations and Mechanical Properties of Crystals, p. 116, John Wiley & Sons, 1957.
8. J. D. Venables and R. M. Broudy, J. Appl. Phys., 29, 1025 (1958).
9. J. J. Gilman, W. G. Johnston and G. W. Sears, J. Appl. Phys., 29, 747 (1958).

DISCUSSION

N. CABRERA (University of Virginia): I do not agree that the strain energy of a screw dislocation does not necessarily influence the process of dissolution. It is true that a screw dislocation has no strain energy at the surface; however, it is the change in the total energy of the crystal that must be considered

and not the energy localized with the surface.   We can illustrate
this by referring to Fig. 1.   Here we show that the nucleation
of attack causing a little island "A" of the surface at the screw
dislocation to go into solution.   The dashed line shows the
original surface.   With the exception of the disturbance due to
the step, the surface configuration is the same before and after
removal of the island.   Consequently this is equivalent to

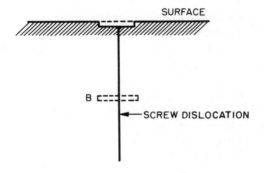

Fig. 1.   Schematic representation of the influence of screw
          dislocation on dissolution.

removing the same amount of strained material from B in the
bulk.   Thus we have reduced the total strain energy of the
screw dislocation.   It is this driving force then that can account
for pit formation at screw dislocations, even though the strain
energy at the surface is zero.   The above argument is based
on the assumption that nucleation occurs at a critical size area
which is substantially more than one atom.

　　　J. J. GILMAN: I think that removing a little island
from the surface of a crystal is not the kinetic equivalent of
removing a like amount of material from the bulk.   Since the
material at the surface is initially unstrained, strain energy is
not available there initially.   The strain energy must flow into
the region from the interior via elastic waves.   This requires

a finite length of time, and therefore will affect the kinetic
process. It seems much more realistic to me to try to interpret
the etching process in terms of the chemical bond configurations
at screw dislocations than to invoke vague ideas about the role of
the non-local elastic strain field.

J. W. FAUST, JR. (Westinghouse): I would like to comment on the atomic arrangement around a dislocation. Certainly
it is true that the surface cannot accommodate a shear stress
at a screw dislocation: however, to prevent the shear stress at
the surface, the atoms in the immediate vicinity of the screw
dislocation must move out of their equilibrium positions. Thus
their bonds are strained and the chemical potential will be
higher than if the screw dislocation were not present. It should
be possible then, as I have stated before, to devise an etch that
produces pitting as a result solely of this difference in chemical
potential: of course, it may in practice be very difficult to devise such etches for some metals.

N. CABRERA: We should not perhaps continue the
argument here; however, one point that we cannot overlook is
that you find no difference in the size of the etch pits at isolated
dislocations and at dislocations in walls where the strain energy
practically disappears.

I have a question concerning dislocations in walls. You
find a difference in etch pits at fresh and at aged dislocations.
Since some of your walls will be formed as a result of polygonization, would not dislocations in such walls be aged making
comparison of dislocation pits more complicated?

J. J. GILMAN: Your statement about dislocations in
polygonized walls is true; however, one also finds no difference
in the pits formed at dislocations in small elongated loops where
the strain energy is confined to a very small region around the
loop; here it is quite clear that the dislocation is fresh. Now,
with regard to the role of impurities that cause a dislocation to
be aged, one popular argument is that the impurities reduce the
strain energy because of Cottrell interaction; this would cause
the aged dislocations to etch more slowly, as we find in LiF.
It should be pointed out, however, that some impurities cause
dislocations to etch more rapidly, as in metals. In other words,
impurities both increase and decrease the chemical dissolution

rate at dislocations; one aspect of this has been mentioned for
III-V intermetallic compounds in a previous discussion by Dr.
Gatos (p. 78). This suggests to me that the effect of impurities
is primarily a chemical effect and changes of strain energy
play only a minor role.

H. C. GATOS (M. I. T.): I think that the zinc blende
type compounds, such as InSb, might really provide the best
proof for the specific chemical reactivity of dislocations mentioned by Dr. Gilman. I would like to illustrate this by briefly
mentioning some of our recent work [H. C. Gatos and M.
Lavine, J. Electrochem. Soc., 107, 427 (1960)]. In the case of
InSb, one face of a wafer cut along {111} planes terminates with
In atoms while the opposite face terminates with Sb atoms. Two
types of edge dislocations may be present in this compound:
(1) the extra plane terminates at the dislocation with a row of
In atoms, and (2) the extra plane terminates with Sb atoms.
Venables and Broudy [J. Appl. Phys., 29, 1025 (1958)] have
shown that only one type of dislocations are revealed by etch
pits and these only on one face. This face has been shown by
E. P. Warekois [unpublished results] to be the one that terminates in In atoms. We have shown that the surface terminating
in Sb atoms has a higher rate of dissolution than the In surface.
It is necessary to have a higher dissolution rate along the dislocation in order to have a pit formed; this is provided by In
dislocations intersecting the In surface. Sb dislocations intersecting the Sb surface, on the other hand, should form no pits
unless something is done to decrease the reactivity of the
surface Sb atoms such as I pointed out in the discussion of
Prof. Cabrera's paper.

B. ROSS (Wesson Metal): When the ferric ion sets
down at a kink would you expect it to form a stable compound
that locks this site completely from further dissolution?

J. J. GILMAN: Yes, the compound is not infinitely
stable but is stable enough to slow down the motion of the kink
by about an order of magnitude.

D. R. MASON (University of Michigan): The dislocation
pits in the photomicrographs you showed seemed to contain
steps of constant height. If this is the case, can you explain it?

J. J. GILMAN: I do not think that the step heights are as constant as you surmise. There is no satisfactory theory to explain how the monomolecular steps cluster as dissolution proceeds to form the observed steps.

S. BAIRD (Texas Instruments): I would like to suggest an experiment. You believe that the iron fluoride complex sets down at a kink and stops its motion. Further insight to this mechanism could be gained by substituting other transition elements that form stable complexes with fluorine; perhaps one or more of them will be too big to fit into the kink. Another way would be to use other complexing agents than fluorine for the iron in order to vary the size of the ion setting down at the kink.

J. J. GILMAN: I refer you to the paper by Gilman, Johnston, and Sears [J. Appl. Phys., 29, 747 (1958)]. We tried thirty different ions in an attempt to correlate the pinning of kinks with atomic radii, valence, and complex formation. The best correlation that was found is that metal ions complexing strongly with fluorine inhibit kink motion. Also, adding anions to an etching solution that form stronger complexes with the metal ions than does fluorine destroys the inhibiting action. We concluded that, in a good etchant, the metal inhibitor ions chemisorb by complexing with the fluorine ions that lie at kinks on the surface of LiF crystals. Adding stronger complexing agents than fluorine causes desorption.

J. W. FAUST, Jr.

*Westinghouse Research
Laboratories*

Etching of Metals
and Semiconductors

ABSTRACT

THE ADVANCES IN the growth, purity, and perfection of crystals has created a demand for etchants to reveal dislocations and to produce specific surface configurations. After a brief review of the etching processes, the various mechanisms by which etch pits form are discussed. Techniques for identifying dislocation pits and the application of pit and sphere studies to mechanism investigations are pointed out.

1. INTRODUCTION

The condition of a surface is of importance not only in studies and processes involving the surface itself but also in many investigations involving the bulk properties of materials. With the recent advances in crystal growth and purification, more rigorous demands are being made on crystal perfection, orientation, and special surface treatments. Etching plays a vital role in the preparation and characterization of crystals.

151

1. 1 Reasons for Etching

The reasons for etching can be grouped into four categories:

(a) Cleaning: In material preparation, it is often necessary to "clean" the surface between various steps. Cutting and other mechanical treatments leave a damaged layer that must be removed before certain studies can be made.

(b) Revealing dislocations: Dislocations and other lattice imperfections affect the strength, surface potential, electrical properties, and other properties of crystals. Etchants that reveal imperfections simplify studies of crystal perfection.

(c) Orientation of crystals: Many studies, such as dissolution, oxidation, and electrical effects require single crystals whose faces are of a definite crystallographic orientation. Crystals can be oriented by x-ray diffraction techniques, in which case the only requirement of the etch is that it remove the damaged layer. Orientation by optical methods, however, can in some cases give results comparable to x-ray diffraction techniques. For optical methods, etchants are required that reveal definite crystallographic planes.

(d) Miscellaneous: In this category, one can include standard metallographic etching and the many different requirements for specific surface properties such as the surface recombination velocity of semiconductors.

1. 2 Etching Processes

Although the scope of this paper is to discuss etch pitting, it seems appropriate to list the various etching processes since pitting can result from any of them.

(a) Chemical: The surface atoms undergo a chemical change. Only reactions that form a product that is removed from the surface during etching can be employed.

(b) Electrolytic: Current flow is employed to cause dissolution of the material in a suitable electrolyte.

(c) Thermal: Material is removed from the surface by vaporization in a vacuum or an inert atmosphere.

(d) Cathodic bombardment: The material is made the cathode in a glow discharge. The energy from the bombarding ions drives off the surface atoms of the material.

(e) Solvation: A liquid is used that is a solvent for the material to be etched.

(f) Alloying: Molten metals can be used as etchants by virtue of their ability to take certain solid materials into solution; this process is commonly known as alloying.

1.3 Definitions and Scope

The metallographer often distinguishes between the terms etching and chemical or electrolytic polishing; here, the term etching will be used not only from the metallographer's point of view but also to designate chemical and electrolytic polishing. Thus it will be necessary to define several terms that are used to characterize etching.

(a) Preferential: The etchant produces pits whose facets have a definite crystallographic orientation.

(b) Polish: The etchant produces a smooth surface with everything obliterated with the possible exception of grain boundaries.

(c) Nonpreferential: The etchant not only produces a polished surface but also reveals dislocations.

Any of the above types of etching can generally be used to satisfy (a) and (d) of Section 1.1; however, (b) and (c) of Section 1.1 require the use of a preferential or a nonpreferential etchant (i.e., etchants that produce definite types of pits).

2. ETCH PITS AND HILLOCKS

The number and origin of pits produced by a given etchant depend, to a large extent, on the type of surface. Basically there are two types of surfaces that are useful for etching, smooth and uniformly matte. Suitable smooth surfaces can be prepared by cleavage, electrolytic polishing, chemical polishing, or occasionally by mechanical polishing. Natural crystal faces or growth flats can often be used without further preparation. The uniformly matte surfaces, whose use will be mentioned later, are obtained by abrasion (1, 2).

When a smooth surface is etched with either a preferential or a nonpreferential etch, the attack is nucleated at discrete points on the surface causing pits. The shape of the pits depends on the etchant and also on the cause of the pit. Although it is possible for an etchant to form a monomolecular pit (a process we shall call surface nucleation), such a process does not lead to large pit formation except under special conditions. Surface nucleation requires a large energy; thus if it were not for edges and surface heterogeneities, etch rates would be quite low. Some of the heterogeneities that can cause pitting are:

(a) Dislocations that extend into the bulk of the crystal.

(b) Dislocations that have been produced by mechanical damage such as abrasion or scratching.

(c) Surface irregularities such as pits and growth or cleavage steps.

(d) Vacancy clusters.

(e) Surface layers such as an oxide that protect the surface except at pin holes or weak spots.

In addition to pit formation, it is possible for hillocks to be formed on the surface. Hillocks may be formed from humps on the pre-etched surface, protective spots on parts of the surface, or the growing together of etch pits.

2. 1 Dislocations

2. 11 Pit Nucleation. There are several mechanisms by which pits are formed at dislocations. They all involve the relative etch rates along the dislocation and of the surface or various planes revealed by the etchant. For pit formation, the etch rate along a dislocation must be greater than other etch rates in its vicinity (Fig. 1). The dislocation line has a certain amount of strain along it, even at the surface. It has been stated that a screw dislocation has no strain energy at the surface. It is true that the surface cannot sustain the stress at a screw dislocation; however, to relieve the stress at the surface, it seems logical that the atoms must rearrange themselves. In so doing, their bonds become strained and it is this strain which may cause nucleation of a pit at a screw dislocation. The

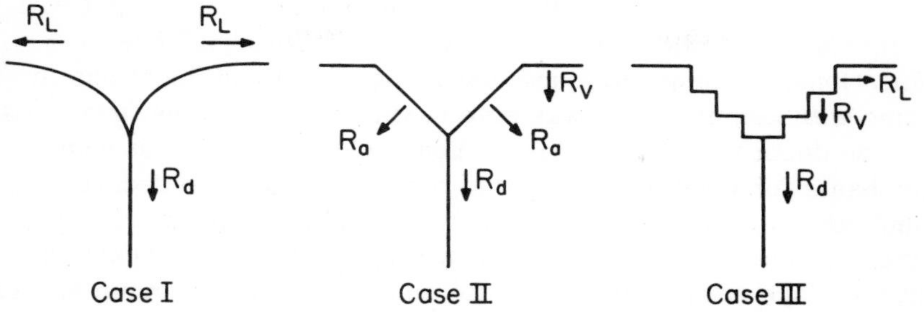

Fig. 1. Etching rates involved in pit formation at dislocations. R_d, etching rate along the dislocation; R_v, rate normal to the surface; R_L, lateral rate; R_a, rate along a crystallographic plane at an angle to the surface.

nucleation of a pit at a dislocation as a result of the strain energy depends upon the etchant. In principle, it should be possible to devise such an etchant for any material; however, it is only recently that it has been possible to do so for metals. There are a number of etchants that will cause the nucleation of pits at dislocations in semiconductors. This may be due solely to the strain energy or to the strain energy plus the existence of a space charge region around the dislocation. Allen and Smith (3) suggest that the extra trapping levels associated with a dislocation cause such a region, and that the number of carriers are reduced in the space charge region; thus the etching will be less and many pits produced at dislocations by the CP4 etchant (a mixture of HNO_3 + HF + Br_2 + CH_3COOH) will leave at least a raised perifery. Levesque (4) showed that electrolytic etching of germanium gave reduced etching along a p-n junction as evidenced by a thin ridge (at a p-n junction, the number of holes equals the number of electrons giving in effect a zero number of carriers).

A space charge region around a dislocation is not possible in metals; thus the strain energy alone or some other mechanism must cause a faster etching rate at the dislocation line. One way in which this can be accomplished is by the

segregation of impurities at the dislocations as shown by
Wyon and Lacombe (5). Purposely adding an impurity that will
segregate at a dislocation is known as "decorating" the dislocations. Gilman (6) found that by decorating dislocations in
zinc with cadmium, he was able to find an etchant that gave pits
at the decorated dislocations. Young (7) has found that some
etchants for copper require that the dislocations be decorated
and others require no decoration. Another method of changing
the relative etch rates is to use a reagent that will adsorb on
the surface causing the etch rate on the planes to become slower
than the rate along the dislocations. Gilman, Johnston, and
Sears (8) have proposed such a mechanism for the action of
ferric ion in the etching of LiF. Gatos and Lavine (9) have
reported that by the addition of surface active agents to etchants for the III-V intermetallic compounds, dislocations can
be revealed on the $\{111\}$ surfaces terminating in group V atoms.

Vermilyea (10) has suggested that pits formed at dislocations in silicon and germanium are the result of oxide films
formed during etching. Such a mechanism may account for the
variation in pit shapes obtained at dislocations in germanium
when the ratio of HF to HNO_3 is varied; however, the oxide
layer present on the surface before it is put into the etchant
cannot be ignored. It was found that an etchant containing 4
parts by volume conc. HF + 2 conc. HNO_3 + 4 of 5% $AgNO_3$ reveals
many tiny pits, including spirals, when the oxide layer is removed with HF prior to etching; the large pits that have been
associated with edge dislocations are also present. The oxide
layer, or other surface layers, formed by electrolytic or
chemical polishing, interfere in some cases with pitting at dislocations; this is evidenced by the fact that some etchants produce pits on freshly cleaved surfaces but not on the same surfaces after they have been chemically or electrolytically polished.

A further complication in revealing dislocations is
found in intermetallic compounds that exhibit a polar axis.
Several investigators (11, 12, 13, 14) have shown that numerous
etchants for the III-V intermetallic compounds produce pits at
dislocations on only one face of a slice whose faces are parallel
to $\{111\}$ planes. White and Roth (15) and Warekois and

Metzger (16) have identified that face as the one that terminates
with group III atoms. Similar results have been shown for the
{0001} faces of hexagonal intermetallic compounds, such as
SiC (17), CdS (18), and ZnS (19). Honess (20) found that HF
produces grooves on the positive edge of a quartz prism but not
on the negative edge. He suggested that on the positive edge
silicon occupied a prominent position.

    2. 12 Pit Morphology. The actual shape of the pit depends
upon the mode of attack of the etchant (i. e. , preferential or nonpreferential). Fig. 1 shows diagrams of three basic pit forms.
The pit formed by a nonpreferential etch (case I) will have
curved sides and frequently appear to be a shallow to deep
cone (Fig. 2) depending on the relative etch rates, R_L and R_d.

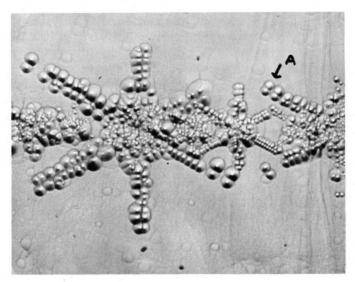

Fig. 2. Dislocations revealed on a natural growth face of
         germanium by a nonpreferential etch. Consult text for
         explanation of pit designated as A.
         X150, before reduction for publication.

The position of the point indicating the actual position of the
dislocation in the conical pit will often signify the angle the
dislocation makes with the surface as shown by Bardsley, Bell,

and Straughan (21) in germanium. If the dislocation should leave the confines of the pit, such as happens in dislocation half-loops or deformation causing it to migrate, R_d is no longer present in the pit and further etching will produce a flat at the point where the dislocation had been (pit marked "A" in Fig. 2). Prolonged etching with the nonpreferential etch eliminates the entire pit.

Case II of Fig. 1 shows the cross-section of a pit formed by a preferential etch at a dislocation on a material whose planes form closed figures, such as the cubic system or the pyramidal planes of the hexagonal system. The relative etch rates are $R_d > R_a \geq R_V$. For example, if the dislocation is normal to a $\{111\}$ surface, triangular pyramidal pits will be formed. These pits have smooth, rather than terraced, sides as shown in Fig. 3. If, however, the dislocation line is at an angle to a $\{111\}$ surface, the triangular pyramidal pit is lopsided (Fig. 5(b)), and two of the pit facets are terraced because the angle these facets make with the surface is no longer the angle of the slowest etching plane. Such pits can also be found in Fig. 5(a); however, they are difficult to distinguish because of the larger crystallographic pits formed by etching a uniformly matte surface.

Case III of Fig. 1 illustrates the cross-section of a pit formed in crystal systems, such as hexagonal, that have sets of planes that do not form closed figures. For hexagonal materials, R_V is the etch rate of the $\{0001\}$ planes and R_L the rate of a set of prism planes. The relationship between the various etch rates is $R_d > R_L > R_V$. The planes revealed depend to some extent on the etchant. Fig. 4 shows this type pit produced on α SiC by molten Na_2O_2 (17). The pyramidal pits are at the dislocations. Here the sides of the pits run in the $< 11\bar{2}0 >$ directions. Reynolds and Czyzak (18) reported that the action of HCl on CdS produced pits whose sides ran in the $< 11\bar{2}0 >$ directions and also pits oriented in the $< 10\bar{1}0 >$ directions.

It may well be that the pits produced by etching minerals (20) were at the sites of dislocations. In the case of apatite (22), the pits have been shown to be at dislocations. Honess and Jones (23) showed that the pits may be oriented symmetrically

Fig. 3.   Etch pits on β SiC.   Etchant: molten Na_2O_2.   X300, before reduction for publication.

or asymmetrically with respect to the structural symmetry of apatite depending on the optical activity of the tartaric acid utilized as the etchant.

When the dislocation leaves the confines of the pit in either case II or III, the faster rate R_d is no longer present and the pit will, on further etching, grow in a manner dictated by R_V, R_L, and R_a.   For example, a triangular pyramidal pit formed at a dislocation normal to a $\{111\}$ surface by an etchant that reveals {111} facets will become truncated, and it will be relatively easy to distinguish the pits that have lost their dislocations. If, however, the etchant reveals only {110} or {100} planes on a {111} surface, the pyramidal pits cannot become truncated, and it may not be possible to determine which pits lost their dislocations. If one knows the planes to which a given etchant is preferential, it is possible, in many cases, to predict the shape of the pits for any orientation.

Fig. 4. Etch pits on α SiC. Pyramidal pits are associated with dislocations; truncated pyramidal pits are not associated with dislocations. Etchant: molten Na_2O_2. X300, before reduction for publication.

2. 2 Mechanically Induced Dislocations

Dislocations can be introduced into some materials by cutting and abrading (1, 2) and by other mechanical processes (24, 25). The importance of care in handling surfaces has been pointed out (24) since scratches and other damage can result.

Etch pits form at these mechanically induced dislocations as at dislocations introduced during growth. In general, the mechanically induced dislocations are in the form of loops confined to thin layers at the surface. These dislocation loops can be removed by etching away the damaged surface layer. When they have been removed, the pits originally associated with these dislocations will be present; but since R_d is eliminated, further etching of the pits will be completely controlled by the etch rates of the various crystallographic planes. In Fig. 2 the pairs of etch pits radiating from the central core are surface half-loops. Pits marked "A" result from shallow surface half-loops being removed during etching. It is sometimes difficult to differentiate the pits at this stage from those caused by processes discussed in sections 2.4, 2.5, and 2.6. They can usually be differentiated from pits produced at surface irregularities (section 2.3) since the latter pits are generally larger.

2.3 Surface Irregularities

Etchants will attack either concave or convex irregularities on the surface, such as formed by gas bubbles during solidification or at irregular growth steps. The pits left after a dislocation has been removed usually give results similar to a concavity (sections 2.1 and 2.2). The shape of these pits or hillocks are determined by the orientation of the surface and the type of attack of the etchant (i.e., preferential or nonpreferential). There is no way at present to predict what planes will be revealed by a given etchant; it is not yet even possible to predict whether a given solution will act preferentially or nonpreferentially.

Studies of the dissolution of germanium in etchant consisting of various combinations of oxidizing agents and complexing agents have shown that the oxidizing agent apparently determines the plane to which the etchant is preferential while the complexing agent affects the rate of attack (26). For example, numerous etchants with HNO_3 as the oxidizing agent gave pits with $\{111\}$ facets; while etchants containing the same complexing agents but H_2O_2 as the oxidizing agent gave pits with predominantly $\{111\}$ and $\{100\}$ facets.

The planes on which an etchant acts preferentially are apparently not always determined by the oxidizing agent if one considers hydrogen ion as an oxidant. Politycki and Fischer (27) have studied the action of solutions of halogen acids on aluminum and found that HI produces pits with cube and octohedral facets, HBr and HCl yield cube facets only and HF at low concentrations yields octohedral facets only. They explained their results on the size of the halogen ion to the spacing of the aluminum atoms, considered as ions at the surface. Gualtieri, Katz, and Wolff (28) have used a similar argument to explain the pit morphology resulting from the gas phase etching of germanium and silicon.

In solvation etching, Gilman (29) reports that the solvent affects the direction of the edge of pits produced on LiF; water gives a < 100 > direction while acetic acid gives a < 110 > direction. Holden and Singer (30) show that square pits are produced on the cleavage face of calcium copper acetate hexahydrate by glacial acetic acid, while rectangular pits are formed in dilute acetic acid, and long streaks appear in pure water.

Batterman (31) has attempted to explain the appearance of facets on hillocks in terms of only the measured orientation dependence of the etch rate. Using this, he concluded that the $\{322\}$ planes are stable hillock facets on germanium etched with an $HF + H_2O_2 + H_2O$ mixture. Irving (32) in a further analysis of this approach concluded that for the same etchant the $\{310\}$ may also be a stable hillock facet on germanium; he also extended the work to include pit facets. This technique has not been used on other systems. Materials that have a polar axis, such as the III-V intermetallic compounds (11), may present further complexities; at least one must take into account the different etching rates at the two directions of the polar axis.

Pits of the nature described here are generally desirable in etching intended to reveal dislocations, as mentioned in section 2. 1; however, these pits faceted along definite crystallographic planes are the basis for orientation of crystals by optical techniques. The accuracy of optical techniques depends, in part, on the flatness of the facets. Wolff, Wilbur, and Clark (33) have listed the accuracy achieved for silicon and germanium. The accuracy obtained thus far for metals is not as good.

Since one desires only light reflections from etched facets, the entire surface of the sample should be covered with etch pits. This can be obtained by etching an abraded surface. Fig. 5 shows the results of the action of a preferential etch for germanium on an abraded and on a polished surface. The multitude of pits on a lapped surface raises an interesting question: are these pits caused mainly by the multitude of irregularities produced on the surface by abrasion or by the multitude of mechanically induced dislocations? In an attempt to answer this

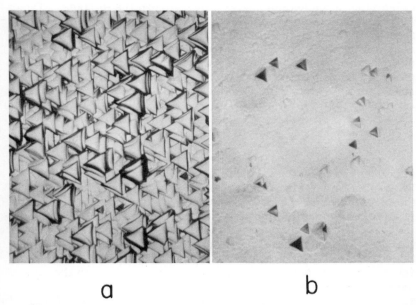

a   b

Fig. 5. $\{111\}$ surfaces of germanium etched for 1 minute (see text). (a) Lapped surface, (b) Chemically polished surface. X200, before reduction for publication.

question, hemispherical pits were abraded into chemically polished germanium surfaces. One group of these were etched with the damaged layer still present while another group had the damaged layer removed by chemical polishing. The samples were then etched in a mixture of $HNO_3 + HF + AgNO_3$ until the pits had assumed their limiting facets. No difference could be found in the pits. Thus the question still remains unanswered;

possibly both mechanisms enter into the pitting.

2.4 Vacancy Clusters

During the growth of crystals, vacancies are introduced in their equilibrium concentration at the melting point. The equilibrium number of vacancies is a function of temperature. Unless the crystal is cooled extremely slowly, it becomes super-saturated with vacancies. If dislocations are present, they will act as vacancy sinks. In dislocation free, or essentially dislocation free, material the supersaturation is relieved by the clustering of vacancies and by migration to the surface. Tweet (34) has associated the smooth tiny pits found on dislocation free germanium etched in CP4 with vacancy clusters. Pits resembling shallow cylinders have been found on essentially dislocation free dendrites. It has been suggested that these pits may be associated with vacancy clusters (35). Pitting associated with vacancy clusters has also been found in neutron irradiated materials.

2.5 Surface Layers

Before an etchant can attack the material it must, in many cases, dissolve a surface layer, often an oxide. This layer may be so thin and dissolve at a much higher rate than the base material that its presence goes unnoticed; if it is slowly attacked, there is a noticeable time delay (induction period). The surface layer can vary in thickness. The etchant will attack through the thinnest part first. Since the oxide confines the lateral etching action, pits will be formed at such spots. In many cases, the etchant dissolves through the rest of the oxide before very deep well-shaped pits can form; the results are shallow pits such as the background of Figs. 2 and 5(b). Amelinckx (36) has shown that this mechanism accounts for shallow hexagonal pits often noticed on etched α SiC. The oxide forms epitaxially and has the direction of its hexagonal sides $30°$ to the $<11\overline{2}0>$ direction in SiC; the shallow pits have this orientation. Higuchi (37) pointed out that Suzuki explained in this matter certain pits formed on α-brass by thermal etching. This process can be used to good advantage; Higuchi (37) employed it in forming etch pits in ice crystals. He coated the surface of the ice with a plastic replica solution and etched the ice by evaporation below freezing in an atmosphere unsaturated with respect to ice. The plastic film had many tiny pin holes through which evaporation could take place. Since the plastic film was not lost, deep pits with crystallographic facets resulted.

2.6 Miscellaneous Causes

Examination of numerous etched surfaces shows a number of pits produced by other causes, not all of which are known. Grease and other materials can protect the surface from etching; these spots generally show up as hillocks (31). Etchants that evolve gases often produce pits or hillocks at the surface due to bubbles nucleating on the surface (3,38). Very small particles of a second phase (29) or imbedded abrasive particles can cause hillocks or pits depending on whether it is less or more rapidly attacked than the rest of the surface. Segregation of impurities has been suggested as the cause of some spiral appearing pits (39). There are many types of pits which have the appearance of dislocation pits (40,41,42), but their origin is not understood (Fig. 6).

3. TECHNIQUES FOR THE IDENTIFICATION OF DISLOCATION PITS

Acceptable techniques for showing a one-to-one correspondence between etch pits and dislocations are:

(a) Count of pits on intersecting lineage lines (43).

(b) Comparison between calculated and observed etch pit densities on plastically deformed samples (44,45).

(c) Comparison of measured distances between pits on a lineage line to those calculated from x-ray orientation differences across the boundary (46).

(d) Direct observation of decorated dislocations (47,48).

(e) Special x-ray techniques (49,50).

4. ETCHING OF HEMISPHERICAL PITS AND SPHERES

In a study of the dissolution of silicon in NaOH (51), it was found that the $\{111\}$ surfaces have a slower etching rate than the $\{100\}$ and $\{110\}$ surfaces. Furthermore, from Fig. 7 it can be seen that within experimental error, the $\{100\}$ and the $\{110\}$ surfaces etch at the same rate. It is known that the slowest etching planes form the limiting facets on a concave surface, while the fastest etching planes form the limiting facets on a convex surface. To prove that the $\{111\}$ planes had the slowest

Fig. 6. Pit produced on germanium by etching in molten indium. Cause of pit unknown. X1200, before reduction for publication.

etching rate, hemispherical pits were produced on {111}, {110}, and {100} surfaces by grinding and then etching to their limiting form. The results are shown in Fig. 8. The angles between the facets, measured with an optical goniometer, showed that the pit on the {111} surface was entirely bounded by {111} planes (three of the side facets of the hexagonal pit "a" are parallel to the opposite facets by undercutting the surface.) The pit on the {100} surface, however, was truncated by a {100} plane and the pit on the {110} surface was bounded at each end with a {100}

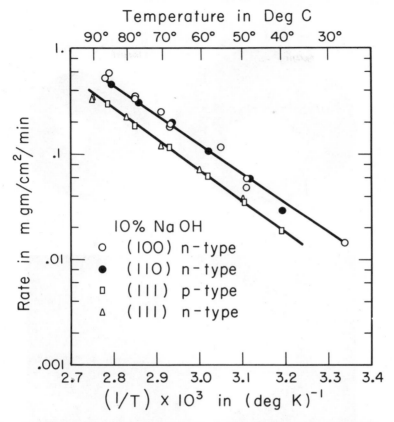

Fig. 7.. Dependence of the dissolution rate of silicon in 10%
        NaOH on temperature.

plane (all other facets on these pits were {111} planes). The
reasons for the {100} facets will appear elsewhere (51). To
determine whether the {110} and {100} surfaces actually etched
at the same rates, spheres of silicon were etched to their
limiting form. Fig. 9(a) shows that the {100} planes have the
fastest etching rate.

The activation energy for the reaction was determined
at several NaOH concentrations. The activation energy for the
10% solution, Fig. 7, was approximately 13 kcal/mole; for 25% and
50% solutions, the approximate value was 17 kcal/mole. Since
the etching rates were found to be in the same order (i. e. ,
{111} < {110} = {100}) and the pits showed the same facets for
all concentrations, a sphere was etched in 30% NaOH. The

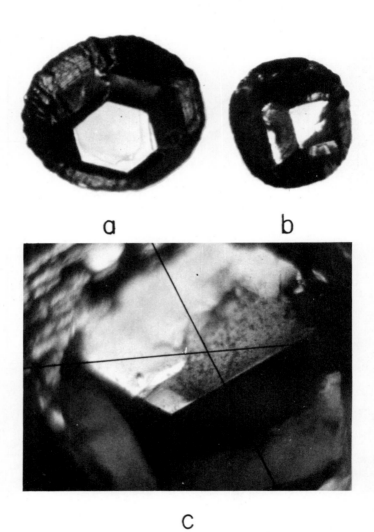

Fig. 8. Facets produced in hemispherical pits in silicon by
         NaOH. (a) {111} surface, (b) {100} surface, and (c)
         { 110} surface. X30, before reduction for publication.

limiting form was found to be a tetrahexahedron, Fig. 9(b), indicating that the fastest etching planes were of the form {hk0 }.

a   b   c

Fig. 9. Silicon spheres etched to limiting shapes. (a) 10%
NaOH, (b) 30% NaOH, (c) CP4. X10, before reduction
for publication.

For comparison, Fig. 9(c) shows that a nonpreferential etchant
leads to a smaller sphere, as would be expected for an etchant
that does not act preferentially on any plane.
    In many respects the action of NaOH on aluminum and
silicon is similar. Streicher (52) reported an activation energy
of 13.7 kcal/mole for the dissolution of aluminum in 2% NaOH.
Orem (53) studied the action of 15% NaOH on spheres of aluminum and on holes drilled into plates whose surfaces were oriented in the three main crystallographic planes. He found that
the relationship between the etch rates was $\{111\} < \{110\} < \{100\}$.

5. SUMMARY

    An attempt was made to show that not all pits or hillocks
produced on surfaces by any of the various etching processes
are formed at dislocations. Some of the causes of etch pitting
were discussed, and techniques for differentiating between the
various pits were described.
    Etching of spheres and hemispherical pits to their limit-
ing form is desirable in the determination of etching mechanisms.

References

1. T. M. Buck, this volume, p. 107.
2. L. E. Samuels, this volume, p. 82.
3. J. W. Allen and K. C. A. Smith, J. Electronics, 1, 439 (1956).
4. P. Levesque, J. Appl. Phys., 27, 1104 (1956).
5. G. Wyon and P. Lacombe, Rept. Conf. on Defects in Crystalline Solids, London, 1954, 187 (1955).
6. J. J. Gilman, J. Metals, 8, 998 (1956).
7. F. W. Young, Jr., Bull. Am. Phys. Soc., 5, 190 (1960).
8. J. J. Gilman, W. G. Johnston, and G. W. Sears, J. Appl. Phys., 29, 747 (1958).
9. H. C. Gatos and M. C. Lavine, J. Appl. Phys., 31, 743 (1960).
10. D. A. Vermilyea, Acta Met., 6, 381 (1958).
11. J. W. Faust, Jr. and A. Sagar, J. Appl. Phys., 31, 331 (1960).
12. H. C. Gatos and M. C. Lavine, J. Electrochem. Soc., 107, 427 (1960).
13. H. A. Schell, Z. Metallk., 48, 158 (1957).
14. J. D. Venables and R. M. Broudy, J. Appl. Phys., 29, 1025 (1958).
15. J. G. White and W. C. Roth, J. Appl. Phys., 30, 946 (1959).
16. E. P. Warekois and P. H. Metzger, J. Appl. Phys., 30, 960 (1959).
17. J. W. Faust, Jr., in J. R. O'Connor and J. Smiltens, eds., SiC - A High Temperature Semiconductor, Pergamon Press, 1960.
18. D. C. Reynolds and S. J. Czyzak, J. Appl. Phys., 31, 94 (1960).
19. S. J. Czyzak and D. C. Reynolds, Bull. Am. Phys. Soc., 5, 190 (1960).
20. A. P. Honess, The Nature, Origin and Interpretation of the Etch Figures on Crystals, J. Wiley & Sons, 1927.
21. W. Bardsley, R. L. Bell, and B. W. Straughan, J. Electronics, 5, 19 (1958).
22. L. V. Lovell, Acta Met., 6, 775 (1958).
23. A. P. Honess and R. J. Jones, Bull. Geol. Soc. Am., 48, 667 (1937).
24. J. W. Faust, Jr., Am. Soc. Testing Materials, Spec. Tech. Publ., No. 246,(1958).
25. W. C. Dash, in H. C. Gatos, ed., Properties of Elemental and Compound Semiconductors, p. 195, Interscience Publishers 1960.

26. J. W. Faust, Jr., unpublished results.
27. A. Politycki and H. Fischer, Z. Elektrochem., 57, 393 (1953).
28. J. G. Gualtieri, M. J. Katz, and G. A. Wolff, Bull. Am. Phys. Soc., 3, 376 (1958).
29. J. J. Gilman, this volume, p. 136.
30. A. Holden and P. Singer, Crystals and Crystal Growing, Doubleday and Co., 1960.
31. B. W. Batterman, J. Appl. Phys., 28, 1236 (1957).
32. B. A. Irving, J. Appl. Phys., 31, 109 (1960).
33. G. A. Wolff, J. M. Wilbur, Jr., and J. C. Clark, Z. Elektrochem., 61, 101 (1957).
34. A. G. Tweet, J. Appl. Phys., 30, 2002 (1959).
35. J. W. Faust, Jr., and H. F. John, Bull. Am. Phys. Soc., 5, 165 (1960).
36. S. Amelinckx, G. Strumane, and W. W. Webb, J. Appl. Phys., submitted for publication.
37. K. Higuchi, Acta Met., 6, 636 (1958).
38. N. Holonyak, Jr., J. Appl. Phys., 26, 121 (1955).
39. A. R. Lang, J. Appl. Phys., 28, 497 (1957).
40. V. V. Damiano and M. Herman, J. Franklin Inst., 267, 303 (1959).
41. H. F. John and J. W. Faust, Jr., unpublished.
42. G. K. Wehner, J. Appl. Phys., 29, 217 (1958).
43. S. Amelinckx, Acta Met., 2, 848 (1954).
44. A. A. Hendrickson and E. S. Machlin, Acta Met., 3, 64 (1955).
45. F. L. Vogel, J. Metals, 8, 946 (1956).
46. F. L. Vogel, W. G. Pfann, H. E. Corey, and E. E. Thomas, Phys. Rev., 90, 489 (1953).
47. W. C. Dash, J. Appl. Phys., 27, 1193 (1956).
48. S. Amelinckx, in L. Marton, ed., Methods of Experimental Physics, Vol. 6, Part A, p. 321, Academic Press, 1959.
49. J. B. Newkirk, Trans. Am. Inst. Mining, Met. Petrol. Engrs., 215, 483 (1959).
50. J. Bonse, Z. Physik, 153, 278 (1958).
51. J. W. Faust, Jr., to be published.
52. M. A. Streicher, J. Electrochem. Soc., 93, 285 (1948).
53. T. H. Orem, J. Research Natl. Bur. Standards, 58, 157 (1957).

DISCUSSION

J. J. GILMAN (General Electric): I would like to comment on the mechanism of the formation of terraced, or striated, etch pits. The terraces are formed, at least in some cases, as a result of variations in the concentration of impurities segregated at dislocations. If one cools a specimen quickly from a high temperature and then allows the specimen to age, impurities tend to segregate at dislocations; the rate of nucleation of mono-molecular pits along such dislocation lines will be affected by the presence of impurity precipitates. If, for example, the impurity slows down dissolution, the rate of nucleation of monomolecular pits will be high until an impurity precipitate (the black dots in Fig. 1) is encountered and then the nucleation rate will drop. During the time when the nucleation rate is low,

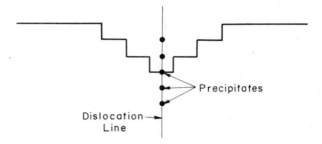

Fig. 1.   Formation of terraced pit.

the step formed during the period of high nucleation rate will advance away from the dislocation line. Then when the precipitate has been excavated by dissolution around it, the nucleation rate will increase and the cycle will repeat, Fig. 1, giving a pit with a number of terraces. Two pieces of fairly direct experimental evidence support this mechanism for LiF. The first involves aged dislocations. One can actually see tiny precipitates coming out of the center of terraced pits; and each time a new terrace appears, a precipitate follows. The second is that fresh dislocations, that is dislocations put into a crystal mechanically at room temperature, which have no such impurity precipitates, form pits with smooth sides rather than terraced ones.

J. W. FAUST, JR.: There are several mechanisms for the formation of terraced pits. You have given one of the mechanisms that account for such pits resulting from an etch that reveals planes which form a closed figure. It is possible that this mechanism also is operative for materials where the planes revealed by the etch form an open figure, such as most of the molten salt etches on hexagonal SiC. Since these etches produce terraced pits, there is no reason to assume that the precipitate mechanism is playing a role here. The terraced pits were found on very pure (colorless) hexagonal SiC as well as more impure (colored) samples. Another mechanism that is operative in materials whose etching planes form closed figures, such as cubic SiC and other materials with a diamond-type lattice, accounts for terraced asymmetric pits. These are formed at dislocations that are inclined to the surface. The actual angle that the dislocation must make with the surface in order to get such pits depends upon the orientation of the surface and the planes revealed by the etch. Such pits are produced on $\{111\}$ surfaces of germanium by some etchants.

W. H. BRATTAIN (Bell Telephone Laboratories): Why is it that electrochemists, or chemists, go on devising etches yet refuse to admit that there is anything intelligent about the process?

J. W. FAUST, JR.: I cannot speak for all the chemists, physicists, and metallurgists working on etches, but I do know of a number of groups that not only admit that these processes are intelligent but that have been studying various systems in detail in an effort to place the devising of etches on a firm scientific basis.

III

ELECTRODE BEHAVIOR
OF METALS
AND SEMICONDUCTORS

H. GERISCHER
Max Planck Institute

Metal and Semiconductor
Electrode Processes

ABSTRACT

THE KINETICS OF reactions at metal and
semiconductor electrodes involving ion transfer
or electron transfer are compared. It is shown
that the electrode behavior depends heavily on the
distributions of electron energy levels in the solid
and its surface. Some examples are given with
emphasis on semiconductors.

1. INTRODUCTION

Electrode reactions are heterogeneous chemical reactions in which stoichiometric transfer of electric charges takes
place between the electrode and the electrolyte. The kinetics
of such reactions depend not only on concentration and chemical structure, but also on the electrical conditions in and near
the phase boundary. Semiconductor and metal electrodes present very different electrical conditions. Here we shall discuss current-potential curves which show the significance of
these differences with respect to the mechanism of electrode
reactions.

It is convenient to distinguish between two types of
electrode reactions:

177

(1) Reactions with ion transfer

(2) Reactions with electron transfer.

Before the reactions themselves are discussed, a brief comparison will be made of the electrical conditions at metals and at semiconductors in contact with an electrolyte.

2. ELECTRICAL PROPERTIES OF ELECTRODE INTERFACES

Because an electrode can exchange charged particles with the electrolyte, charges of opposite sign will normally be accumulated near the electrode-electrolyte interface. Thus a potential difference arises between the electrode and the electrolyte which changes the free energy of the charged particles in the two phases. Although the real potential difference is not measurable in absolute terms, different states can be compared easily on a relative scale.

The distribution of the charges in the electrical double layer follows the laws of electrostatics as long as equilibrium conditions can be assumed (little or no current). The system behaves like a plate capacitor with thick plates of different type of conductivity and with different concentrations of mobile carriers near them (1).

The electrical charges in the double layer are not actually concentrated in two planes at the interface but have a more or less diffuse part extending into the interior of the phases. The depth of this diffuse part depends predominantly on the concentration of mobile carriers in each phase. In a metal the concentration of mobile electrons is so high that practically all the charges behave like surface charges. In the electrolyte solution the situation is similar only at very high electrolyte concentrations. In dilute solutions, part of the potential difference occurs in a region of 10 - 100 Å in the solution phase. This has been verified by comparing experimentally measured capacities with calculated ones using a model of this type.

In most semiconductors the concentration of mobile carriers (electrons or holes) is very low. Therefore a diffuse part of the double layer can extend into the interior of a semiconductor electrode (2) (this point is discussed in more detail by

H. J. Engell in this volume). An important consequence is
that concentrations of electrons and holes in the surface can
change with polarization by several orders of magnitude; in a
metal surface the concentration of electrons remains relatively
constant and only their potential energy changes with polarization.

Other aspects of the electrode-electrolyte interface
must also be considered, such as specific adsorption of charged
particles from the solution at the electrode and the formation
of traps at the semiconductor surface. These aspects will be
only schematically illustrated here. Fig. 1 shows several
cases of electrode-electrolyte interfaces and points out the
most important differences between metal and semiconductor
electrodes.

3. KINETICS OF ELECTRODE REACTIONS WITH ION TRANSFER

Electrolytic dissolution processes will be discussed
here since it is normally very difficult to electrodeposit semiconductors. Results obtained with silver on one hand and with
germanium on the other will be presented since these cases
are best understood.

3.1 Metals

The dissolution process begins with an atom in a half
crystal position at the surface. In the case of silver, it can
be shown that two steps can be experimentally distinguished
(3, 4): (1) moving of half crystal atoms into adsorption positions
on the surface and (2) transfer of silver ions from adsorption
positions through the inner double layer into the solution.

The adsorbed atoms formed in step 1 are mobile on the
surface and must be considered as belonging to the metallic
phase although their bonding to the metal is considerably ionic
in character. Pertinent results were obtained by investigating
the dependence of the equilibrium concentrations of adsorbed
atoms on the equilibrium potential in the case of a silver electrode (3). It was shown that the adsorbed atoms are partially

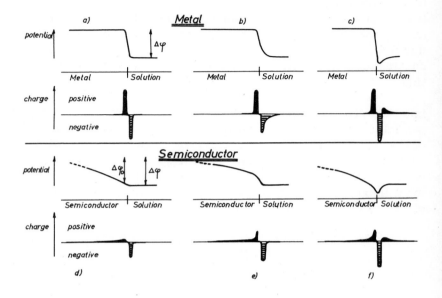

Fig. 1.   Electrical potential (φ) and charge distribution at the metal-electrolyte interface (a-c) and semiconductor-electrolyte interface (d-f).

(a) very concentrated solution; (b) moderately dilute solution; (c) dilute solution with specific anion adsorption; (d) semiconductor with no surface states; (e) semiconductor with surface states (traps); (f) semiconductor with traps and specific adsorption of anions (dilute solution).

hydrated which reflects some contribution of the ionic state of these atoms, although the quantum states of the valency electrons of the adsorbed atoms remain in close resonance with the other metal electrons.

Complete hydration and ionization occurs in step 2 in a more or less continuous way. In the case of silver, step 2 is much faster than step 1, but that cannot be expected as a general rule. Generally step 2 should be slow when the solvation shell is very stable and differs in structure from the adsorbed state which in many cases is true.

In addition to the two-step mechanism of dissolution a direct reaction of half crystal atoms forming hydrated ions (step 3) is possible. This direct reaction path can be favored under strong electrical polarization (5). Fig. 2 illustrates the reaction mechanism at a silver electrode in a noncomplexing aqueous solution.

Electrolytic polarization of such an electrode changes primarily the rate of the charge transfer reaction (step 2 or 3) while the rate of step 1 can be altered appreciably only by changes of the concentration of the adsorbed atoms or the half crystal atoms. The reason is that the activation energy of the charge transfer reaction varies with the shift of electrical

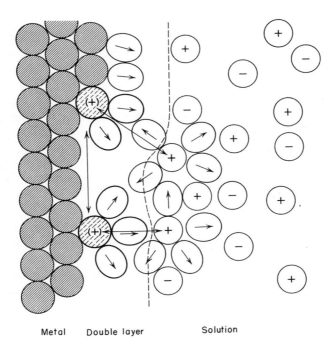

Metal   Double layer   Solution

Fig. 2. Schematic illustration of the reaction paths for the dissolution of metals (silver).

potential in the inner region of the Helmholtz double layer where the activated complex of the reaction is formed. The linear shift of the activation energy with the electrode potential or overvoltage η leads to an exponential relationship between the reaction rate (current, j^+ or j^-) and electrode potential:

$$j^+ \sim \exp\left(\alpha \frac{\mathcal{F}\eta}{RT}\right) \tag{1a}$$

$$j^- \sim \exp\left(-\beta \frac{\mathcal{F}\eta}{RT}\right) \tag{1b}$$

which has been confirmed many times experimentally. The transfer coefficients α and β represent the fraction of the total free energy change for the transfer of the ion to the transition state in the double layer. $\mathcal{F}$ is the Faraday constant.

Silver is a rather noble metal. Most of the less noble metals behave in a more complex fashion because they often form intermediate surface compounds by reacting chemically or electrochemically with the solution. Such systems are often very similar to semiconductors because the surface compounds form films with semiconductor properties. The best known examples of this type are associated with passivity where semiconducting oxide films cover the metals. It is therefore possible to find examples which are intermediate in behavior between metals and semiconductor electrodes.

3.2 Semiconductors

The behavior of semiconductors is expected to be different from that of metals first of all because of differences in crystal structures. Generally the atoms in metals have a greater number of nearest neighbors than the atoms in semiconductors. The situation is similar for atoms in half crystal positions. All complex chemical reactions, where many chemical bonds are broken and rearranged, occur in steps. Usually a reaction involving a greater number of steps and with a relatively small change in structure in a single step takes place faster than a similar reaction with more pronounced changes in a single step. Therefore metals should normally react faster than semiconductors (they should require a smaller overvoltage for electrolytic dissolution at a given rate) because metallic bonds can be broken much more continuously than chemical bonds in semiconductors.

Experience with germanium and silicon confirms the fact that high overvoltages are needed to overcome the energy barrier for dissolution. Moreover the normal chemical bond in these crystals is so stable that dissolution can only occur at places where chemical bonds are associated with defects. This has been shown by the experiments of Brattain and Garrett (6) who found that the supply of holes to the surface could become rate determining for the dissolution of a germanium electrode. Thus at least one hole is needed in the rate determining step to break the chemical bond of a surface atom with the crystal. The situation here is very unusual in that the breaking of a single chemical bond at a solid surface can be directly recognized. Fig. 3 shows the electrolytic dissolution of two n-type Ge electrodes, where the supply of holes is limited, which is to be contrasted to the dissolution of a p-type electrode where there is an unlimited supply of holes at the surface (7). As shown in Fig. 4, the dissolution rate can also be limited by the supply of chemical species needed for the formation of the final ions in solution (7). Fig. 4 also shows that hydroxyl ions lead to formation of metagermanate ions much faster than do water molecules. A similar behavior has also been found with fluoride ions.

As a result of our investigation of the dissolution of germanium (7) we arrived at a detailed mechanism of germanium dissolution in alkaline solutions (Fig. 5). This mechanism is an extension of that given previously by Turner (8).

For the present purpose, the important point in connection with the behavior of metal and semiconductor electrodes is the following: In semiconductor electrodes the rate-determining step is not primarily influenced by the change in the electric field in the region between the electrode surface and the electrolyte. The electric field in this region is, in fact, only slightly altered because of the very diffuse distribution of electrical charges in the interior of the semiconductor (see Fig. 1), provided there is no degeneracy of states in the surface.

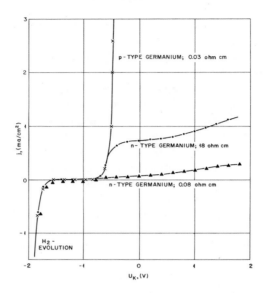

Fig. 3. Current-potential curves for dissolution of germanium
in 0. 05N NaOH (potential vs. N-calomel electrode).

The rate of the dissolution reaction is changed with
changes in electrode potential only indirectly and as a result
of changes in the surface concentration of holes. The situation
is somewhat more complicated if the surface traps and specific
adsorption of OH⁻ ions (7) are taken into consideration. These
aspects will not be discussed here. However as long as the
concentration of holes in the surface varies exponentially with
the total potential difference, an exponential relation is obtained between electrode potential and rate of dissolution of the
type expressed by Eq. (1a). Such a relationship has been demonstrated experimentally (2, 6, 7, 8). But for semiconductors
the physical meaning of the transfer coefficient is very different than for metals. In semiconductors, a change in overvoltage hardly affects the activation energy but it affects appreciably the concentration of the reactants at the interface.

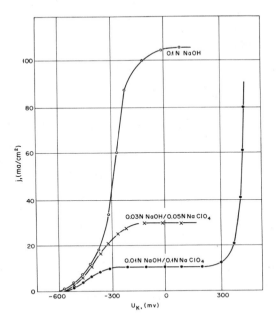

Fig. 4. Current-potential curves of p-type Ge in solutions containing different amounts of OH⁻ ions.

4. KINETICS OF ELECTRODE REACTIONS WITH ELECTRON TRANSFER

Transfer of electrons from or to an electrode results
in reduction or oxidation of species in the solution. If the solution contains both components of a redox system a definite
equilibrium potential difference is established by means of electron exchange. Following the treatment of Gurney and
Fowler (9) electrons can be exchanged only between levels of
equal potential energy. Using the Frank-Condon principle, the
energy levels (ΔE) of electron states in the solution are given
by the energy change associated with the reaction:

$$\text{Ox}_{(solv.)} + e_\infty^- \;\rightleftarrows\; \text{Red}_{(solv.)}$$

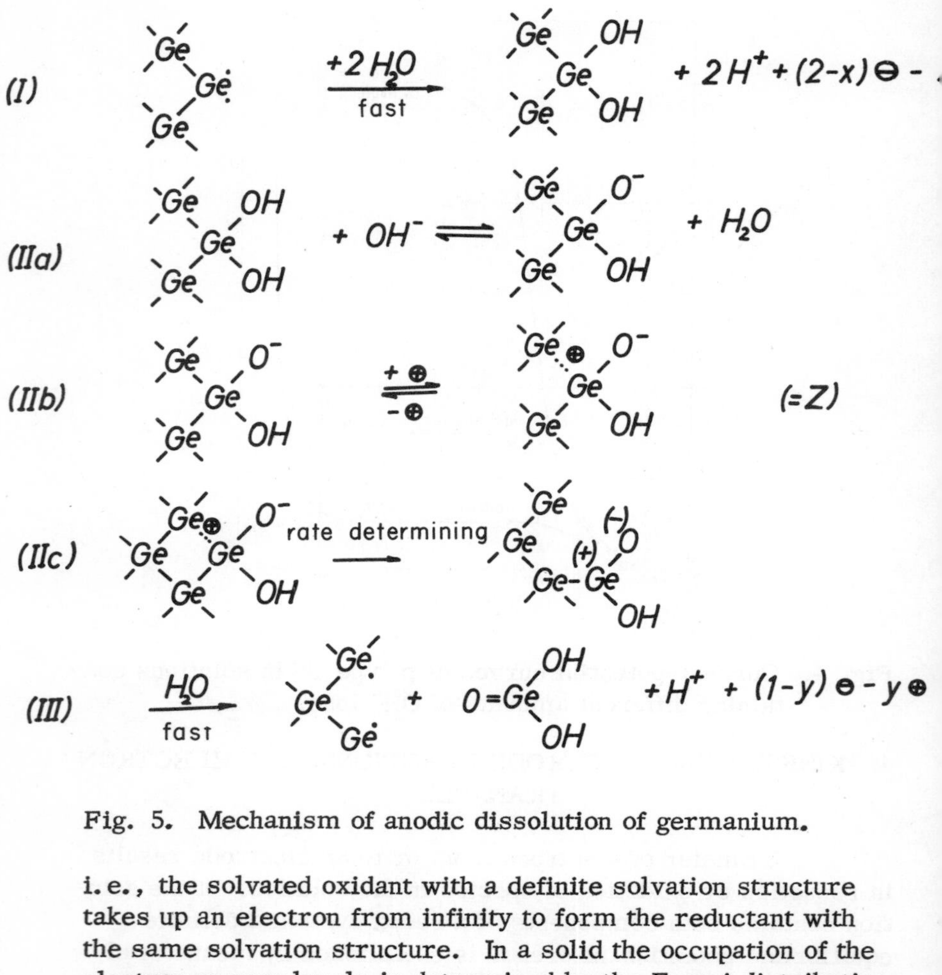

Fig. 5. Mechanism of anodic dissolution of germanium.

i.e., the solvated oxidant with a definite solvation structure takes up an electron from infinity to form the reductant with the same solvation structure. In a solid the occupation of the electron energy levels is determined by the Fermi distribution function. In an electrolyte also, there are occupied (reduced species) and unoccupied (oxidized species) electron levels with a statistical distribution of energies which is governed by the thermal distribution of solvation structures. The density of occupied electron levels D_{red} (ΔE) is proportional to the concentration of the red. constituent and its distribution function W_{red} (ΔE). An equivalent situation exists for the density function D_{ox} of unoccupied electron levels in the solution which is proportional to c_{ox} and W_{ox} (ΔE):

$$D_{red} = c_{red} W_{red} (\Delta E) \tag{2a}$$

$$D_{ox} = c_{ox} W_{ox} (\Delta E) \tag{2b}$$

Distribution functions W (ΔE) for a redox system are shown schematically in Fig. 6. Different redox systems differ mainly in the amount of overlapping of these two functions.

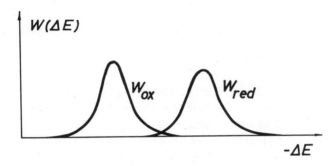

Fig. 6.   Thermal distribution of energy levels for electron transfer between infinity and a redox system in solution.

Let us assume now that the density function of energy levels for electrons in the solid is D (ΔE). The distribution of electrons is governed by the Fermi distribution function:

$$f (\Delta E - E_F') = \cfrac{1}{1 + \exp (\cfrac{\Delta E - E_F'}{RT})} \tag{3}$$

E_F' being the Fermi level under these special conditions where the solid is in contact with the electrolyte on a scale related to ΔE. Because the energy of electrons in the solid in relation to the solution depends on the electrical potential difference $\Delta\varphi$ between the solid and the solution we have:

$$E_F' \equiv E_F - \mathcal{F}\Delta\varphi \qquad (4)$$

E_F being the Fermi level of uncharged metal in molar units and $\mathcal{F}$ the Faraday constant.

Then the anodic and cathodic currents are proportional to the following integrals:

$$j^+ \sim c_{red} \int_{\Delta E=-\infty}^{\infty} \kappa(\Delta E)D(\Delta E)\,[1-f(\Delta E - E_F')]\,D_{red}(\Delta E)d(\Delta E)$$
$$(5a)$$

$$j^- \sim c_{ox} \int_{\Delta E=-\infty}^{\infty} \kappa(\Delta E)D(\Delta E)f(\Delta E - E_F')\,D_{ox}(\Delta E)d(\Delta E) \quad (5b)$$

κ is a probability factor for the tunneling of electrons through the energy barrier at the surface which also will depend on the energy level ΔE of electrons.

When the Fermi level of electrons in the solid is the same as the mean free energy ΔF_o for the redox reaction in the solution,

$$E_F' \equiv E_F - \mathcal{F}\Delta\varphi_o = \Delta F_o \qquad (6)$$

then we have equilibrium conditions:

$$j^+ = j^- = j_o \qquad (7)$$

where j_o is the exchange current density at equilibrium.

It is seen that the density function D of electron levels in the solid must have very great influence on the reaction rate of a redox process at solids. Therefore significant differences between metals and semiconductors as redox electrodes are to be expected and will be discussed below.

This problem can also be approached by using the rate theory with thermodynamic analogues as has been done by Randles (10) and Marcus (11). Applying this method on semiconductor redox reactions, Dewald (12) arrived at very similar conclusions as those presented here. The method used here, however, shows more directly the influence of the solid itself and it can yield more information for nonequilibrium conditions.

4.1 Metals

The behavior of metal redox electrodes in general will now be discussed in connection with Eq. (5). For this purpose the distribution functions for free and occupied electron levels are plotted on the same scale in parallel and are integrated graphically over the products of these functions for equilibrium conditions (Fig. 7). For simplicity it is assumed that κ should be approximately constant. The scales are related to one another by Eq. (6). It can be shown that the energy level equivalent to ΔF_0 must be between the peaks of W_{ox} and W_{red} in Fig. 6. It is further assumed that the concentrations c_{ox} and c_{red} are equal.

As a result of product formation as shown on the right hand side of Fig. 7, the electron exchange occurs preferentially in a narrow energy region near $E_F^!$ where the greatest overlapping of unoccupied and occupied levels in both phases occur. The magnitude of the exchange current depends apparently on the value of D (contribution from the solid) and on the height of D_{ox} and D_{red} in this energy region (contribution of the special redox system itself).

If equilibrium conditions are disturbed by changing $\Delta\varphi$ by an overvoltage $\eta = \Delta\varphi - \Delta\varphi_0$, the distribution functions shift relative to each other by the amount of $\mathcal{F}\eta$. As a result the integrations according to Eq. (5) will now give different values for j^+ and j^- as shown in Fig. 8 for the case of anodic polarization. Here the electron transfer from the solution to the solid is increased greatly and the reverse process is correspondingly decreased. Under certain conditions the currents depend exponentially on the change of potential difference in a similar way as given in Eq. (1a) and (1b), but this is the case only if the chemical activation of solvation structures remains rate determining. Clearly, such a relation can be verified only with metals sufficiently inert not to be attacked in this region of polarization.

4.2 Semiconductors

Let us first compare the energy levels in an intrinsic semiconductor and in a redox system before and after contact. The situation is represented in Fig. 9. The energy scale with respect to an electron at infinite distance is given by the distribution functions of Fig. 6 for the redox system, and by the

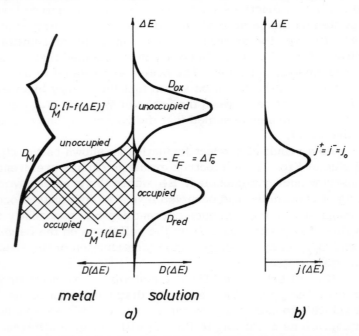

Fig. 7. (a) Distribution of electron energy levels in a metal and in a solution containing equal concentrations of the constituents of a redox system. System is at equilibrium. (b) Distribution of currents over energy levels given by Eq. (5).

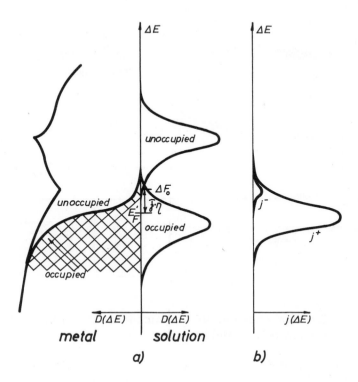

Fig. 8. System of Fig. 7, anodically polarized.

energies of electrons in the conduction and in the valence band
for the semiconductor. Bringing the two phases into contact,
the Fermi level in the interior of the semiconductor will change
(electrical potential difference between the semiconductor and
the solution) until $E_F' = E_F + \mathcal{F}\Delta\varphi_0 = \Delta F_0$. Taking the interior
of the solution as the reference point of our energy scale we
arrive at the situation represented in Fig. 9. When there is no
surface charge or specific adsorption of ions or dipoles, as is
assumed in Fig. 9, the energy scale of electron levels in the
semiconductor surface remains unchanged during the contact
charging process, when compared with the energy of electrons
in solution. But the concentration of electrons in these states
will be altered largely because the concentration of electrons

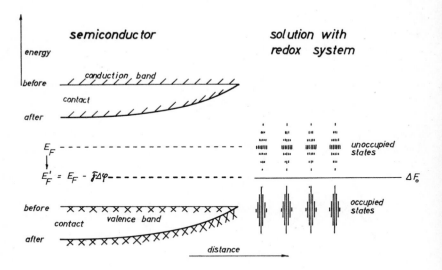

Fig. 9.   Electron energies in a semiconductor and in a redox
system before and after contact.

in the interior of the semiconductor $_ic_\ominus$ and on the surface $_sc_\ominus$
depends exponentially on the electrical potential drop in the
space charge near the surface (diffusion potential):

$$_sc_\ominus = {}_ic_\ominus \exp \frac{(\mathcal{F}\Delta\varphi_0)}{RT} \tag{8a}$$

$$_sc_\oplus = {}_ic_\oplus \exp \frac{(\mathcal{F}\Delta\varphi_0)}{RT} \tag{8b}$$

When there are special surface states and specific adsorption of ions or dipoles, a shift occurs in the energy scale
of the surface states; normally the shift will be of minor importance as long as no degeneracy of states occurs in the surface.
    The electron transfer will be discussed here also by
applying Eq. (5). The density functions of electron levels in the
semiconductor and the electrolyte interface are plotted again in

Fig. 10 under equilibrium; i.e., the Fermi levels are the same
in both phases (compare with Fig. 9). Because of a gap in the
distribution function of electron levels where the Fermi level
is normally found, exchange of electrons cannot occur in this
region. Exchange occurs only at energy levels in two separated energy regions, the conductance band and the valence band,
where the number of exchangeable levels is very small compared with the region where exchange takes place at a metal.
Therefore the total exchange rate must be very much smaller
at a semiconductor. The electron exchange in the valence band
can best be discussed in terms of minority carriers (holes).

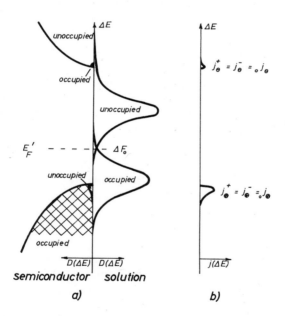

Fig. 10. (a) Distribution of electron energy levels in a semiconductor surface and in a redox system at equilibrium. (b) Distribution of currents.

According to the principle of microscopic reversibility, under equilibrium conditions the transfer of charge in each
band must have equal rates in the anodic and cathodic directions. It is obvious from Fig. 10 that the exchange currents

for electrons $_0j_\ominus$ and for holes $_0j_\oplus$ can differ very much depending on the position of ΔF_0 in relation to the energy gap of the
semiconductor. ΔF_0 depends only on the redox system and its
normal potential is a convenient measure of this value. $|\Delta F_0|$
increases with increasing positive redox potentials. In highly
oxidizing redox systems, it is therefore expected that the Fermi
level on the surface is near the valence band and the concentration of holes in the surface is much higher than that of free electrons. Hence the exchange of holes should be predominating
in such a redox reaction. On the other hand, redox systems
with very negative normal potentials should preferentially exchange electrons with the conduction band. This general result
has been presented by Dewald (12) who employed the above
thermodynamic approach to redox reactions.

    The two types of electron transfer in a redox reaction at
semiconductors can be distinguished by a number of experimental methods (12,13,14). The mechanisms of some redox reactions
at germanium electrodes are summarized in Table I. It is
seen that the mechanism of redox reactions with positive normal potentials is associated with the valence band, whereas the
mechanism of redox reactions with more negative normal potentials is associated with the conduction band if there is any reaction at all. The situation remains the same when the electrode
is moderately polarized in the anodic or cathodic direction. An
example is shown in Fig. 11 using a redox system with properties
equivalent to those assumed in Fig. 10.

    Redox reactions can be studied at germanium electrodes,
undergoing no rapid dissolution or hydrogen evolution, only in
a region of polarization over approximately 0.9 volts. Under
high currents the assumptions of electronic equilibrium in the
interior of the semiconductor are not valid (compare the limited
hole current at n-type germanium in the region of dissolution).
But on the basis of our model one can consider an ideal case
with a semiconductor which is not attacked and a solvent which
is not subject to electrolytic decomposition.

    When the Fermi level is shifted in the semiconductor
under very high anodic polarization, degeneracy of surface
states sets in. The surface then behaves like that of a metal
and an effective Helmholtz double layer forms at the surface.

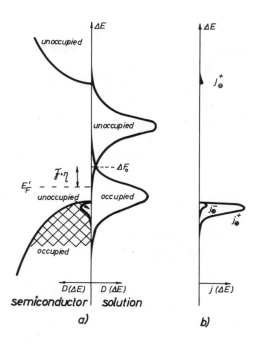

Fig. 11.   System   of Fig. 10 under moderate anodic polarization.

Therefore the energy scale of the electron states will be shifted
relative to the states in solution as shown in Fig. 12.   In this
case the electron transfer to the conduction band will be strongly favored and should occur predominantly at very high anodic
polarization.   On the other hand, with cathodic polarization the
electron transfer from the valence band increases to a smaller
degree than the electron transfer from the conduction band.
Another change in the prevailing mechanism can be expected
when the Fermi level approaches the conduction band.   With
the concentration of free electrons high enough and the density
of free electron states not very small in the energy range of
interest, a conduction band mechanism would prevail during
cathodic reduction under strong polarization.   Under very
strong cathodic polarization and in the case of degenerate surface states, reduction takes place through a valence band mechanism.   The above two cases are shown in the Figs. 13 and 14.

196   H. GERISCHER

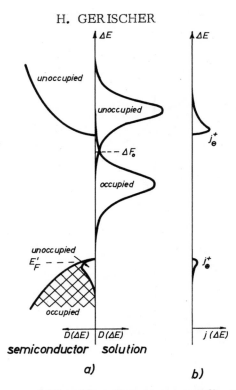

Fig. 12.   System   of Fig. 10 under strong anodic polarization.

When $|\Delta F_0|$ of the redox system is greater than $|_iE_F|$, a
valence band mechanism is favored (see summary in Table
II). It is apparent from the above discussion that for a given
system the mechanism can change depending on the degree of
polarization.

The potential-current curves of redox systems at semiconductor electrodes will be briefly discussed. An exponential
relationship between current and overvoltage is again to be
expected provided the surface states do not contribute substantially to the change of potential. As already pointed out, however, small exchange currents are to be expected owing to the
small number of states under equilibrium conditions. Thus
high overvoltages must be associated with moderate currents.
In addition, the charge transfer coefficients must have rather
unusual values. They are expected to have values either close

TABLE I

Redox Reactions at Semiconductor Electrodes

Redox System	Electrolyte	Formal Potential U_K (Volt)	Observed Reaction	Prevailing Electron Transfer Mechanism
MnO_2/MnO_4^-	1 N H_2SO_4	+1.38	reduction	valence band[13)14)]
Ce^{+3}/Ce^{+4}	1 N H_2SO_4	+1.15	reduction	valence band[13)]
$Cr^{+3}/Cr_2O_7^{--}$	0.1 N H_2SO_4	+1.07	no reaction	—[13)]
OH^-/H_2O_2	0.1 N NaOH	+0.71	reduction	valence band[13)]
HNO_2/HNO_3	–	+0.65	reduction	valence band[12)]
Fe^{++}/Fe^{+3}	1 N $HClO_4$; 1 N H_2SO_4	+0.40	reduction	valence band[12)13)]
$[Fe(CN)_6]^{-4}/[Fe(CN)_6]^{-3}$	0.1 N H_2SO_4	+0.28	reduction and oxidation	valence band[13)]
OH^-/O_2	0.1 N NaOH	+0.17	reduction	valence band[13)]

TABLE I (Cont.)

Redox Reactions at Semiconductor Electrodes

Redox System	Electrolyte	Formal Potential U_K (Volt)	Observed Reaction	Prevailing Electron Transfer Mechanism
$[Fe(CN)_6]^{-4}/[Fe(CN)_6]^{-3}$	0.1 N NaOH	+ 0.13	reduction	valence band [13] [14]
V^{+3}/VO^{++}	1 N H_2SO_4; 1 N HCl	+ 0.02	no reaction	[13]
Ti^{+3}/TiO^{++}	1 N HCl	- 0.19	no reaction	[13]
$H_2/2H^+$	1 N H_2SO_4	- 0.28	reduction	conduction band [6]
V^{++}/V^{+3}	0.1 N H_2SO_4	- 0.59	oxidation	conduction band [13] [15]
Cr^{++}/Cr^{+3}	0.1 N HCl	- 0.70	no reaction (?)	[13]
$C_2O_4^{--}/CO_2$	0.1 N HCl	- 0.77	oxidation	conduction band [16]

TABLE II

Mechanism of Electron Transfer at a Semiconductor Electrode
for Various Types of Redox Systems

Polarization		$\|\Delta F_o\|$ of Redox System		
		$\approx\|_i E_F$	$>\|_i E_F\|$	$<\|_i E_F$
Equilibrium		v.b. or c.b.	v.b.	c.b.
Anodic	small	v.b. (favored)	v.b.	c.b.
	medium	v.b.	v.b.	c.b. (or v.b.)
	very high	c.b.	c.b.	c.b.
Cathodic	small	c.b. (favored)	v.b.	c.b.
	medium	c.b.	v.b. (or c.b.)	c.b.
	very high	v.b.	v.b.	v.b.

v.b., valence band mechanism

c.b., conduction band mechanism

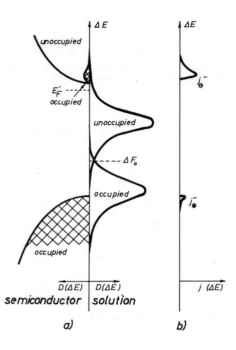

Fig. 13. System of Fig. 10 under moderate cathodic polarization.

to unity (cathodic reaction under conduction band mechanism, or anodic reaction under valence band mechanism) or close to zero (anodic reaction under conduction band mechanism or cathodic reaction under valence band). Simple exponential current-potential curves are not to be expected under degeneracy of surface states or when there is a substantial contribution by special surface states to the charging process which influences the electrode potential.

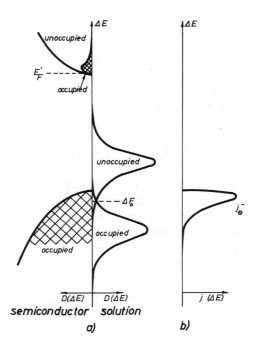

Fig. 14.   System of Fig. 10 under very strong cathodic polarization.

References

1.   cf. D. C. Grahame, Chem. Revs., 41, 441 (1947); R. Parsons, in J. O'M. Bockris, ed., Modern Aspects of Electrochemistry, p. 103, Butterworths Scientific Publications, 1954.
2.   see also K. Bohnenkamp and H. J. Engell, Z. Elektrochem., 61, 1187 (1957).
3.   H. Gerischer and R. P. Tischer, Z. Elektrochem., 61, 1159 (1957); H. Gerischer, ibid., 62, 256 (1958).
4.   W. Mehl and J. O'M. Bockris, J. Chem. Phys., 27, 818 (1957); Can. J. Chem., 37, 190 (1959).
5.   H. Gerischer, Electrochimica Acta, 2, 1 (1960).
6.   W. H. Brattain and C. G. B. Garrett, Bell System Tech. J., 34, 129 (1955).

7. F. Beck and H. Gerischer, Z. Elektrochem., 63, 500
    (1959).
8. D. R. Turner, J. Electrochem. Soc., 103, 252 (1956).
9. R. W. Gurney, Proc. Roy. Soc. (London) A, 134, 137 (1931);
    Ions in Solution, Cambridge University Press, 1936;
    R. W. Gurney and R. H. Fowler, Proc. Roy. Soc. (London),
    A, 136, 378 (1932).
10. J. E. B. Randles, Trans. Faraday Soc., 48, 828 (1952).
11. R. A. Marcus, O.N.R. Technical Rep. 12, Project
    NR-051-339 (1957); 2, Project NR-051-400 (1959); Electro-
    chem. Soc., abstract No. 183, Philadelphia meeting,1959 .
12. J. F. Dewald, in N. B. Hannay, ed., Semiconductors, p.
    727, Reinhold Publishing Co., 1959.
13. H. Gerischer and F. Beck, Z. physik. Chem. (Frankfurt),
    13, 389 (1957); Z. Elektrochem., 63, 943 (1959).
14. Iu. V. Pleskov, Doklady Akad. Nauk S.S.S.R., 126, 112
    (1959).
15. Iu. V. Pleskov and B. N. Kabanov, Doklady Akad. Nauk
    S.S.S.R., 123, 884 (1958).
16. E. A. Efimov and I. G. Erusalimchik, Doklady Akad. Nauk
    S.S.S.R., 128, 124 (1959).

DISCUSSION

D. A. VERMILYEA (General Electric):

I do not feel that the two step mechanism of electrolytic deposition or dissolution of metals has been unambiguously proven as
yet. In studies at our Laboratory [J. Chem. Phys., 28, 720
(1958)] we found a rate constant for the overall reaction which
was about equal to that which Dr. Gerischer [Z. Elektrochem.,
61, 1159 (1957); Z. Electrochem., 62, 256 (1958)] and Mehl and
Bockris [J. Chem. Phys., 27, 818 (1957)] found for just one step
of the reaction. This discrepancy still must be resolved.

In the study of adsorption from the gas phase, one sometimes finds differences between the extent or mechanism of
adsorption of gases on metals and semiconductors. Hydrogen,
for example, is dissociatively adsorbed on many metals but
must be dissociated before it is adsorbed on semiconductors.

It seems possible that one may find similar differences between the adsorption of various ions or molecules from solution onto metals and semiconductors. Have you made any studies of the effects of impurities on reactions at metal and non-metal electrodes? If so, have you found any correlations?

H. GERISCHER: There are very few cases in which we can treat the kinetics in much detail; silver is one of them. I believe that there is good evidence to support the two step mechanism for silver electrodes at or near equilibrium conditions. The two steps being (1) atoms in half crystal positions moving into adsorption positions on the surface, and (2) the transfer of atoms from adsorption positions into the solution. Naturally we have in parallel the possibility of a one step process, namely the direct dissolution or deposition of atoms in the half crystal positions. The one step mechanism is favored by high concentration of half crystal places in the surface and by strong electrical polarization [Electrochimica Acta, 2, 1 (1960)]. Thus the same metal electrode may have different mechanisms of dissolution or deposition under different conditions. In the experiments of Dr. Vermilyea the number of half crystal places in the surface probably was extremely high.

We have not yet studied the influence of inhibitors on germanium electrodes. The problem is that germanium dissolves in parallel with most redox reactions at germanium electrodes. The dissolution causes a steady cleaning of the surface which should hinder the effect of contamination. The situation is very complicated in the case of cathodic polarization where the surface is covered with hydrogen atoms which act in some respects as inhibitors for others like catalysts.

J. V. PETROCELLI (International Nickel): For equilibrium, or close to equilibrium conditions, the electrode reaction is a two step process. You said that the surface diffusion step is the slow one. If so, then how does the electric field accelerate that step?

H. GERISCHER: The main effect of the electric field during electrolytic polarization on the slow crystallization process by means of ad-atoms is that the concentration of ad-atoms is changed in the neighborhood of half crystal places, increased during cathodic polarization, decreased during anodic

polarization. Therefore the concentration gradients of ad-
atoms vary with polarization. So, we have some kind of concentration polarization in the surface of the metal because the
thermodynamic activity of the metal surface is correlated with
ad-atom concentration. But this concentration polarization is
not uniform on the surface and must cause local cell action between surface parts with high concentration of half crystal positions and smooth parts of the surface. In parallel to this main
effect we have also a small influence of the electric field at the
interface on surface mobility. That is because the ad-atoms
are to some degree already in an ionic state and therefore the
activation energy for surface diffusion depends on polarization
[cf. Electrochimica Acta, 2, 1 (1960)].

M. STERN (Union Carbide): You noted, as we have
also from our work, that exchange rates on passive metals are
much smaller than similar exchange reactions on active metals.
You point out that the passive layer in many cases has the
properties of a semiconductor. What type of experiments could
be carried out to determine whether a layer exhibits semiconductivity?

H. GERISCHER: I believe that the fact that the exchange
reactions are so much slower on these surfaces gives some
evidence that the passive surfaces are semiconductors. The
difficulty lies in determining the electronic structure of these
layers. It may be possible to make certain deductions about
the structure of these layers by a rigorous study of the rates
of a number of different redox reactions in combination with
a study of the action of light on a special electron exchange reaction.

J. F. DEWALD

Bell Telephone
Laboratories

Experimental Techniques
for the Study
of Semiconductor Electrodes

ABSTRACT

EXPERIMENTAL TECHNIQUES FOR the
study of semiconductor electrodes are reviewed,
and the theory involved in the treatment of the resulting data is discussed for several specific
cases. A new transient technique, which is particularly useful with large-energy-gap semiconductors, is described.

1. INTRODUCTION

Brattain and Garrett's classic study (1) of the germanium
electrode was made more than five years ago, but there has been
relatively little recognition of the generality of the concepts and
techniques used by them. That their paper was written in language unfamiliar to many chemists is partly the cause; in addition
no attempt was made by the authors to show how their techniques
could be generalized for use with the far more numerous class
of compound semiconductors. The present paper is an attempt
to remedy this situation and constitutes a review of the techniques and concepts involved in the study of semiconductor electrodes in general. Many of these techniques are useful in obtaining information about the bulk properties of semiconductors.

However, we will be primarily concerned here with the techniques involved in studying the interfacial properties per se.

Metal electrodes have been so extensively studied in the past that one may profitably ask the question: How does a semiconductor electrode differ from a metal electrode? Although there are many differences, the two essential distinctions are (1) the low and readily variable electron density and (2) the existence of an energy gap, i.e., of a region of unallowed electronic energies. The many other differences can be shown to arise from these two. For example, because of the low electron density, one has sizable penetration of the interfacial electric fields into the bulk of the electrode. With metals significant fields penetrate no more than an angstrom or so inside the electrode; with typical semiconductors the fields may be sizable at depths in excess of 10, 000 Å. In consequence the distributions of charge and potential at a semiconductor electrode are almost of a different kind from those at a metal electrode.

The existence of the energy gap in a semiconductor electrode introduces even more striking differences. With metal electrodes transitions between the various electronic levels are too rapid to allow distinctions regarding their energy; with a semiconductor electrode there are always at least two distinguishable kinds of electrons, i.e., conduction band and valence band, and therefore at least two distinguishable paths for any given charge-transfer process. Large photovoltaic effects are also characteristic phenomena with semiconductor electrodes. As we shall see below, these arise because the carrier densities are so readily varied and the rates of interband transitions are slow.

Probably the most apparent result of the low electron density is the decisive role played by impurities in the semiconductor. Impurities in a semiconductor electrode, even at levels as low as 1 part in 10^8, can contribute significantly to the space charge, can act as catalysts for the recombination of holes and electrons, or can furnish additional charge-transfer paths for electrochemical reaction. It is essential, therefore, to have control and knowledge of the impurity distribution before any meaningful kinetic measurements can be made on a semiconductor electrode.

An example of the size of the impurity effects that may arise is shown in Fig. 1, which gives the electrode kinetics for the ferro-ferricyanide reaction on three different zinc oxide single crystals of varying conductivity. Each of the crystals was in excess of 99.999% pure. As can be seen, each crystal gives a linear Tafel plot under cathodic bias. However, the exchange currents, i.e., the extrapolations back to the reversible potential (+.19 volts), differ by a factor of about 1000 and

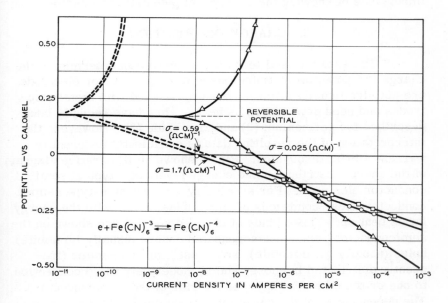

Fig. 1. The electrode kinetics for the $Fe(CN)_6^{-3}/Fe(CN)_6^{-4}$ reaction at three zinc oxide electrodes of varying impurity content. The curves marked $\sigma = 0.59$ and $\sigma = 1.7$ contained only strongly dissociated donors. The curve marked $\sigma = 0.025$ contained weakly ionized donors at a concentration of 1 part in about 10^6.

the Tafel slope on the lowest conductivity crystal differs from the others by more than a factor of two. Since the Tafel slope on the two highest conductivity crystals (0.065v/decade) agrees almost exactly with that predicted for a simple electron exchange from the ferrocyanide ion to the conduction band ($0.059v/$ decade) we distrusted the results on the $\sigma = 0.025(\Omega\text{-cm})^{-1}$ crystal even though, judged by room temperature conductivity and Hall-effect measurements, it appeared to be of higher purity. This distrust was subsequently confirmed by capacitance measurements on these crystals which showed the presence of a low-lying donor in the $0.025(\Omega\text{-cm})^{-1}$ crystal and only completely ionized donors in the other two. This illustrates the importance of knowing the charge and potential distribution.

2. CHARGE DISTRIBUTION

The experimental techniques involved in determining the charge and potential distributions at a semiconductor electrode are not significantly different from those used with metal electrodes and need not concern us here. They have recently been described for germanium (2) and zinc oxide (3). However, the interpretation of the resulting data is sufficiently different to warrant a brief discussion. Fig. 2 shows an illustrative diagram of the charge distribution and energy levels at a typical semiconductor electrode. For specificity we show an n-type semiconductor under conditions of anodic bias, i. e., with the energy bands bent up. Three kinds of charged species are shown on the semiconductor, viz., uncompensated donors (usually immobile), holes (usually quite mobile), and "fast" surface-states (frequently distributed in energy and in moderately rapid connection to one or the other bands in the interior of the semiconductor). The dependences of the capacitance upon electrode bias, frequency, crystal doping, and illumination are used to unravel the complexities involved.

The zinc oxide electrode is a particularly simple example of a semiconductor electrode, because its large energy gap (3.3 ev) makes the minority-carrier contribution to space charge negligible in the dark and because the fast surface state effects are negligible. This latter fact has been demonstrated by data of the sort shown in Fig. 3 (3).

The simplest possible model of the surface assumes completely ionized donors and the absence of surface states. In this case one has a large Helmholtz capacitance, on the solu-

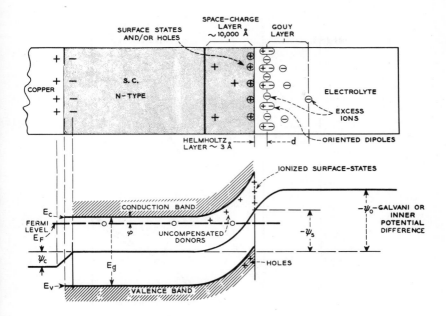

Fig. 2. The charge distribution and energy-level diagram at
an n-type semiconductor/electrolyte interface.

tion side of the electrode, in series with a space-charge capacitance which can be computed from the Poisson-Boltzmann equation to be of the form

$$C_{sc} = \frac{\alpha \left| e^{Y}-1 \right|}{\{e^{Y}-1-Y\}^{1/2}} \qquad (1)$$

where Y is the amount by which the bands are bent down (in units
of kT/q) and α is a known constant involving only the donor density, the dielectric constant, and the temperature. For strongly anodic conditions, i.e., bands bent up, Y is strongly negative, the exponential terms in (1) are negligible; a plot of $1/C^2$
vs V should give a straight line if the surface-state density is
small and changes in electrode potential occur primarily within

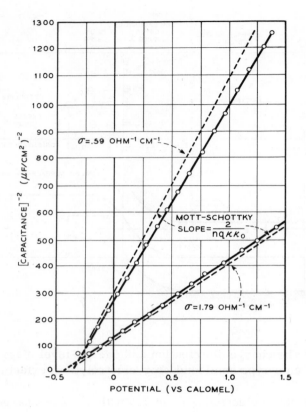

Fig. 3.   Mott-Schottky plots of capacitance^{-2} vs bias for two
typical zinc oxide crystals.   The dotted lines represent absolute theoretical predictions in the absence of
surface states.

the space-charge layer in the semiconductor.   Such linear behavior, with near-theoretical slopes and intercepts, is exhibited by the data shown in Fig. 3 and by most of the data obtained
on zinc oxide crystals over a wide range of crystal doping, frequency, and electrode bias.   Since surface-state effects would
not vary with impurity content of the crystal at the low doping
levels in question one concludes that these effects are inopera-

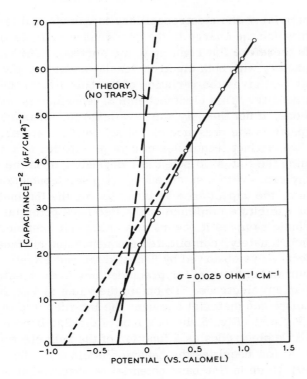

Fig. 4. The Mott-Schottky plot for the $\sigma = 0.025$ crystal of
Fig. 1. The dotted line shows the theoretical slope
predicted from the room temperature Hall effect and
conductivity measurements. The slope at strongly
anodic bias (V positive) is a measure of the total donor
density in this crystal.

tive on zinc oxide electrodes. In consequence maverick crystals
such as the 0.025 $(\Omega\text{-cm})^{-1}$ sample of Fig. 1, which gave a
strongly nonlinear $1/C^2$ vs V plot, can be detected and characterized by capacitance measurements such as those shown in
Fig. 4.

Another very important use of capacitance measurements
in dealing with semiconductor electrodes is as a means of determining the "flat-band potential"(3). This quantity is analogous

to the potential of the electrocapillary maximum and is the potential at which the charge in the semiconductor is zero and
the bands therefore flat right up to the surface. The variation
of this quantity with bulk electron density under any given surface treatment gives the variation of the bulk Fermi level with
electron density. This electrochemical technique is one of the
few methods, if not the only one, available for measuring this
bulk property in the presence of "slow" surface states.

     Two distinct techniques of data processing are used in
determining the flat-band potential, depending upon the size of
the energy gap. With a small energy gap semiconductor like
germanium, the capacitance vs bias plot for the intrinsic semiconductor exhibits a minimum at the flat-band potential (V_{FB}).
For extrinsic samples it occurs at a calculable distance from
V_{FB}. Unfortunately, complicated frequency and surface treatment effects were observed by Bohnenkamp and Engell (2) with
germanium which have so far precluded any exact treatment of
the germanium electrode. To obtain the value of V_{FB} for a
large-energy-gap material one uses the intercepts of the
$1/C^2$ vs V plots. Fig. 5 shows a plot of the flat-band potential
on zinc oxide electrodes as a function of the bulk electron density (3). At low densities the behavior is classical but a start-
ingly sharp bump in flat-band potential is observed at electron
densities just below 10^{18}-cm^{-3}. This is taken to imply a similar variation in bulk Fermi level as the impurity atoms start to
interact with one another and the transition to metallic conduction begins.

3. CHARGE TRANSFER

     Phenomena which involve the concept of minority car-
riers are perhaps most characteristic of semiconductor electrodes. The study of charge-transfer processes is one of the
most direct ways of getting at the details involved. Dewald (4)
has given an introduction to the subject, and in the present section we extend some of these ideas to cover the response to
transient conditions.

     The essential idea here is that, because of the slow rate
of interband transitions, there is more than one way of trans-
ferring charge across the interface. This may be symbolized
by the chemical equations

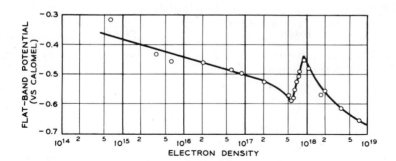

Fig. 5.   The flat-band potential of the ZnO electrode as a
function of the bulk electron density. H_3PO_4 etched
crystals in buffered (pH = 8.5) KCl solution. The
straight line at low density is drawn with the theoretical slope (.059 volts/decade) expected if the electrons
form an ideal solution.

$$M^+ \rightleftharpoons M^{++} + e_s^-$$ (2)

$$M^+ + e_s^+ \rightleftharpoons M^{++}$$ (3)

$$M^+ + t \rightleftharpoons M^{++} + e_t^-$$ (4)

Here we consider the simplest possible case of an electron-
transfer reaction with no nuclear rearrangements. Eq. (2)
shows the electron coming from and going to the conduction band
at the surface while (3) involves the valence band. In cases like
the maverick crystal of Fig. 4, impurities can catalyse electron
transfer, and Eq. (4) shows one possible mechanism, the electron going to and from an impurity trap, t, and then to one or
the other bands. These three reactions represent parallel paths
for the overall reaction.

One can determine the various kinetic parameters, exactly as for any other chemical reaction, by independently varying the concentrations of the various species; the only difference

between this and ordinary chemical kinetics is that the concentrations of holes and electrons are not usually considered as chemical variables and require somewhat subtle methods for their measurement. The rates of reactions (2) and (3) may be written in the forms

$$I_n = I_n^o \left(1 - \frac{n_s}{n_s^o} \right) ; \quad I_p = I_p^o \left(\frac{p_s}{p_s^o} - 1 \right) \tag{5}$$

where I_n^o and I_p^o are the exchange currents, i.e., the rate constants at unit concentration of M^+ and M^{++}, for the two reactions. p_s^o and n_s^o are the carrier densities at the surface at the equilibrium potential. To simplify our treatment we neglect the reaction involving traps in the semiconductor (Eq. (4)). This can be handled without great difficulty by similar methods.

One assumption which is usually made in determining the reaction orders with respect to the various carriers in the semiconductor is that the electrons and holes are essentially in translational equilibrium across the space-charge layer. Their concentrations may be very far from equilibrium with respect to recombination, analogous to having water with an ion product (at room temperature) very different from 10^{-14}. However, the very high mobility of holes and electrons tends to make the gradients of their chemical potentials (Fermi levels) quite small. Under such conditions, the hole and electron concentrations at the surface (p_s and n_s) are related to their concentrations (p_l and n_l) just to the semiconductor side of the space-charge layer by the equations

$$n_s = n_l e^Y ; \quad p_s = p_l e^{-Y} \tag{6}$$

where as before Y is the surface potential in units of kT/q.

As can be seen from Eqs. (6), there are two ways in which one can vary the concentrations of carriers at the surface; by varying Y and by varying n_l or p_l. We have already seen how the value of Y may be varied and its value determined from capacitance measurements. The determination of n_l and p_l is less obvious. A number of methods have been employed.

One of the most direct methods, due to Brattain and Garrett (1), is illustrated in Fig. 6. It is applicable to any semiconductor with which one can form a p-n junction.

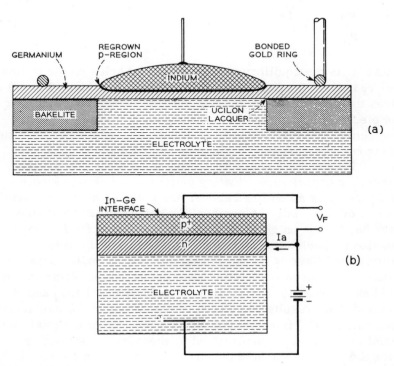

Fig. 6. The "floating-potential" method of measuring the minority carrier density near the surface.

Brattain and Garrett took a thin wafer of germanium and by alloying one side of it with indium formed a p-n junction with the p-side very much more heavily doped than the n-side, so that any current flow across the junction would be due to holes (5). The n-side of the junction was brought into contact with the electrolyte and current was then passed across the electrolyte interface under various potentials. Under these conditions the voltage which develops between the two ohmic contacts to the semiconductor is a measure of the minority-carrier density on the less-heavily-doped side of the junction,

216   J. F. DEWALD

i. e., of holes on the n-side in Fig. 6.* In reasonably good
approximation, the hole density (p_1) is given by (1)

$$\frac{p_1}{p_o} = e^{V_f}$$ (7)

where p_o is the equilibrium bulk density of holes on the n-side
and V_f is the "floating potential." Strictly speaking, Eq. (7)
gives the hole density at the p-n junction rather than that near
the electrolyte interface. However with thin slices of semiconductor, this distinction is of importance only under conditions
of strong depletion and corrections can be made if necessary.

No complete characterization of an electrode process,
combining capacitance, floating junction, and simple kinetic
measurements as outlined above, has yet been made on a semiconductor electrode. A number of semi-quantitative studies
have been made on germanium electrodes using the floating-
junction technique (or variations on it) described above.
Brattain and Garrett (1) and Turner (6), for example, have
studied the hydrogen evolution reaction on n-type electrodes in
KOH and Turner (6) has studied the reduction of HNO_3 and O_2.
Some of their results are shown in Fig. 7 where the interfacial
hole current (I_p) is shown plotted as a function of the total interfacial current. I_p is determined by measuring the floating
potential (to give the hole density), the saturation current I_s
across the p-n junction, and the minimum value of the floating
potential (V_f^{min}) of the same junction under anodic bias (to give

---

*See Shockley (5) for a demonstration of this conclusion. The
essential point here is that the holes are in much better equilibrium across the junction because their concentration on the n-
side is much larger than is the concentration of electrons on
the p-side. In consequence the electrochemical potential (quasi-
Fermi level) for holes is essentially constant across the junction while the quasi-Fermi level for electrons takes on whatever
gradient is required to satisfy the continuity and charge neutrality conditions.

the rate of generation of holes). *

$$I_p = I_s \; \frac{\left(e^{\beta V_f} - 1 \right)}{\left(e^{\beta V_f^{min}} - 1 \right)} \quad ; \quad \beta = q/kT \tag{8}$$

The only assumption involved in (8) is that the surface recombination velocity does not vary significantly with bias.

As seen in Fig. 7, the hydrogen reaction from KOH proceeds almost completely via electron transfer from the conduction band while the reduction of nitrate ion proceeds entirely by injection of holes. In fact the injected hole current appears

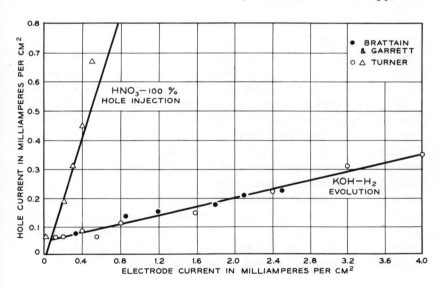

Fig. 7. The hole current (I_p) as a function of the total current across a germanium electrode under cathodic bias.

---

*The reasoning here is given by Brattain and Garrett (1). Note that their Eq. (12) contains an error of sign in the denominator.

to exceed the total current. This latter behavior could be due
to the corrosion reaction or possibly to a variation of the
surface-recombination velocity with bias but is presently not
completely understood.

One other feature of the data in Fig. 7 is of interest;
the extrapolation of the hydrogen data does not go through the
origin. This is almost certainly because a different chemical
reaction, oxygen consumption, (which involves hole injection)
(6) takes over. The changeover occurs at current densities
comparable with the oxygen diffusion current and is strongly
sensitive to the introduction or removal of oxygen from the
solution.

Another interesting technique has been used by Pleskov
(7) for studying the relative rates of the hole and electron reactions at the germanium electrode. In this method a thin n-
type germanium slab is used to separate two solutions each of
which contains a reference electrode. The germanium crystal
is biased anodically with respect to one of the solutions until
the current saturates. The crystal is then biased with respect
to the other solution (the one of interest); if minority carriers
are involved in the interfacial reaction, they cange the saturation current at the other interface, decreasing it if holes are
"collected" and increasing it if holes are "injected." Basically this is no different from what could be done with the p-n
junction technique of Brattain and Garrett. However, it might
be useful on semiconductors with which narrow p-n junctions
were difficult to obtain. To generalize the technique, one requires only that the diffusion length of the minority carriers be
large compared to the thickness of the sample and that some
electrode reaction of known kinetics be available.

4. PHOTO-EFFECTS

One of the most important and generally applicable techniques for studying semiconductor electrodes is the response
of the electrode to illumination. However, the complete significance of these effects, particularly of the transient responses,
has not been generally recognized. To see what is involved,
consider, for example, an n-type semiconductor electrode under

open circuit conditions and initially at the equilibrium potential for the reactions

$$M^+ + e^+ \rightleftharpoons M^{++}$$

$$M^+ \rightleftharpoons M^{++} + e^-$$

Furthermore consider that this reaction is such as to bend the bands up at the surface. The interfacial hole and electron currents are given by (see Eqs. (5) and (6))

$$I_p = I_p^o \left(\frac{p_1}{p_o} e^{\Delta} - 1 \right) \tag{9a}$$

$$I_n = I_n^o \left(1 - \frac{n_1}{n_o} e^{-\Delta} \right) \tag{9b}$$

where Δ is the difference (+ for anodic bias) between the potential of the electrode and its equilibrium potential, i.e., the overpotential. These currents are both initially zero by virtue of the initial equilibrium condition. Now let us abruptly illuminate the electrode. The first thing to happen is an increase within a minority-carrier lifetime (typically a few hundred microseconds or less), in the hole and electron densities just outside the space-charge layer, p_1 and n_1, by the same absolute amount Δn. The concentrations of holes and electrons in the space-charge layer also change in such a way as to keep the total charge within the semiconductor initially constant and the quasi-Fermi levels constant across the space-charge layer. Thus Y changes in a direction to make the bands flatter regardless of the magnitude or sign of Y, as shown in Table I. This qualitative behavior was observed by Brattain and Garrett (1) on germanium. Measurement of the "instantaneous" photoresponse is thus seen to afford a method of determining the value of the flat-band potential. Unfortunately Brattain and Garrett's data are not sufficient for a quantitative treatment because they did not distinguish between the "instantaneous" photoresponse and the subsidiary response which arises as charge-transfer across the interface takes place (see below). An important point here

TABLE I

The "Instantaneous" Change in Y on Illumination for the Four Conditions of Bias and Majority Carrier.

Majority Carrier	ΔY	
	Negative Y	Positive Y
	+	−
negative	large	small
	+	−
positive	small	large

is that the "instantaneous" effect will be measurable only if $\Delta n e^{Y}$ or $\Delta n e^{-Y}$ are sizable in comparison to the other space-charge terms.

The magnitude of the instantaneous photoresponse may be simply computed from the Poisson-Boltzmann equation. For an n-type semiconductor it is

$$\frac{d^2 y}{dx^2} = \frac{q^2 N_D}{kT \kappa \kappa_0} \left\{ \left(1 + \frac{p_1}{N_D}\right) e^y - 1 - \frac{p_1}{N_D} e^{-y} \right\} \tag{10}$$

where x is the distance from the surface, y is the potential measured from the bulk, N_D the donor density, and the other symbols have their customary meaning. The equation may be integrated once with respect to y, and if we insert the boundary conditions at $x = \infty$ ($y'(\infty) = 0$) and at $x = 0$ ($y'(0)$ unchanged on illumination), we obtain the equation

$$\left(1 + \frac{p_o}{N_D}\right) e^{Y_o} - Y_o + \frac{p_o}{N_D}\left(e^{-Y_o} - 1\right) = \left(1 + \frac{p_1}{N_D}\right) e^{Y_1} -$$

$$Y_1 + \frac{p_1}{N_D}\left(e^{-Y_1} - 1\right) \tag{11}$$

where Y_0 and Y_1 are the values of the surface potential before
and after illumination and p_1 now refers to the hole density under
the illuminated condition. The instantaneous open-circuit photovoltage, Δ_0, is of course just $Y_1 - Y_0$.

Two extremes of Eq. (11) are of interest in considering
the behavior following the instantaneous response. If the hole
density at the surface ($p_0 e^{-Y_0}$ or $p_1 e^{-Y_1}$ in the two conditions)
is very small compared to the bulk donor density, N_D, then Y_0
is equal to Y_1 and Δ_0 is close to zero, i.e., there is no instantaneous photoresponse. On the other hand, if the hole density
at the surface is large compared to the bulk donor density (and
p_1 still small compared to N_D), then the instantaneous photovoltage is given by

$$\Delta_o = -\ln \frac{p_1}{p_0} \tag{12}$$

In either case Eqs. (9a) and (9b) show that a finite current flow
across the interface will result. In the former case, ($\Delta_0 \sim 0$)
the hole current is initially positive, while the electron current
is initially zero. As a result the bands will bend down with
time at a rate initially proportional to I_p^0. Then as Δ becomes
more negative (at constant p_1*), the hole current will decrease
and the electron current will increase until the two currents become equal and a new steady-state of zero interfacial current
is obtained with $I_p = - I_n$. An important point to note here is
that the absolute magnitude of the hole density plays no direct
role in determining the size of the slow photovoltage. In large
energy-gap semiconductors the equilibrium hole density in the
dark may be as low as one hole per sidereal universe while under illumination it may be as low as one hole per cm^3. It will
still give a large slow photoeffect so long as the hole exchange
current, I_p^0, is sufficiently large compared to the electron exchange current, I_n^0.

In the second extreme case mentioned above, when Eq.
(12) applies we have a somewhat different situation. In this

---

*Strictly speaking, p_1 would increase slightly with time under
these conditions, as the hole current, a recombination process
of sorts, decreases.

222   J. F. DEWALD

case Eqs. (9a) and (12) show that the interfacial hole current is
initially unchanged on illumination while the interfacial electron
is negative i. e., cathodic. As a result of this interfacial current the space-charge layer becomes more positive. Thus the
slow response will be in the opposite direction to the "instantaneous" effect. This slow response continues until a steady-
state with finite hole and electron currents of equal magnitude
and opposite sign is once again attained.

The detailed analysis of the transient photovoltaic responses affords one of the most direct methods of evaluating
the individual exchange currents, I_p^o and I_n^o, for any reaction.
Details will be given in papers presently in preparation.

References

1. W. H. Brattain and C. G. B. Garrett, Bell System Tech. J.,
   34, 129 (1955).
2. K. Bohnenkamp and H. J. Engell, Z. Elektrochem., 61, 1184
   (1957).
3. J. F. Dewald, Z. Physik., in press.
4. J. F. Dewald, in N. B. Hannay, ed., Semiconductors, p.
   727, Reinhold Publishing Co., 1959.
5. W. Shockley, Electrons and Holes in Semiconductors, D.
   Van Nostrand Co., 1950.
6. D. R. Turner, personal communication.
7. Iu. V. Pleskov, Doklady Akad. Nauk S.S.S.R., 126, 111 (1959).

DISCUSSION

W. MEHL (RCA): Over what range of frequencies did
you measure, and how did the capacity vary in your zinc oxide
studies?

J. F. DEWALD: The capacitance was essentially independent of frequency in the range from 50 cps to as high as
100 kc.

S. L. MATLOW (Hoffman Electronics): Could you tell
me what the reaction product is in the reduction of nitric acid?
Why are holes rather than electrons postulated?

J. F. DEWALD: The answer to the first question is "I would rather not. " This is a very complex chemical-kinetic system to talk about without knowing all the experimental results. The work of Cretella and Gatos [J. Electrochem. Soc., 105, 487 (1958)] tends to show that the reaction goes via the NO_2/NO_2^- electron exchange. However, I certainly am not the authority on this point. The answer to your second question is that holes are found, experimentally, to be the important "charge-transfer" carriers. The data of Fig. 7 demonstrate this. One can attempt to predict this result theoretically, and I have tried to do so [in N. B. Hannay, ed. , Semiconductors, p. 727, Reinhold Publishing Co. , 1959]. However, I do not trust the theory very far when one deals with complicated, as well as rapidly corroding, systems like germanium in nitric acid.

H. C. GATOS (M. I. T.): You have stated that the nitric acid reduction on germanium involves the injection of holes into the germanium. We have found that during the dissolution of germanium in nitric acid the reduction of germanium controls the dissolution process. We have also found that the dissolution rate is affected by the resistivity of the germanium. The rate can change by a factor of two in going from p- to n-type. Is this consistent with the proposed mechanism of 100 percent hole injection?

J. F. DEWALD: No. It is not consistent with the simple picture given in Hannay.

H. GERISCHER (Max Plank Institute): I would like to comment on Dr. Gatos' question. We have studied corrosion rates of germanium electrodes with various redox systems. When the redox potential was high enough we found no difference between p- and n-type material. Nitric acid is not a very convenient system to study because its redox reaction is in itself very complicated. The reduction scheme for nitric acid contains a step which appears to be catalyzed at the surface. The catalytic activity of a germanium surface is probably influenced by the doping; perhaps this could explain your results. We did not find any difference in p- and n-type when we used ferricyanide or ceric salts as oxidizers.

H. C. GATOS: The reduction of nitric acid during dissolution is autocatalytic, and we believe that the surface plays no

224   J. F. DEWALD

significant catalytic role. Although I agree that the reduction
of nitric acid is rather complex, we found the dissolution results
to be quite reproducible and rather straight forward.

M. EISENBERG (Lockheed): Would you please define the
flat-band potential and explain how it is measured.

J. F. DEWALD: The flat-band potential is the potential
of the semiconductor electrode (with respect to some reference
electrode like calomel for example) when the charge inside the
semiconductor is zero. At this point the "bands are flat" -
right up to the surface. It is closely analogous to the potential
of the electrocapillary maximum at a metal electrode, differing
significantly only if there are a sizable number of surface
states. There are a number of ways of determining V_{FB} as
discussed above, capacitance and photovoltaic measurements
being most prominent.

H. J. ENGELL
K. BOHNENKAMP
Max Planck Institute

Electrode-Solution Interfaces

ABSTRACT

DIFFERENCES IN THE distribution of charges between a metal and a semiconductor electrode surface are considered. Using a simplified model the densities of the charge carriers in a semiconductor electrode can be calculated. Calculated results are in agreement with differential capacity measurements in germanium electrodes. The influence of current through the electrode surface and of the formation of surface traps is considered.

1. INTRODUCTION

If two phases with a measurable electric conductivity are in contact with one another, a potential drop exists at their interface. This potential drop is caused in part by the formation of a very thin charge double layer next to the interface. The charges are carried by the charge carriers which are mobile in the phases in question, i.e., by ions, electrons, or holes. Another part of the potential drop at the interface is due to a layer of dipoles at the surface of each phase.

225

The most simple model for the distribution of the charges at the electrode-electrolyte interface consists of an electrode surface layer with excess electrons or ions and a layer of an equivalent number of ions in the electrolyte. This layer of ions has a thickness δ corresponding to the radius of the ions. It is called the Helmholtz layer.

In an improved model (1) it is assumed that the ions are distributed in the electrolyte in a space charge layer near the electrode surface. The distribution of the ions and the corresponding potential are ruled by Boltzmann statistics and the Poisson equation.

The model introduced by Stern (2), which is in best agreement with all experimental facts, combines a distribution of charges in a space charge layer (diffuse part of the double layer) and the Helmholtz layer (rigid part of the double layer). Ions are assumed to be adsorbed on the electrode and thus bound to the surface by chemical forces. If strongly adsorbed ions are present at the interface, the rigid double layer predominates in determining the electrical properties of the interface.

The thickness of the diffuse double layer decreases with increasing concentration of ions in the electrolyte and approaches the structure of a rigid double layer. This is valid even if no specific adsorption of ions occurs at the electrode surface. If the electrode is a metal, it is most likely that the charges therein are arranged as a surface charge layer. For mercury electrodes, Rice (3) assumed that the electrons form a diffuse double layer in the metal phase. He calculated the distribution of charge using Boltzmann statistics and quantum statistics. From this calculation he concluded that most of the potential drop at the interface must occur in the metal phase, and therefore the electrolyte has little effect on the properties of the interface. This conclusion is not in agreement with experimental facts.

If, however, the electrode is a semiconductor, the distribution of charges in the solid will be similar to that in the electrolyte, for the concentration of carriers in semiconductors is significantly smaller than in metals. In pure germanium for example the concentration of electrons and holes at room temperature is 2.5×10^{13} cm^{-3} or 4×10^{-8} mole/l; i.e., the same order of magnitude as the concentration of H^+ and OH^- in pure water. The striking similarities between the charged species in the bulk of a semiconductor and the ions in aqueous solutions has already been pointed out (4). It can be expected that this similarity also exists in the structure of the double layer. Therefore a space charge region can be assumed in a semiconductor electrode near the surface. The thickness of this layer decreases with increasing carrier concentration and approaches the form of a surface layer in crystals with nearly metallic conductivity like the inverse spinels.

However the formation of a surface charge layer is also possible at low carrier concentrations, for a certain amount of carriers can be bound by surface states. These surface states can exist as a result of the geometrical distortion of the lattice at the surface (5), or they can be formed by adsorption of ions from the electrolyte. While the formation of surface states by adsorption processes is an experimental fact (6), their existence at a clean semiconductor surface is doubtful (7).

On a semiconductor electrode, as on a metal electrode, another part of the double layer will be built up by a dipole layer at the surface of the solid. These dipoles again result from the geometrical discontinuity of the lattice at the surface and from adsorption of ions.

2. EXPERIMENTAL RESULTS

The most convenient method to obtain information about the distribution of charges at a charged interface is the measurement of the electrode capacity and its dependence upon the potential drop at the interface and the frequency of the a-c used. In the case of a semiconductor electrode, the carrier density in the solid is influenced by illumination and by temperature. Therefore the dependence of the capacity on applied light and on temperature is also of importance for the interpretation of the results.

While a number of investigations have dealt with different properties of semiconductor electrodes (8), the first measurements of the differential electrode capacity have been carried out by the present authors (9). An a-c bridge with a Wagner

auxiliary arm was used for the measurements. The circuit
diagram is shown by Fig. 1. The alternating voltage was sup-

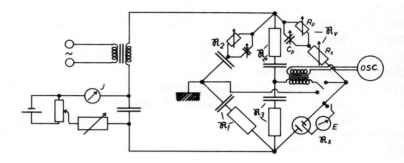

Fig. 1.   Circuit diagram of the measuring bridge. $\mathcal{R}_1$, $\mathcal{R}_2$
Wagner auxiliary arm; $\mathcal{R}_3$ = $\mathcal{R}_4$; $\mathcal{R}_V$ equivalent
circuit; $\mathcal{R}_x$ measuring cell.

plied by an AC-generator. An oscilloscope was used as the
zero-instrument of the bridge. The germanium electrodes used
were disk-shaped single crystals with a diameter of 6 mm and
a thickness of 2 to 4 mm. An ohmic metal contact was soldered
to one side of the disks. Then the specimen was sealed into a
glass tube by a resin in such a manner that only the plane of
the disk bearing no metal contact was in contact with the electrolyte. The electrodes were placed in an electrolytic cell
containing a large platinum electrode and a calomel electrode
for potential measurements. This cell is represented by $\mathcal{R}_x$
in Fig. 1. The potential of the germanium electrode was
changed by a direct current passing through the electrolyte, the
germanium and the platinum electrodes. Before each experiment, the germanium electrode was etched in the electrolyte
used in the experiment by applying an anodic current of about
1 ma/cm^2. To avoid contributions to the measured capacity
from a diffuse double layer in the electrolyte, concentrated
electrolytes were employed (1 mole/l). In this case the average thickness of the diffuse part of the double layer in the solution is about 3 Å. Thus the double layer in the solution can be
assumed to be on a fixed plane. Most of the experiments have
been carried out in sodium hydroxide and sulfuric acid solu-

tions and a few in sodium sulfate and potassium chloride solutions.

The equivalent circuit for the calculation of the differential electrode capacity is shown in Fig. 2. It consists of a series resistance R_s, which represents the internal ohmic resistance of the germanium disk and of the metal contact. Since

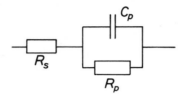

Fig. 2. Equivalent circuit.

this resistance can change by enrichment or depletion of carriers in the space charge region near the surface of the electrode, the value of this resistance was determined in each measurement by a pulse technique. It is to be expected that the resistance in the space charge region is not purely ohmic, for some capacity must exist between regions of different carrier concentration. The imaginary component is, however, without importance in the region of frequencies used in these experiments, provided there is no depletion of carriers resulting in a noticeable change of the resistance in the semiconductor. R_p is the ohmic part of the impedance of the electrode surface contributed by the passage of carriers (ions, electrons, or holes) from the semiconductor to the electrolyte or vice versa. This resistance is of importance regarding the kinetics of the electrode reaction in question. C_p is the differential capacity of the electrode surface.

The results of the measurements with intrinsic, p-, and n-type germanium ($N_A = 3.5 \times 10^{14}$ cm^{-3}, $N_D = 7.5 \times 10^{15}$ cm^{-3}) in 1N KOH at 25° and 45°C are shown in Figs. 3-5. The circular frequency, $\omega = 2\pi f$, used for the measurement is indicated at each curve. All measurements were made with and without illumination of the electrodes. The capacity-potential curve

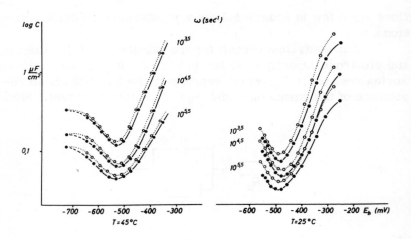

Fig. 3. Measured values of the capacities related to the geometric surface. Intrinsic Ge in 1 N KOH. ● without
light, O with light.

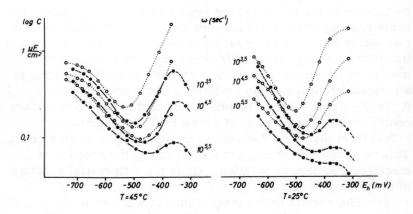

Fig. 4. Measured values of the capacities related to the geometric surface. N-type Ge in 1 N KOH. ● without
light, O with light.

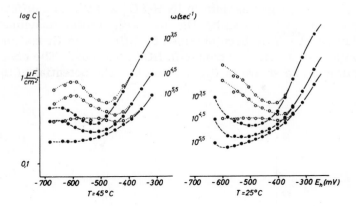

Fig. 5. Measured values of the capacities related to the geometric surface. P-type Ge in 1 N KOH. ● without light, ○ with light.

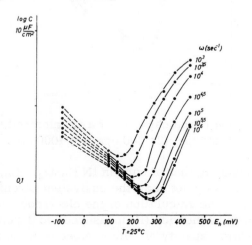

Fig. 6. Measured values of the capacities related to the geometric surface. Intrinsic Ge in 1 N H_2SO_4.

of intrinsic-type germanium in 1N H_2SO_4 at 25°C and different a-c frequencies is shown by Fig. 6. With similar techniques, similar results have been obtained by Efimov and Erusalimchik (10) with germanium electrodes in HCl solutions. The observed two minima are shown in Figs. 7 and 8. The potential of the

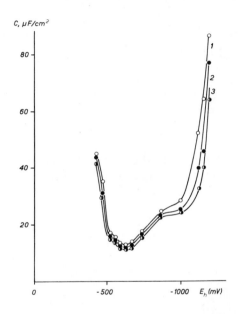

Fig. 7.   Dispersion of the capacity of a Ge electrode in 0.1 N HCl.   (1) 60 cps; (2) 200 cps; (3) 1000 cps.

second corresponds to that of ours in 1N H_2SO_4. Unfortunately the Russian authors do not show the equivalent circuit they used in the bridge or in the calculation of the electrode capacity.

Zviagin and Liutovich (11) measured the dependence of the phase boundary capacity of silicon electrodes on the potential in sulfuric acid. Their results are shown by Fig. 9.

3. THEORETICAL CONSIDERATIONS

As pointed out in the introduction, the structure of the double layer between a semiconductor electrode and an elec-

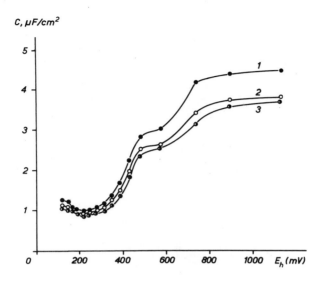

Fig. 8. Dispersion of the capacity of an n-type Ge electrode
with ρ = 25 ohm cm during anodic dissolution in
0.1 N HCl. (1) 200 cps; (2) 1000 cps; (3) 500 cps.

trolyte consists of the following parts: a diffuse space charge
in the semiconductor near the interface, a surface charge layer at the semiconductor surface, the charge in the Helmholtz
plane in the solution, and a diffuse space charge (diffuse double
layer) in the solution near the interface.   There may also be
a potential drop outside the semiconductor caused by orientated
dipoles. In solutions of high concentrations (> 0.1 mole /l) the
thickness of the diffuse double layer is so small that the excess
charge can be assumed to be located in a fixed plane. Thus
the double layer in the electrolyte degenerates to a surface
charge layer in the case of concentrated solutions. In the
following this will be assumed to be valid.
    The charge distribution and electrolytic potential within
the diffuse space charge layer in a solid electrode, as well as
the capacity of this layer, can be treated in the same manner as
in an electrolyte as shown by Rice (3), Verwey and Niessen (12)
and Grimley (13). In the case of a semiconductor with electrons
and holes, the charge distribution obeys the Boltzmann equations

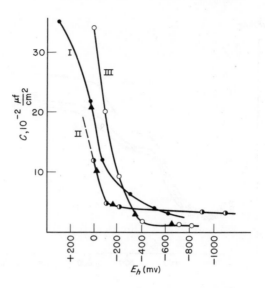

Fig. 9.　Barrier capacity for p-type Si in 0.01 N H_2SO_4.
    ● 　I　Surface polished, then boiled in distilled water.
    ◑ 　II　Surface etched in KOH.
    ○ 　III　Surface etched electrolytically in NaF/KCl.
    ▲ 　Calculated values.

$$n = n_0 \exp\left(\frac{\overline{V}}{A}\right) \ ; \ p = p_0 \exp - \left(\frac{\overline{V}}{A}\right) \qquad (1)$$

where n and p are the concentrations of electrons and holes; the subscript $_0$ indicates the values in the field-free interior of the electrode. $\overline{V}$ is the electric potential against the field-free interior and A $= kT/e$ designates the voltage equivalent of the temperature. Considering the Poisson equation,

$$\overline{V}'' = \frac{d^2\overline{V}}{dx^2} = -\frac{\rho}{\epsilon\epsilon_0} \qquad (2)$$

(ρ = space charge density, ϵ = dielectric constant of the electrode material, ϵ_0 = general dielectric constant), Bohnenkamp and

Engell (9) showed that:

$$q = - \sqrt{8\pi\epsilon\epsilon_o n_i eA} \; \sinh \left(\frac{\overline{V}(0)}{2A} \right) \tag{3}$$

for intrinsic conducting germanium with $n_o = p_o = n_i$; q is the space charge per unit area and $\overline{V}(0)$ the electric potential of the surface of the electrode against the space charge free interior.* In doped semiconductors, the existence of non-mobile charged particles (ionized acceptors or donors) must be taken into consideration. For n-type germanium with a concentration of donors of N_D, if $N_D \gg n_i$ and $p_o \approx n_i^2/N_D$, the authors showed that

$$q = \text{sgn}\varphi \sqrt{2\epsilon\epsilon_o eAN_D}$$

$$\sqrt{\exp\left(\frac{\overline{V}(0)}{A}\right) - 1 - \frac{\overline{V}(0)}{A} + \left(\frac{n_i}{N_D}\right)^2 \; 2 \left[\cosh\left(\frac{\overline{V}(0)}{A}\right) - 1\right]} \tag{4}$$

These expressions agree with the formula of Kingston and Neustadter (14), where $\exp(E_F - E_I/kT) = n_o/n_i$, $\exp(E_I - E_F/kT) = p_o/n_i$; E_F is the Fermi level of the semiconductor and E_I is the Fermi level of an intrinsic semiconductor.

If no surface charge is present at the semiconductor or if it does not change, we can neglect the potential drop outside the space charge or its change. The differential electrode capacity for an intrinsic semiconductor then is given by

$$c = e \sqrt{\frac{2\epsilon\epsilon_o n_i}{kT}} \; \cosh\left(\frac{\overline{V}(0)}{2A}\right) \tag{5}$$

This is exactly the same expression as for the diffuse part of the double layer in an electrolyte (1). Under the same assumptions, the capacity of an n-type germanium electrode is given by

---

*If a surface charge exists at the electrode $\overline{V}(0)$ is the potential drop in the space charge region.

$$c = e \sqrt{\dfrac{2\epsilon\epsilon_0 N_D}{kT}}$$

$$\left[\dfrac{\exp(\dfrac{\overline{V}(0)}{A}) - 1 + (\dfrac{n_i}{N_D})^2 \; 2 \sinh (\dfrac{\overline{V}(0)}{A})}{2\sqrt{\exp (\dfrac{\overline{V}(0)}{A}) - 1 - \dfrac{\overline{V}(0)}{A} + (\dfrac{n_i}{N_D})^2 \; 2 \left[\cosh (\dfrac{\overline{V}(0)}{A}) - 1 \right]}} \right] \tag{6}$$

For p-type germanium, the capacity is obtained by changing the sign of $\overline{V}(0)$ and replacing N_D by N_A.

The electrode capacity of intrinsic, p-, and n-type germanium as a function of $v_i = -\overline{V}(0)$ according to Eq. (5) and Eq. (6) is shown in Fig. 10. Fig. 10 further shows a comparison of the calculated and experimental capacity-potential curve of intrinsic germanium in 1 N KOH at 25°C, measured with $\omega = 10^6$. $V_i = 0$ is chosen arbitrarily at - 500 mV (hydrogen scale).

Assuming that the real surface of the electrode is twice the geometrical surface area, the measured capacity values at the minimum would agree with the calculated curve. In interpreting the differences in the shape of the curves, it can be assumed that only part of the applied change of the d-c potential affects the space charge. Then another part causes a change in the surface charge density.

A comparison of the capacities measured at the highest frequencies and the current-potential curves shows that the current i passing through the electrode is proportional to the concentration of holes at the surface

$$i = \text{const. } p(0) = i_0 \exp \dfrac{\alpha \Delta E_h}{A} \tag{7}$$

The value of the constant is nearly independent of the electrolyte used and the type and value of the conductivity of the electrode. Furthermore, all Ge samples showed identical current-potential curves in the same electrolyte in the region of small currents, where no deviations from the equilibrium $n(x) \, p(x) = n_i^2$ are to be expected. Consequently different values of V_i exist at the same electrode potential for differently doped samples. There-

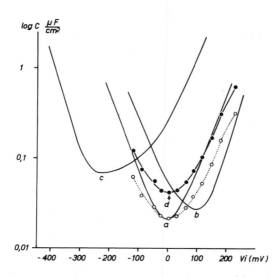

Fig. 10. Theoretical values of the space charge capacities as a function of the space charge potential V_i; (a) Intrinsic Ge; (b) n-type Ge with $N_D = 3.5 \times 10^{14}$ cm^{-3}; (c) p-type Ge with $N_A = 7.5 \times 10^{15}$ cm^{-3}; (d) Measured values of the capacity at the interface intrinsic Ge - 1 N KOH. $T = 25°$, $\omega = 10^6$ sec^{-1}. Related to the geometric surface (●) and to the real surface (o) assuming a roughness factor of 2.

fore the measured minima of the capacities are observed at potentials less different than those of the minima of the calculated curves (Fig. 10).

The concentration of the carriers near the surface is increased by illumination. The steady state concentration increase corresponds to $np = (n_i + \Delta n_i)^2$. Thus the applied light increases the electrode capacities also. This increase is proportional to $\sqrt{1 + \Delta n_i / n_i}$ for intrinsic samples. For doped Ge it is most pronounced if the minority carriers are enriched in the space charge, in agreement with theoretical considerations. As already shown by Brattain and Garrett (8), illumination increases the dissolution current of Ge. If Δi is the change in the current and Δp_0 the change in the concentration of holes, $\Delta i/i \sim \Delta p_0/p_0$ holds. Therefore light has a large effect on the dissolution current of n-type Ge, a smaller one for intrinsic Ge, and no measurable effect for p-type Ge.

Assuming a roughness factor of 2, the theoretical values of the capacities for the doped samples were also nearly obtained at the highest frequencies used. Stronger deviations occurred when the minority carriers were enriched in the space charge, i.e., for the n-type samples in the more anodic, for the p-type samples in the more cathodic region.

Since holes are consumed at the surface during the anodic dissolution, the n-type samples show increasing differences between the measured and the calculated capacities with increasing rate of dissolution, i.e., with increasing anodic polarization. In this case d-c potential curves also show deviations from the initial exponential slope. At higher anodic potentials a saturation current occurs. Illumination compensates for or decreases the influence of the anodic current on the concentration of holes. Fig. 11 shows schematically the influence of anodic dissolution and illumination. For p-type Ge the same effects occur, when electrons are consumed by the electrode reaction, i.e., in the cathodic region.

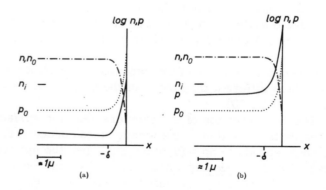

Fig. 11. Schematic representation of the concentration of the free electrons (n) and holes (p) in the space charge layer of an n-type semiconductor. (a) with anodic cur-current, (b) with light; ..... equilibrium distribution of electrons and holes with $n(x)\, p(x) = n_i^2$; _____ real distribution $n(x)\,p(x) \neq n_i^2$.

Raising the temperature from 25 to 45°C we found an increase of the capacities, which is to be expected as a result of the temperature dependence of n_i. The light effects and the deviations due to the anodic current are smaller in this case.

The frequency dependence of the measured impedances has not yet been explained. A qualitative explanation can be made with special assumptions about the time constants of charging and discharging of the surface states. The number of such states contributing to the differential capacity must decrease with increasing frequency of the a-c signal used. The analysis of the frequency dependence shows that a single time constant is not sufficient. The shortest time constant seems to be larger than the reciprocal value of the highest a-c frequency used, at least in the neighborhood of the capacity minimum. The similarity of the curves measured with different frequencies could be explained with the assumption that the rate of charging and discharging of the surface traps is proportional to the concentration of the free carriers and the occupation of the surface traps respectively. This assumption raises the question whether there exists an electrochemical equilibrium between the free charge carriers and the occupation of the surface states.

The potentials of the capacity minima are strongly dependent on the pH of the electrolyte. The current potential curves show the same dependence. These potential differences are not caused by changes in the space charge. It must be assumed that the source of these potential differences lies between the semiconductor surface and the Helmholtz plane in the electrolyte. Adsorption of OH^- ions may be an explanation of this effect.

Efimov and Erusalimchik (10) have criticized the results of Bohnenkamp and Engell (9). They state that the capacity values of the minimum of the capacity-potential curve reported by Bohnenkamp and Engell are too small, compared with their own measurements, and assume that this is due to a poor contact at the reverse side of the germanium electrodes and an inadequate preparation of the surface. We tested the contact on the reverse side with the help of a sample contacted at both sides and found no capacitive component large enough to influence the measured values. As shown above, the values measured by Bohnenkamp and Engell are nearly in agreement with the theory, whereas the values of the Russian authors are more than an order of magnitude higher. Similar high values we found only when the surface was not cleaned by an anodic treatment. Further, Efimov and Erusalimchik assume that the minimum capacity has to be at the same potential, independent of the electrolyte used, for it should be connected with the "zero charge potential." This is the potential at which the electrode is free of any excess charge and the electrostatic potential has a constant value throughout the electrode. As we have shown (9) the minimum of the capacity is connected with the zero charge potential only for intrinsic Ge. Considering the dipole layer, which is partially formed by adsorption of ions on the electrode, a potential drop exists also between an electrode and the solution at the zero charge potential. Therefore the value of the zero charge potential and thus the potential of minimum electrode capacity, can depend on the chemical composition of the solution.

Zviagin and Liutovich (11) found similar minimum values for p-type Si as we did for the Ge samples. The theoretical curve of the Russian authors is calculated on the assumption that the minority carriers are depleted. This is possible for a p-type semiconductor only in the case of cathodic polarization. Since the Russian authors did not take into account the possibility of enrichment of the minority carriers, they did not get a distinct minimum of the theoretical capacity-potential curve. We found the minimum for n-type Ge under reverse bias, i.e., under anodic current. This result is to be expected (in contrast to a common rectifier) as long as the resistance across the phase boundary (R_p) is high compared to the recombination rate or the rate of formation of free carriers. It is to be expected, in other words, as long as the electrochemical potential of the free carriers remains nearly constant across the space charge up to the surface. The Russian authors point out that the measured capacity is not equal to the space charge capacity, but should be related to it. This relationship is indicated by the measured frequency dependence of the measured impedances. It is in agreement with our assumption that the measured capacities approach the calculated values of the space charge capacity with increasing frequencies.

References

1. G. Gouy, J. Phys., 9, 457 (1910); D. L. Chapmann, Phil. Mag., (6) 25, 475 (1913).
2. O. Stern, Z. Elektrochem., 30, 508 (1924).
3. O. K. Rice, J. Phys. Chem., 30, 1501 (1926); Phys. Rev., 31, 1051 (1928).
4. C. Wagner and W. Schottky, Z. physik. Chem., B, 11, 163 (1930); C. Wagner, J. Chem. Phys., 18, 62 (1950); W. H. Brattain and C. G. B. Garrett, Ann. N. Y. Acad. Sci., 58, 951 (1954).
5. I. Tamm, Physik. Z. Sowjetunion, 1, 733 (1932); R. H. Fowler, Proc. Roy. Soc., A, 141, 56 (1933).
6. W. Schultz and H. V. Harten, Z. Elektrochem., 60, 20 (1956).
7. H. J. Engell, in W. Schottky, ed., Halbleiterprobleme, Vol. I, p. 249, Friedr. Vieweg & Sohn, 1954.
8. W. H. Brattain and C. G. B. Garrett, Bell System Tech. J., 34, 129 (1955); W. W. Harvey and H. C. Gatos, J. Electrochem. Soc., 105, 654 (1958); J. Appl. Phys., 29, 1267 (1958); M. C. Cretella and H. C. Gatos, J. Electrochem. Soc., 105, 487 (1958).
9. K. Bohnenkamp and H. J. Engell, Z. Elektrochem., 61, 1184 (1957).
10. E. A. Efimov and I. G. Erusalimchik, Zhur. Fiz. Khim., 33, 441 (1959).
11. V. I. Zviagin and A. S. Liutovich, Izvest. Akad. Nauk Uzbek. S. S. R., Phys. - Math. series, No. 1, 25 (1959).
12. E. J. W. Verwey and K. F. Niessen, Phil. Mag., (7) 28, 435 (1939).
13. T. B. Grimley, Proc. Roy. Soc., A 201, 40 (1950).
14. R. H. Kingston and S. F. Neustadter, J. Appl. Phys., 26, 718 (1955).

DISCUSSION

J. F. DEWALD (Bell Telephone Laboratories): In the circuit diagram, Fig. 1 of your paper, there is a variable resistance marked R_s. Is the value of it significant with respect to the observed frequency dependence? Also, you mentioned a resistivity of the space charge layer; where is this included and is it significant compared to the bulk resistivity?

H. J. ENGELL: R_s represents the internal ohmic resistance of the semiconductor and of the metal contact on its reverse side. R_s must be carefully set to correspond to the measured value for each specimen otherwise the frequency dependence will be altered. Since this is important, the value of the resistance was determined in each measurement by an impulse technique, and R_s adjusted when necessary. The resistivity of the space charge layer is included in R_s.

H. GERISCHER (Max Planck Institute): Efimov and Erusalimchik [Zhur. Fiz. Khim. 33, 441(1959)] reported much larger values of the capacity than you and Bohnenkamp. Do you know if they calculated their capacities in the same way that you did? Do you think that their calculated capacities included a pseudo capacity resulting from a chemical reaction taking place during their measurements? I can add that our own measurements confirmed your results.

H. J. ENGELL : The paper of Efimov and Erusalimchik is very brief. They give no equivalent circuit nor do they discuss their method of measurement; thus, it is difficult to say just what they have measured. Their measurements were made, however, at a potential of about -500 mv in acid solutions. Under these conditions the rate of hydrogen evolution is relatively fast; therefore, it is possible that their minimum in the capacity could have been influenced by kinetic effects. I should also point out that we obtained higher values of the capacity when we did not etch the surface by applying an anodic current before each experiment.

W. H. BRATTAIN (Bell Telephone Laboratories): I want to comment in connection with some of the questions that were asked this morning in regard to how sure you can be that the electrode capacity, or to be more general that one of the measured surface parameters has been obtained under conditions that will yield true values. If you are at all suspicious of your measurements, the thing to do is to measure one of the other parameters and see how it is behaving. If you measure at least two or preferably three parameters, then you will be able to tell what is spurious and what is truly associated with the space charge layer or the electrode. I have read Dr. Engell's paper, and I am quite sure that he is measuring the real capacity.

P. LACOMBE

*Ecole Nationale
Superieure des Mines*

Electrolytic Etching
of Metals

ABSTRACT

ELECTROLYTIC ETCHING OF metals
produces various results: intergranular attack,
attack of crystalline surfaces which is orientation dependent, formation of etch pits, and anodic
oxide films. The behavior of a metal or alloy
depends on composition, temperature of the electrolyte, and above all on the electrode potential
which varies with the metal. Applications to
Al, Fe, stainless steel, Ti, Zr, U, and their
alloys will be discussed.

1. INTRODUCTION

Electrolytic polishing, discovered by Jacquet in 1935,
has the distinct advantage of completely eliminating the structural surface damage caused by classical mechanical polishing.
However, it is not always possible to clearly reveal the
structure of high purity metals by electropolishing alone, even
in the most simple case of grain size determination of a recrystallized material. Consequently, electropolishing must

244

always be followed by chemical or electrolytic etching. The principal factors of this anodic etching are the electrolyte composition, the temperature, the current density and the duration of the electrolysis.

For the same material, by varying the composition of the electrolyte, the current density, and the duration of etching, it is possible to obtain three different types of etching.

2. TYPES OF ELECTROLYTIC ETCHING

2.1 Preferential Etching of the Grain Boundaries

Etching of stainless steel represents the most typical case of the application of electrolytic etching. This technique has been used on the 18/8 stainless steels in order to obtain a reliable and rapid measure of their sensitization to intergranular corrosion after a thermal treatment at 600 to 900°C. Several organic electrolytes such as oxalic acid (1) and tartaric acid (2) as well as inorganic electrolytes such as chromic acid (3) and sodium cyanide (4) have been employed. All these electrolytes attack preferentially the grain boundaries in which a second phase has precipitated. The composition of this phase responsible for the etching is not always known.

The sensitivity of the grain boundaries to electrolytic etching is most conclusively demonstrated in the case of high purity metals such as Al where the intergranular etching by hydrochloric acid can only be explained by the concentration of residual impurities in the grain boundaries (5).

2.2 Formation of Etch Pits and Etch Figures

Etch-pit formation techniques have been extensively developed since the first observations on Al by Lacombe and Beaujard (6) and on semiconductors (Ge) by Vogel et al (7). Besides their seemingly random distribution etch pits are frequently aligned on intragranular boundaries of subgrain boundaries, which are the boundaries of polygonization.

A comparison between the linear density of the etch pits in these polygonization boundaries and the degree of misorientation of two adjacent subgrains has permitted the unambiguous

identification of dislocations: each etch pit was found to be
associated with a single dislocation in the sub-boundary. *

Electrolytic etching reagents are especially suited for
the detection of the distribution of dislocations in a heterogeneous strained metal. It is also possible to distinguish an even
slightly work-hardened metal from a perfectly recrystallized
one. Electroetching is so sensitive that it is possible to distinguish a crystal of secondary recrystallization from a crystal
of primary recrystallization by differences in etch-pit densities (10).

For the detection of dislocations by electroetching as
well as by chemical etching, it is frequently necessary to "dec-
orate" the dislocations by means of one or more impurities in
the base metal. The impurity atoms interact with the dislocations. This idea was first put forward by Wyon and Lacombe
(11) in the case of the Al. The same approach has also been
extended to Fe (12), Si-Fe alloys (13), Zn (14), Cu (15), and
others.

Prolonged etching in an electrolyte developing etch pits
may lead to the formation of a multitude of superimposed etch
figures covering the surface almost uniformly. The facets of
these etch figures remain parallel to crystallographic planes
of simple Miller indices (6) $\{(100)$, (110) or (111) for cubic
metals$\}$. Consequently a beam of light normal to the surface
becomes elliptically polarized when reflected by the different
grains of a polycrystalline material. The degree of ellipticity
varies according to the orientation of the facets with respect to
the incident beam. As a result even an isotropic metal can be
observed between crossed Nicols reflecting polarized light of
varying color depending on the orientation of the facets of the
etch figures. Jones (16) was the first to use this technique and
Dunsmuir (17) extended it to the evaluation of the degree of

---

*A distinction must be made between the macro etch pits with
geometrical contours (8, 9, 6), which are observed even at low
magnifications and the micro etch pits which have no distinct
geometrical shape. The former probably reveal only a fraction
of the dislocations, whereas the latter give a better measure of
the total number of dislocations (13, 12, 30).

preferential orientation in the case of polycrystalline sheets of
Si-Fe alloys.

2.3 Formation of Anodic Insoluble Products

Electrolytic etching can be represented by the equation:

$$M - ne^{-} \rightarrow M^{n+} \tag{1}$$

The removal of electrons from a metal resulting in the formation of positive ions is achieved by the application of an emf
(in the case of electroetching) or by an oxidizing agent (in the
case of chemical etching). Electrolytic or chemical etching
may lead to the formation of soluble or insoluble oxides depending upon the metal and the electrolyte employed.

If the oxide (or hydroxide) is insoluble, its thickness
depends either on the crystal orientation or on the length of
electroetching: Thin oxide films may be grown in this way exhibiting interference colors with white light (18). Thicker
films (several microns) can be examined with polarized light
(19, 20, 21, 22). This technique, at first limited to Al and its
alloys (anodic oxidation), has been recently extended to other
metals and particularly to U (23), Zr (24), Ti (25-29) and their
alloys.

Other anodic reactions are also of interest when there
is formation of an insoluble product. Sulfide films were used
(30, 31) in the case of Cu and Cu-Zn alloys. These methods
can serve for the determination of the relative orientation of
the grains in a polycrystalline pure metal or homogeneous
solid solutions. In the case of pure metals, the color of the
surface film depends on the orientation of the grains. In the
case of solid solutions, their composition affects the rate of
oxidation and, therefore, the color of the films. It is possible
in this way to detect composition heterogeneities in a solid solution.

A typical application is the detection of sub-boundaries
in Al-Zn solid solutions with enough Zn to allow precipitation-
hardening at room temperature after quenching. During such
aging, Zn atoms concentrate at the sub-boundary dislocation
walls to a sufficient extent to cause a color variation of the

oxide film (18, 32) (Fig. 1).

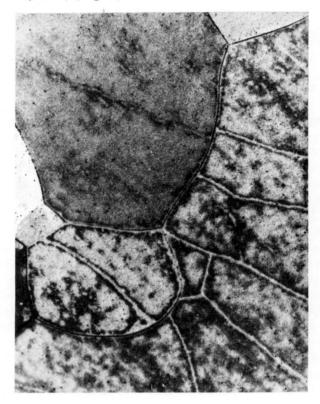

Fig. 1. Polygonization sub-boundaries in a solid solution Al-
        Zn after quenching and aging at room temperature;
        thin anodic film with interference tints (18).

These oxidation methods are also applied for the detection of the various phases of complex alloys. Each phase exhibits a different oxidation rate (depending on composition) and,
therefore, a different color if electroetching is carried out under well controlled conditions. The method has been applied
for some time in the identification of different carbides in
stainless steels (4) and high speed steels (33). More recently

Ence and Margolin (25) applied the same method for examining complex Ti alloys such as Ti-Mo, Ti-MnO and Ti-Mo-O. Hiltz (27) employed the method as a cumulative etching technique, whereby the metal undergoes several successive etchings of short duration in order to follow the color variation of each phase through every oxidation stage. Picklesimer (24) extended this technique to Zr and Zr alloys, such as Zr-Ag and Zr-Sn.

3. VARIOUS ELECTROLYTIC ETCHING TECHNIQUES

3.1 The Etching Electrolyte is the Same as the Electropolishing Solution

This method is generally applicable and probably the most efficient one. It is surprising that it is not more extensively used in view of its simplicity. The method is based on the classical current-voltage curve of electropolishing (Fig. 2). The curve is divided into three parts: In the first part the current density is approximately proportional to the voltage; in the second part, the current density is independent of the voltage; and in the last one the current density increases again with the voltage. At the second part of the curve the metals undergo electropolishing; in the first part etching takes place and in the last part some localized pitting occurs. Thus electroetching involves two steps. In the first step the voltage applied between the two electrodes (the metal anode and the auxiliary electrode) corresponds to the plateau of the current-voltage curve leading to polishing. In the second stage, the voltage is decreased suddenly to a value falling in the ascending part of the curve. The time at this low potential is very short (generally a few seconds) as compared with the time necessary for electropolishing (a few minutes). The applications of this technique to three specific cases is discussed below.

3.11 Copper. Copper (34) is electropolished in an aqueous solution of phosphoric acid (700 cc H_3PO_4, sp gr 1.71, per liter). The copper cathode is far larger than the anode to be polished. After 25-30 minutes of electropolishing, the current is switched off and the two electrodes are short-circuited.

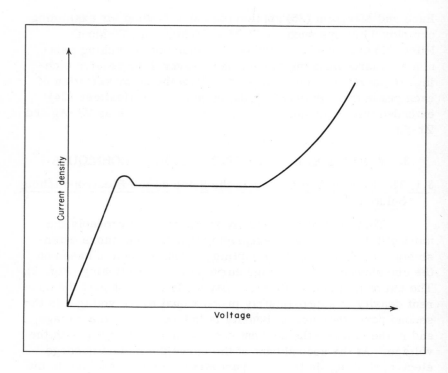

Fig. 2.   Typical voltage - current density curve of electrolytic
polishing.

The difference of electrolyte composition near the two electrodes caused by polarization during electropolishing is sufficient to cause a current of a few milliamperes.   The intensity
of this current decreases rapidly and falls to zero after 5 to 6
minutes.   A short-circuit of 50 to 90 seconds' duration is sufficient to produce not only the etching of grain boundaries but
also of areas revealing plastic deformation heterogeneities and
very small inclusions of Cu_2O or Cu_2S, hardly visible after
electropolishing only.

According to Jacquet (34) the above very low electroetching current results from the fact that a viscous layer of
high resistivity forms at the anode during electropolishing.

This layer contains a larger amount of dissolution products than the bulk of the electrolyte. When the polishing current is turned off after the two electrodes are short-circuited, the viscous layer is gradually eliminated by diffusion and the polarization current progressively decreases. Fig. 3 shows the variation of the current density with time for different size anodes

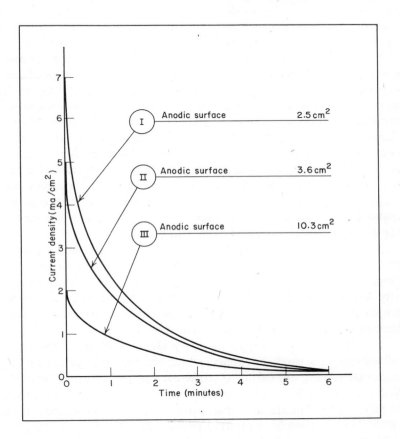

Fig. 3.   Density of polarization current versus time for copper specimens of different sizes.

and the same cathode. The initial current density is greater than the smaller total anode surface. Thus the electroetching

time necessary to detect all the structure variations of the
metal will be shorter for a small anode. For example, for the
anode with the area of 10. 3 cm^2, etching of two minutes with a
current density varying from 1. 8 to 0. 5 ma/cm^2 is quite insuf-
ficient, whereas good results are obtained with the two other
anodes after one minute at a current density three or four times
greater. In fact, the anodes to be etched should not exceed 4 to
5 cm^2. This technique has been applied successfully by Jacquet
in cases where classical etching techniques are inadequate.

An interesting case is the detection of structural flaws
due to plastic deformation. Tension or compression produce
strains which are visible as slip lines. Electropolishing yields
smooth surfaces and reveals no trace or plastic deformation.
Similarly, chemical reagents lead to no preferential etching
along the intersection of the slip planes and the surface. In
contrast electroetching reveals some bands of preferential
etching on the surface which are parallel to the initial slip lines
but far broader. Consequently it seems that the structure disturbance caused by the slip process is not limited to the slip
plane but also extends to a more or less significant distance in
the lattice on both sides of each slip plane.

Another important fact revealed by electroetching is
that plastic deformation of a metal (polycrystalline or even
single crystal) is extremely heterogeneous. This heterogeneity depends upon the type of deformation; cold-rolling for example produces some slips which are not homogeneous in the
bulk of each grain, but rather localized.

A third observation made by electroetching is the development of a work-hardened structure in a recrystallized
material during annealing at different temperatures. Jacquet
(34) rolled (90%) a copper sheet consisting of three large grains
of different orientation. After annealing at a low temperature
(200° C) electroetching clearly showed that each of the three
deformed crystals had its structure developing differently depending on the crystallographic orientation. In particular,
electroetching revealed very clearly the work-hardened regions
of the crystal and those presenting recrystallization nuclei.
The very small size of these nuclei does not permit their iden-

tification by classical x-ray techniques. *

Electroetching of Cu by this technique is highly reproducible in addition to exhibiting great sensitivity to structural
defects.

3.12 Uranium. Micrographic examination of α - U presents two principal problems associated with its orthorhombic
structure and its chemical reactivity.   Like all anisotropic
metals (hexagonal, tetragonal and others), U is very sensitive
to mechanical deformation.   Furthermore it forms an oxide in
air even at room temperature.   During electropolishing, uranium is gradually covered with an oxide layer which bears no
structural relationship to the underlying metal. **   In contrast,
prior to air oxidation, electroetching leads to epitaxial oxide
growth as shown by Robillard et al (23).

Uranium is electropolished under 30 volts for 10 to 20
minutes in the following electrolyte: 50 g Cr_2O_3, 600 cc glacial CH_3COOH, 60 cc H_2O at 6 to 8°C.   Upon electropolishing,
and without removing the specimen from the electrolyte, the
potential is suddenly decreased to 2-3 volts, then maintained
at this value for 8 to 12 minutes, according to the extent of
etching required.   These conditions are convenient for samples
with total surface of 3 to 10 cm^2.   The etching clearly reveals

---

*It should be pointed out that Jacquet has developed other elec-
trolytic etching techniques which are even more sensitive.
They have been particularly applied to copper alloys such as
65/33 brass, employing sodium thiosulfate electrolyte.   The
techniques made possible the study of the microstructure of
strained brass and showed the piling of dislocations on grain
boundaries (30).   The etching techniques were also able to
detect heterogeneities in the plastic deformation of a poly-
crystal (Fig. 4) and to follow its transformation into a polygonized structure during a low temperature anneal (Fig. 5).

**This observation is valid only for the aceto-chromic electro-
lyte.   Indeed Jacquet (35) and Englander (36) have shown epitaxial growth of an oxide on uranium by electropolishing in
other electrolytes.

Fig. 4. 65/35 brass annealed for 15 hrs at 200°C, polished to
        dissolve 100μ, annealed again for 3 hrs at 400°C, re-
        polished to dissolve 15μ, annealed for 1 hr at 500°C
        and finally polished to dissolve 10μ. The specimen is
        anodically etched in a thiosulfate solution and the
        colored film is dissolved (30); X 630.

grain-boundaries, twin boundaries, or kink bands. Electropolishing alone does not disclose any structure. Prolonged
electroetching causes surface roughening which varies with
crystallographic orientation.

Uranium has various types of substructure. The α -
substructure represents the subdivision of the α - grains of a

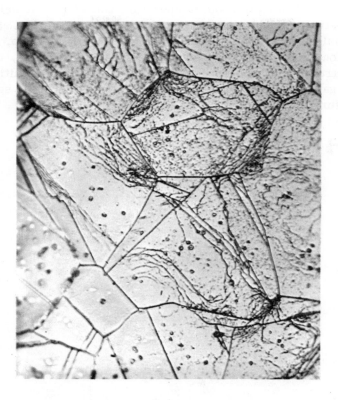

Fig. 5. Same specimen as in Fig. 4 after annealing for 2 hrs
at 500°C, polishing to dissolve 5μ, annealing for 45
min. at 600°C and repolishing to dissolve 6μ. The
specimen is anodically etched in a thiosulfate solution
and the colored film is dissolved. Some sub-boundaries have disappeared due to annealing at higher temperature (30); X 630.

polycrystalline sample. Because of the anisotropy of the expan-
sion coefficients along the three axes a, b, c, of the orthorhombic cell this subdivision occurs invariably when the metal is
heat treated in the α - phase. Even if a polycrystalline sample
consists of perfect single crystal grains, heating from 20° to

600°C and cooling to room temperature causes plastic deformation between neighboring grains of different orientation. Such
thermal deformation introduces, during the cooling step, dislocations which may be detected in polygonization walls, forming intragranular sub-boundaries in each grain of the initial
aggregate. The resulting network is referred to as the substructure of α - polygonization (Fig. 6).

Fig. 6.   Polygonized α - U after annealing in the β - phase and
         slow cooling. The sub-boundaries stop abruptly on
         the JJ' grain boundary between two crystals (37); X150.

Another network of sub-boundaries called β - substructure
may be superimposed on the α - substructure, as shown by

Robillard, Calais and Lacombe (37). These authors used the same technique of electroetching. The β - substructure appeared only when α - U was reheated in the γ - phase region. When cooled to room temperature and annealed in the γ - field, U undergoes a two phase-transformation: $\gamma \rightarrow \beta$ transformation at 774°C and $\beta \rightarrow \alpha$ at 665°C. During the $\gamma \rightarrow \beta$ transition, a significant decrease in volume occurs which introduces internal stresses. The dislocations thus induced give rise to the poly-gonization of the β - U crystals (Fig. 7). During the cooling of the β - phase, the impurities of U diffuse and concentrate

Fig. 7. β - substructure of uranium superimposed to the grain boundaries of the final structure after a slow cooling from the γ - phase (37); X 150.

around the dislocations forming a network of β-subgrains. This precipitation of impurities in the β - polygonization substructure enables the substructure to persist during the $\beta \rightarrow \alpha$ second transformation. Only electroetching permits the detection of the β - substructure superimposed to the boundaries and sub-boundaries of the final α-structure with great sensitivity and reproducibility. It is possible also to detect the former γ - grain boundaries (Fig. 8).

Another interesting aspect is the oxide film formation

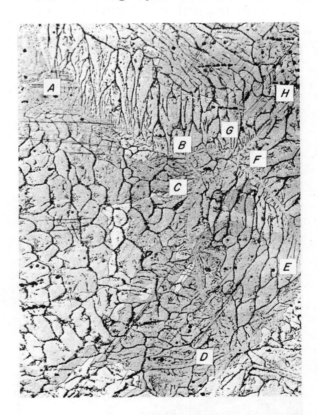

Fig. 8. Discontinuities in the network of the substructure of β - phase, forming a polygonal net ABCDEFGH which represents the former γ - boundaries of uranium (37); X 150.

on α-uranium either by air oxidation or anodic oxidation. Its growth is related to the crystalline orientation of the underlying metal. As a matter of fact, the oxide in both cases grows slowly enough to allow the observation of the development of interference tints, which vary with the orientation of the individual grains. But surprisingly, epitaxial growth cannot be observed on uranium which has been submitted only to electropolishing; during atmospheric or anodic oxidation, the oxide film always has the same color which has no relation to the metal structure, as if the metal were covered with an amorphous skin before oxidation. It is likely that electropolishing of uranium forms an amorphous oxide film controlling the further development of the atmospheric (or anodic) oxide film, at least in the aceto-chromic electrolyte. Electroetching, however, eliminates the amorphous film by pickling the surface; the epitaxial growth of an oxide layer is then possible. These epitaxial films allow the differentiation of the various types of deformation in a α - U (slip-bands, twins, kink bands) and the detection of impurities such as uranium hydride (UH_3). This hydride appears in the form of particles surrounded by a ring of metal resistant to oxidation (23, 37) (Fig. 9).

3.13 Aluminum. Electrolytic etching of Al is actually an anodic oxidation rather than real etching. But the technique as employed by Hone (20) is in principle the same as those discussed for Cu and U: the same electrolyte is used for the electropolishing and electroetching; the growth of the oxide film takes place during the decrease of the potential. Electropolishing takes place in a mixture of H_3PO_4 + carbitol + HF + H_2O under high current density (50 to 150 amp/dm^2). The oxide layer is formed when voltage is lowered and the current density becomes 1 - 2.5 amp/dm^2. Depending on the duration of electrolysis, either oxide layers exhibiting interference tints or thick oxide layers (10μ after 20 minutes) are obtained. The thicker layers must be examined with polarized light through crossed Nicols.

Using 10μ films, Beck and his collaborators (21, 22) studied the continuous and discontinuous recrystallization strain-induced growth and polygonization of Al. It should be pointed out that these oxide films have the same properties with regard to metallographic applications as the anodic films formed in

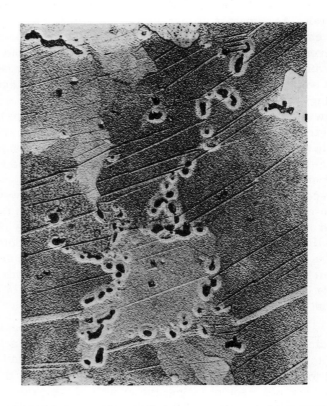

Fig. 9.   Intergranular precipitation of UH_3 revealed by electroetching (23); X150.

sulphuric electrolytes (19, 38).   The thin films were studied by
Lacombe and Mouflard (18) in the case of Al, and Berghezan
(39) in the case of Al-Mg alloys.

3. 2   The Etching Electrolyte Differs from the Electropolishing Solution

Several electrolytic solutions have been proposed for
the etching of different metals and alloys.   The reason for this
variety is not apparent.   For example in the case 18/8 stainless

steel, several electrolytes have been recommended, particularly for the identification of carbides precipitated along the
austenitic grain boundaries by a sensitization heat treatment.
The qualitative observations reported are hardly sufficient to
decide whether the oxalic, citric or tartaric electrolyte is the
most sensitive for the detection of very small traces of carbides along the grain boundaries. We shall return to this point
in the last section. Nevertheless a comparison of these different reagents shows that the surface preparation before etching
is the most essential factor. It is quite obvious that electropolishing, or perhaps chemical polishing, constitutes the best
means of preparation. Mechanical polishing must be excluded
since electroetching can reveal even a small amount of cold-
work (30, 34). It is therefore difficult to appreciate the merits
of the proposed etching electrolytes if the method of surface
preparation is not specified. But even in the case of electropolished surfaces, the choice of the polishing electrolyte is important. Depending on the chemical composition of the electrolyte, a thin oxide layer may or may not form on the surface
during electropolishing. For instance in the case of Al only
anhydrous perchloric acid-acetic anhydride gives polished surfaces free of oxides, as shown by electrode potential measurements (40). On the other hand, some electrolytes such as
Hone's solution (20) lead to oxide formations during polishing.
The presence of an oxide film, even if very thin, may affect
the process of electroetching.

It is still difficult to propose simple rules for defining
the desirable composition of the electrolyte. Nevertheless
many of the electrolytes employed are oxidizing agents. In
order to show the possibilities of these reagents, a comparison
will be made of the different techniques proposed recently for
the etching of easily oxidized metals, such as Ti, Zr and U.

Ence and Margolin (25) have identified the different
phases of complex Ti-alloys, using their technique based on the
different rates of oxidation. The sample is put on a stainless
steel rod wrapped with a cotton-wool pad soaked in etching
solution (10% NaCN); the rod serves as the cathode. Upon
etching for 60 seconds (under 8 to 10 volts and 0.14 amps) the
carbides appear yellow or orange while the α - and β-Ti phases

appear violet or blue. The borides Ti_2B, TiB or TiB_2 may also be identified.

Another technique (cumulative etching) permits a better differentiation of the phases in complex alloys, like Ti-Mo-Fe and Ti-Mo-O (26). The specimen (Fig. 10) undergoes several successive etchings for short times (0.3 sec.) under high voltage (125 volts) in order to develop thin oxide films of increasing thickness. The thickness, however, varies for the different phases. The best contrast of interference tints is obtained when the richest Ti-phase acquires a second order interference blue color (Figs. 11 and 12).

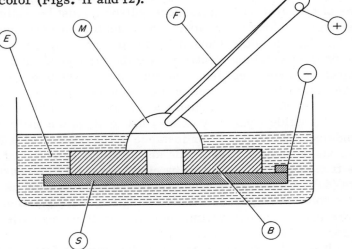

Fig. 10. Apparatus used for cumulative etching. Current densities are determined by the thickness of the Bakelite mask (B) and the size of the opening of the mask (M-sample, F-stainless steel forceps, S-stainless steel cathode) (25).

Hiltz (27, 28) modified the Ence and Margolin electrolyte in order to study Ti and Ti-alloys in the wrought and recrystallized state. Two objections can be raised against the Ence and Margolin technique: the total etching time is very short (3 seconds) and the etching process cannot be easily controlled; secondly, the identification of the different phases is

Fig. 11 Microstructure of an as-cast Ti - 54.5 Mn alloy etched
with HF + glycerol + H_2O (1:1:10) shows two or three
phases. The microconstituents are: Ti-Mn and β-
Ti (25); X 350.

based on their coloration which in turn depends on the composition and the orientation of each phase. Thus in the case of pure
Ti, Hiltz and Douglas (29) have shown that the grains with surfaces
parallel to the basal (0001) plane present the smallest oxidation
rate. Consequently a polycrystalline Ti specimen will appear
with a uniform blue color after prolonged etching if all its grains
have an orientation differing from (0001). But if a few grains have
the (0001) orientation, they will not oxidize so rapidly and will maintain their yellow color. This result could lead to the conclusion that
a second phase is present. In fact, it is possible to differentiate rapidly between a 98% cold-rolled material annealed at 793°C and
the same material hot-rolled at 793°C. The metal re-crystal-
lized at 793°C after cold-rolling does not present any grains
with the (0001) orientation and will be uniformly colored blue.

Fig. 12. The same alloy as Fig. 11 electrolytically stained for
1.5 sec. at 125 V shows three phases: Ti-Mn bluish-
green (A), ε-phase violet (B), and black β-Ti purplish-
red (25); X 350.

On the contrary hot-rolling at 793°C gives a (0001) texture and
the grains are colored yellow or orange for the same etching
time. Picklesimer (24) adopted the Ence and Margolin technique to study Zr and Zr-alloys such as Zr-Ag and Zr-Sn.
Table I shows the great similarity of the baths used in the case
of Ti and Zr. The Picklesimer electrolyte is very sensitive in
detecting Zr-hydride.

In the case of U, two electrolytes were found to lead to
oxide film formation. One has been developed by Picklesimer
(24) (20 cc of concentrated NH_4OH + 80 cc of absolute ethyl
alcohol); the other electrolyte (23g ethyl glycol + 500 cc concentrated NH_4OH sp gr 0.925 + 500 cc H_2O) is used after electroetching at low voltage in the Robillard et al electrolyte (23).
The best conditions for obtaining the maximum contrast of
colors for different crystallographic orientations can be deter-

TABLE I

Electrolytes Employed for Electrolytic Etching of Ti and Zr and Their Alloys

Electrolyte Composition	Ti (25)	Ti (27)	Ti (29)	Zr (24)
Oxalic Acid	5 g	5 g	5 g	-
Citric Acid	5 g	5 g	5 g	2 g
Orthophosphoric Acid	5 cc	3 cc	3 cc	5 cc
Tartaric Acid	-	5 g	5 g	-
Lactic Acid (85%)	10 cc	-	-	10 cc
Water	35 cc	50 cc	20 cc	35 cc
Methanol	-	27 cc	-	-
Ethanol (95%)	60 cc	-	27 cc	60 cc
"Carbitol"	-	20 cc	20 cc	-
Glycerol	1 Vol /1 Vol	-	-	20 cc
Applied Potential, Volts	125	6	6	20
Etching Time	0. 3 to 3 sec.	-	5 to 120 sec.	3 to 10 sec.

mined from the logarithmic plots of current density versus time. The curves consist of two parts: The first corresponds to the formation of thin epitaxial oxide layers with interference tints (Fig. 13); the second corresponds to a slowing down of the oxide growth which suggests the formation of layers analogous to those formed on Al in sulfo-phosphoric electrolytes employed for the preparation of replicas for electron microscopy. Therefore it is not necessary to prolong electroetching beyond the bend of the curve (Fig. 13). The best contrast of colors is obtained with an oxidation of 20 minutes at 40 volts (Fig. 14).

A comparison of the results obtained for Ti, Zr, and U bears out the importance of surface preparation prior to etching. If the oxidation of U takes place immediately after electropolishing without any intermediary etching, the anodic film on

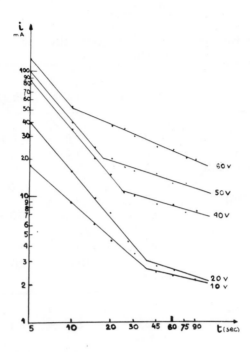

Fig. 13. Current during anodic oxidation of U at different potentials (23).

all grains is quite uniform in color regardless of orientation.
In contrast, after electroetching the growth of the anodic oxide
is epitaxial and its colors vary with orientation. In the case of
the electrolytes of Ence and Margolin or Hiltz (except for (0001)
grains), the weak dependence of color on orientation is probably due to the lack of electroetching prior to the anodic oxidation.
The authors recommend chemical etching prior to oxidation in
order to improve the color contrasts but they do not specify the
nature of this etching.

4. POTENTIOSTATIC STUDY OF ELECTROLYTIC ETCHING

The choice of the baths for electroetching is primarily
the result of empirical observations. At present it is difficult

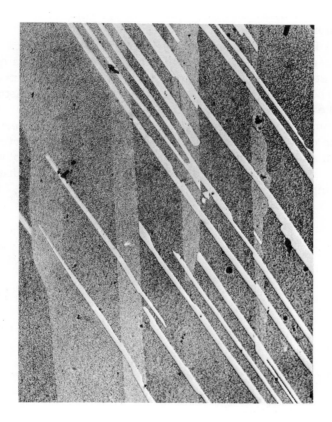

Fig. 14. Twins produced by plastic deformation and broadened by annealing at 650°C in an imperfect single crystal of α - U grown by progressive phase-change from β to α. The bands with different shades correspond to the recovery of the subgrains of the initial crystal. Electroetching reveals small disorientations between the subgrains; X 150. (D. Calais, P. Lacombe and Mme Simenel, Rev. mét., 56, 261 (1959)).

to explain why an electrolyte leads to etch-pit formation or to a preferential attack of grain boundaries or specific phases of a given alloy. Furthermore, it is not frequently known for a given electrolyte, that the applied voltage represents the best condition for the desired type of etching.

It was first suggested by Edeleanu (41), in the case of stainless steels, that a potentiostat approach permits a quantitative study of electroetching. The potential of an electrode immersed in a given electrolyte can be maintained constant with the potentiostat such as that used by Roberts (42). There is a simple relationship between the potential of the electrode and the dissolution rate. Fig. 15 shows the type of curve obtained with an 18/8 stainless steel in 20% sulphuric acid solution at 25°C. The concentration of the electrolyte, temperature, and the composition of the steel are important parameters. If the

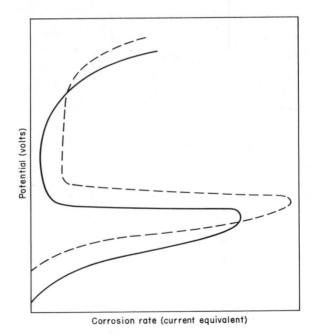

Fig. 15. Corrosion-potential curves of Cr-Ni stainless steels in sulphuric acid. Solid line represents a steel lower in chromium and higher in nickel than the dotted line (44).

two first factors are maintained constant, it is possible to determine the role of the steel composition in the corrosion rate potential curve. In the case of 18/8 stainless steel the curve consists of three distinct parts corresponding to the different rates of the surface oxide dissolution.

At high potentials (about + 1 volt) the corrosion rate increases with the potential in agreement with the increasing solubility of the oxide, the composition of which lies beyond its normal stoichiometric composition. As a matter of fact, iron, which does not oxidize easily beyond the trivalent state in acid solutions, does not undergo any important increase of its corrosion rate at high potentials. On the other hand, alloys with chromium, like 18/8 steels, are etched because chromium can be oxidized to a valence of six. In fact, the corrosion products contain mainly hexavalent chromium and only traces of trivalent iron.

At intermediate potentials (+ 0.8 to - 0.2 volts) stainless steel becomes passive owing to the formation of stoichiometric Me_2O_3 oxides. For lower potentials (lower than -0.2 volts) corrosion takes place again since the oxides are partly reduced before dissolution. At the lowest potentials (from -0.3 to -0.5 volts) the corrosion decrease represents the classical cathodic polarization curve.

The curves of Fig. 15 correspond to a homogeneous steel quenched from 1100^0 - 1150^0C. The solid curve corresponds to an alloy with less Cr and more Ni than the alloy represented with the dotted line. If the alloy contains two phases, each phase will behave more or less independently. The potentiostat technique permits determination of the optimum potential for each of the phases (43).

Edeleanu (44) applied the technique for the metallographic etching of stainless steels of the following composition: 18.42% Cr, 8.73% Ni, 2.85% Mo, 0.70% Mn, 0.55% Si, 0.24% Ti, 0.05% C. After quenching from 1150^0C the steel contains δ - ferrite and γ - austenite. The δ - phase is richer in Cr and poorer in Ni than the second phase. Consequently δ - ferrite will be selectively etched over a wide range of potential whereas γ - austenite will remain unetched (Fig. 15). Below this potential, the two phases will be passive over a large

range of potentials. At lower potentials, austenite will be selectively etched whereas ferrite will again undergo etching at a
still lower potential (Fig. 16). If the same alloy is tempered
at 850°C after quenching, σ - phase precipitates from the δ -
ferrite and at the same time a new austenite is formed with a
composition that is probably different from that of the initial
austenite. Employing a potentiostat, Edeleanu (44) could reveal at a high potential (+ 1. 05 volts) the untransformed δ -
ferrite and the σ - phase; at a potential of 0. 35 volts the initial
austenite could be distinguished from the one formed during
precipitation of σ - phase (Figs. 17 and 18).

However the main advantage of the potentiostatic technique is in detecting minor phases, like chromium carbides
which form during sensitization tempering of stainless steels
between 600° and 900° C. The precipitation of carbides has
been considered to be responsible for the intergranular corrosion of stainless steel. Such precipitation involves a decrease
in Cr - content of the austenitic solution in the vicinity of the
grain boundaries. In this case, owing to the very small amount
of material dissolved, it is not possible to determine accurately
the optimum potential for the preferential and selective corrosion of the grain boundaries from the potential - weight loss
curve. For this reason Edeleanu proposed a modification of
this technique. The current delivered by the potentiostat is
measured as a function of the applied potential. Instead of remaining fixed, the potential is allowed to vary slowly (0. 4 volts/
hr) by means of a constant speed motor. Under these conditions
for potentials below -0. 3 volts, the potential-current curve resembles the potential-weight loss curve of a quenched 18/8
steel (Fig. 19a). If the alloy is slowly cooled in air from
1050°C or tempered at 550°C the potential - current curve is
altered (Fig. 19b), indicating the formation of a solid solution
depleted in Cr around the carbide precipitate. The amount of
Cr - depleted solid solution increases with the length of treatment. For very long tempering (6 weeks at 550°C) the Cr -
concentration gradient decreases owing to diffusion (Fig. 19c).
It should be pointed out that in the case of a steel cooled in air
from 1050°C, the presence of a precipitate cannot be detected by
classical methods. Its presence was however revealed in a

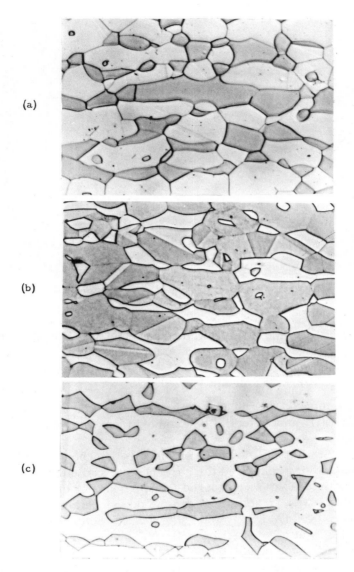

Fig. 16. 18/8 Mo-Ti steel water-quenched from 1150°C. Etched in 20% H_2SO_4 at different voltages (44); X 1250, before reduction for publication. (a) at + 1.05 volt for 5
min; (b) at -0.35 volt for 1 hr; (c) at -0.45 volt for 1 hr.

272   P. LACOMBE

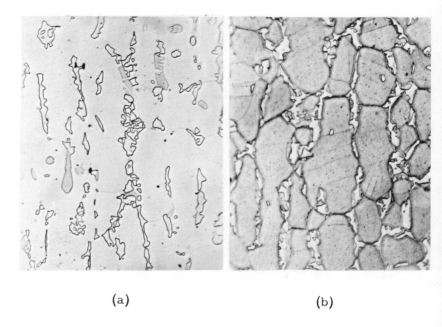

(a)   (b)

Fig. 17.   18/8 Mo-Ti steel water-quenched from 1150°C and heat
treated for 4 hrs at 850°C (44); X 1250, before reduction
for publication.   Etched at: (a)+ 1. 05 volt for 5 min;
(b) -0.35 volt for 1 hr.

steel tempered at 550°C for 1 hour by electroetching with oxalic acid (1) at a potential determined from the potential-current
curve.
    Similar results were obtained by Clerbois et al (45).
These authors compared the current-potential curves of two
18/8 stainless steels tempered for two hours at 650°C; one of
the steels was Ti-stabilized and the other contained no Ti.   The
Ti-free-steel (A. I. S. I. 302) shows a characteristic peak in
20% H_2SO_4 at a potential of - 50 mV.   This peak corresponds
to the corrosion sensitization of the grain boundaries.   The
Ti-stabilized steel (A. I. S. I. 347) is not sensitized by the same
tempering and does not show any peak at - 0. 50 mV (Fig. 20).
Similar observations have been presented more recently by
Berge and Jacquet (46).
    Edeleanu has pointed out the significant advantages of

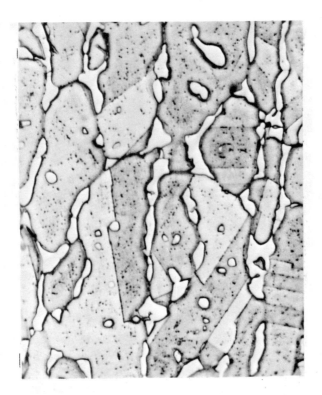

Fig. 18. 18/8 Mo-Ti steel water-quenched from 1050°C and heat treated for 6 days at 850°C, etched at -0.35 volt for 1 hr (44); X 1250.

the potentiostatic technique over the classical etching techniques, chemical or electrolytic. The etching reagents usually contain oxidizing or reducing agents or complexing ions. During etching the metal-electrolyte system tends to an equilibrium-potential characteristic of the oxidizing or reducing components. Thus conventional etching works like the potentiostat technique, but with less flexibility and accuracy. The potential of a metallic sample immersed in an etchant depends in part on the etching rate and will be approximately the same for the

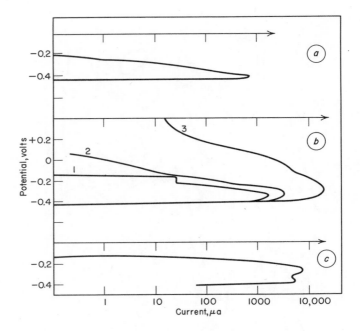

Fig. 19. Potential-current diagrams of an 18/8 steel after different treatments (44). (a) Water-quenched from
1050°C; (b) 1 - Air-cooled from 1050°C; 2 - Water-
quenched from 1050°C and annealed at 550°C for 1 hr;
3 - Water-quenched from 1050°C and annealed at 550°
C for 14 days; (c) Water-quenched from 1050°C and
annealed for 6 weeks at 650°C.

various phases present especially in the case of alloys. In contrast, by means of a potentiostat it is possible to apply a perfectly defined and constant potential which permits either the preferential etching of grain boundaries or the selective etching of
a given phase.

The idea that an etching reagent behaves like a redox
system has been verified by Clerbois et al (45) in the case of
the Strauss reagent (2N, H_2SO_4 + 10% $CuSO_4$) which has been
recommended for testing of the intergranular sensitivity of
stainless steels (47). Provided that metallic copper is present,

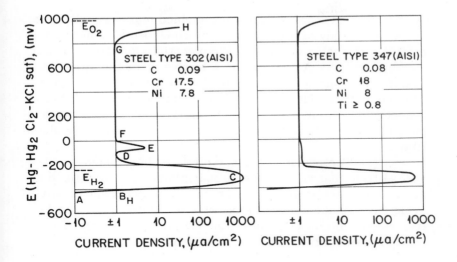

Fig. 20. Potential-current density diagrams of two stainless
steels (45). (a) AISI 302 steel without Ti, after sen-
sitizing; (b) AISI 347 steel with Ti, after same annealing.

the redox potential of the Strauss reagent is about 50 mV which
corresponds to the peak of the current-voltage curve (Fig. 20).
When the Strauss solution is depleted in copper, the redox potential drops well below 50 mV and general corrosion sets in.
By the same method these authors showed that the Huey (48)
test (65% boiling HNO_3) is not convenient for determining the
susceptibility of a stainless steel to intergranular corrosion.

5. GENERAL CONCLUSIONS

(1) Among the proposed methods of electrolytic etching
it seems that only the methods using the same electrolyte for
electropolishing and etching can be generally applied to all
pure metals. However, this technique of lowering the voltage
in the electropolishing bath to obtain etching cannot perhaps be
considered as a general method for complex alloys if selective

etching of a phase is desirable.

(2) Only the potentiostatic method makes possible the systematic study of all solutions for electroetching in order to establish the value of the specific potentials for intergranular etching, uniform corrosion, or selective etching of a phase. Systematic plotting of a large number of potentiostatic curves can make it possible to specify the chemical composition of a reagent for obtaining any of the three types of etching: etch-pit formation, intergranular etching, or formation of insoluble films.

(3) The problem of electrolytic etching cannot be divorced from that of the prior preparation of the metallic surface. Electropolishing is an absolute prerequisite, not only to avoid any surface cold-work but also to realize a surface as free as possible of insoluble films (oxides or others). The case of uranium bears out the importance of this factor.

Acknowledgments

The author wishes to thank Dr. P. Jacquet for reading the manuscript and for making valuable suggestions. He is greatly indebted to Professor Margolin and Dr. Ence, Dr. Jacquet, Dr. Hiltz and Dr. Edeleanu for permission to reproduce some of their results. Thanks are also due to my collaborators Dr. Calais, Dr. Robillard and Mme. Simenel who have contributed to the uranium study.

References

1. G. E. Ellinger, Trans. Am. Soc. Metals, 24, 26 (1936).
2. A. Molaroni, Congress of "Associacione de Metallurgia Italiana, " Firenze (1951).
3. M. Boeyertz, Trans. Am. Soc. Metals, 25, 1185 (1937).
4. W. Arness, Trans. Am. Soc. Metals, 24, 701 (1936).
5. P. Lacombe and N. Yannaquis, Metaux & corrosion, 22, 35 (1947); Rev. mét., 45, 68 (1948).
6. P. Lacombe and L. Beaujard, J. Inst. Metals, 74, 1 (1948).
7. F. L. Vogel, W. G. Pfann, H. E. Corey and E. E. Thomas, Phys. Rev., 90, 489 (1953).

8. R. Jacquesson and J. Manenc, Compt. rend., 230, 959 (1950).
9. J. Bardolle and J. Moreau, Compt. rend., 238, 1416 (1954).
10. C. G. Dunn and E. F. Koch, Report 57-RL-1718, General Electric Research Lab., 1957.
11. G. Wyon and P. Lacombe, in Defects in Crystalline Solids, p. 187, Physical Society, 1954.
12. J. Suits and J. Low, Acta Met., 5, 285 (1957).
13. W. R. Hibbard and C. G. Dunn, Acta Met., 4, 306 (1956).
14. J. J. Gilman, Trans. Am. Inst. Mining Met. Petrol. Engrs., 206, 998 (1956).
15. F. W. Young and N. Cabrera, J. Appl. Phys., 28, 789 (1957).
16. O. Jones, Phil. Mag., 48, 207 (1924).
17. P. Dunsmuir, Metallurgia, 41, 240 (1950).
18. P. Lacombe and M. Mouflard, Metaux Corrosion-Inds., 28, 390 (1953).
19. P. Lacombe and L. Beaujard, Report of Commission Technique des Etats et Propriétés de surface des Métaux, p. 73, Paris, 1944; P. Lacombe, Chim. & ind. (Paris), 53, 222 (1945).
20. A. Hone and E. Pearson, Metal Progr. 53, 363 (1948).
21. P. Beck and P. Sperry, J. Appl. Phys., 21, 150 (1950).
22. P. Beck and H. Hu, J. Appl. Phys., 21, 420 (1950).
23. A. Robillard, R. Boucher and P. Lacombe, Metaux Corrosion-Inds., 31, 433 (1956); A. Robillard and D. Calais, Compt. rend., 245, 59 (1957).
24. M. L. Picklesimer, Report ORNL-2296 TID-4500, Oak Ridge National Lab., May, 1957.
25. E. Ence and H. Margolin, J. Metals, 6, 346 (1954).
26. P. A. Farrar, L. P. Stone and H. Margolin, J. Metals, 8, 595 (1956).
27. R. H. Hiltz, Report NO-WAL 132/24, Watertown Arsenal Laboratory, 1956.
28. R. H. Hiltz, Report NO-WALTR 401/266, Watertown Arsenal Laboratory, 1957.
29. R. H. Hiltz and R. W. Douglas, J. Metals, 11, 286 (1959).
30. P. Jacquet, Compt. rend., 237, 1248 (1953); Acta Met., 2, 752, 770 (1954).

31. S. Yoshida, J. Phys. Soc. Japan, 11, 129 (1956).
32. P. Lacombe and A. Berghezan, Alluminio, 4, 3 (1949).
33. S. Zeffries, Trans. Am. Inst. Mining Met. Engrs., 60, 1917 (1919).
34. P. Jacquet, Rev. mét., 42, 133 (1945).
35. P. Jacquet, Metallurgia, 42, 252 (1950).
36. M. Englander, J. Stohr and Mme Laniesse, Report of Commissariat à l'Energie Atomique, Saclay, 1959.
37. A. Robillard, D. Calais and P. Lacombe, Rev. met., 55, 815 (1958).
38. J. Herenguel and R. Segond, Rev. mét., 46, 377 (1949).
39. A. Berghezan, Metaux Corrosion-Inds., 30, 359 (1955).
40. P. Lacombe, P. Morize and G. Chaudron, Rev. mét., 44, 87 (1947); G. Chaudron, P. Lacombe and G. Youssov, Compt. rend., 229, 201 (1949).
41. C. Edeleanu, Nature, 173, 739 (1954).
42. M. H. Roberts, Brit. J. Appl. Phys., 5, 351 (1954).
43. C. Edeleanu, J. Iron Steel Inst., 188, 122 (1958).
44. C. Edeleanu, J. Iron Steel Inst., 185, 482 (1957).
45. L. Clerbois, F. Clerbois and J. Massart, 10th Symposium, Commission Internationale de Thermodynamique et de Cinétique Electrochimique (CITCE), Amsterdam, 1958.
46. P. Berge and P. Jacquet, Third Metallurgical Symposium, Commissariat à l'Energie Atomique, Saclay, June, 1959; P. Berge, Compt. rend., 245, 1239 (1957).
47. B. Strauss, H. Schottky and J. Hinnuber, Z. anorg. u. allgem. Chem., 188, 309 (1930).
48. W. R. Huey, Trans. Am. Soc. Steel Treating, 18, 1126 (1930).

DISCUSSION

J. F. DEWALD (Bell Telephone Laboratories): Have you performed any experiments which convince you that it is the potential rather than the current density which determines the etching characteristic?

P. LACOMBE: I have no personal experience with the potentiostatic method. But it can be said from a thermodynamic point of view that the potentiostatic method gives far more in-

formation about the nature of the passive layer of the Fe-Cr or
Fe-Cr-Ni steels than the amperostatic method. For example,
the Cr content of these alloys affects considerably the conditions
of their passivation. This is due to the relative proportion of
Fe_2O_3 and Cr_2O_3 in the passive film. With the potentiostatic
method, it is possible to specify, according to the Cr content,
the potential range in which passivation may occur. Of interest
in this respect is the work of Bartlett [Trans. Electrochem.
Soc., 87, 521 (1945)], Bartlett and Stephenson [J. Electrochem.
Soc., 99, 504 (1952)], Frank [Thesis, Göttingen 1954] and
Oliver [International Committee for Electrochemical Thermodynamics and Kinetics, p. 314, Butterworths, 1955]. The
greatest interest in the potentiostatic method as compared to
the amperostatic method is apparent by the increasing number
of researches carried out in England by Edeleanu, in Belgium
by Pourbaix, in France by Jacquet and his co-workers.

N. CABRERA (University of Virginia): In discussing
your anodic films you refer to them as epitaxial films yet you
say that they are amorphous. How can this be?

P. LACOMBE: The term epitaxy has of course a specific crystallographic meaning, particularly following Royer's
classical researches. However, metallographers use the term
in thin oxide or sulfide layers or films of any other compounds
giving rise to interference tints which vary with the orientation
of the underlying metal. The term of epitaxy merely describes
a phenomenon and does not imply the origin and the mechanism
of formation of these tints. In fact, these tints may be due to
different causes. For instance, the metallic surface may become slightly faceted during the anodic formation of an oxide
film. This is very likely the case in the anodic oxidation of
Al. Another cause may be the phase shift of the light when
reflected at the oxide-metal interface in the case of a trans-
parent film.

H. C. GATOS (M. I. T.): What is the sensitivity of the
anodic oxidation technique in determining low angle boundaries?

P. LACOMBE: This depends upon the material and the
technique used for electroetching. For example the use of
polarized light to determine the existence of sub-grain structure
in α-uranium is not very good. Misorientations smaller than

1^0 are not perceptible under polarized light. The technique of oxide layers is far more sensitive yet the sensitivity in orientation determinations by the oxide layer formed on Al by anodic oxidation depends on its thickness. Layers with a thickness of 10μ or more are not very sensitive. Very thin films, however, exhibiting interference tints present a sensitivity of 1^0 or less.

M. A. STREICHER (DuPont): A number of detailed investigations provide information on several points raised in this paper in connection with the use of electrolytic etching to detect susceptibility of stainless steels to intergranular corrosion. A brief summary of pertinent aspects is given below.

The grain boundaries of austenitic stainless steels may be made susceptible to accelerated intergranular corrosion (sensitized) by exposure of the steels to temperatures in the range of $800\text{-}1600^0F$ ($426\text{-}871^0C.$). Depending on the composition of the steel, either or both of two types of precipitates may be formed in the grain boundary zones. The most important of these consists of chromium carbides in stainless steels containing more than about 0.025 percent carbon.* In 18 Cr-8 Ni-2.5 Mo steels, a second type of susceptibility, associated with the formation of sigma phase at grain boundaries, may also be produced. However, this second type may be present either as a distinct, microscopically visible phase or in an invisible, pre-precipitation form [Streicher, J. Electrochem. Soc., 106, 161 (1959)]. To date, the only means whereby this latter form of sigma phase can be detected is by exposure (48 hr. or more) of the steel to boiling (65%) nitric acid which leads to rapid intergranular disintegration of the steel. **

---

*Heat treatments of one or two hr. are assumed. When heat treatments lasting from one day to three weeks are used, chromium carbides can be precipitated in steels containing as little as 0.007-0.009% C [Heger and Hamilton, Corrosion, 11, 6 (1955); Rosenberg and Irish, J. Research Natl. Bur. Standards, 48, 40 (1952)].

**The selection of a test for detecting susceptibility to intergranular attack can, therefore, not be based solely on convenience, as is implied in the last paragraph of Section 4 of this paper.

Discrete, visible sigma phase may be present as very fine particles when heat treatments in the range of 1200-1300°F (468-704°C) are applied. During electrolytic etching small etch pits are formed at the sit es of these particles [Warren, Corrosion, 15, 221 (1959)] . Heating for 4 hr. or more at 1600°F (871°C) produces relatively large islands of sigma phase. All types of susceptibility to accelerated intergranular attack may be eliminated by dissolving the precipitates (chromium carbides, visible and invisible sigma phase) in the austenitic matrix at about 2000°F (1093°C) and rapidly cooling from this temperature.

Solutions used for electrolytic etching of stainless steels may be divided into two classes: (a) Electrolytes which readily etch grain boundaries in the form of grooves regardless of the presence or absence of intergranular precipitates. Nitric acid is of this type [J. Electrochem. Soc., 106, 161 (1959)] .
(b) Electrolytes which readily reveal the presence of (1) precipitated chromium carbides, (2) ferrite, and (3) sigma phase, but only when present as a distinct phase. The pre-precipitation form of sigma phase is not revealed by any of these etches. The following electrolytes are of this type: oxalic, formic, maleic, citric, tartaric, chromic, sulfuric and phosphoric acid, sodium cyanide and ammonium persulfate.

The electrolytes of class (b)   differ in the rate and clarity with which they detect the presence of carbides and the sigma constituent. For example, sodium cyanide is the most sensitive etchant because its etching action is slow and there is almost no etching of the austenitic matrix. Oxalic acid gives a very rapid etch of carbides and sigma phase along with appreciable dissolution of austenite. Because of the difference in rates of dissolution of various crystal faces of austenite crystals, steps are formed between grains on annealed steel (Fig. 1). On a sensitized steel the same etching conditions produce extensive grooving at the grain boundaries (Fig. 2). The action of the other etchants listed above lies between these two extremes.

Electrolytic etching of stainless steels has been used industrially to simplify and accelerate the evaluation of stainless steels for their susceptibility to intergranular attack. Be-

Fig. 1. Annealed steel. 18 Cr-8 Ni stainless steel etched
electrolytically in 10% oxalic acid for 1.5 min. at 1
amp/sq. cm; X500.

Fig. 2. Sensitized steel. 18 Cr-8 Ni stainless steel etched
electrolytically in 10% oxalic acid for 1.5 min. at 1
amp/sq. cm; X500.

cause of the general preference for a quantitative basis for
evaluation, the electrolytic etch is used as a screening method
in conjunction with a standarized corrosion test in which weight
loss (or some other measurable quantity) is the basis for evaluation. Examples of such tests are nitric acid [Streicher, ASTM
Bulletin No. 188, 35 (Feb. 1953)], ferric sulfate-sulfuric acid
[Streicher, ASTM Bulletin No. 229, 77 (April, 1958)] and
nitric-hydrofluoric acid [Warren, ASTM Bulletin No. 230, 45
(1958)]. In these testing methods the steels being evaluated
are first etched electrolytically in oxalic acid under standardized conditions to determine the presence and amount of precipitated chromium carbide and/or visible sigma phase. The
resulting etch structures are classified into one of three well-
defined types whose corrosion behavior in the given corrosion
test is known. Steels having etch structures revealing no intergranular precipitates, or only small amounts which do not
completely envelope individual grains, have low corrosion rates
in these acid tests and, therefore, do not need to be tested further. Any steels which show envelopment of grains by precipitates must be tested further to determine whether their corrosion rate in the given test exceeds the maximum permissible
rate.

The electrolytic etches in oxalic acid, as described
above, are carried out under standardized conditions of current
density and length of etching time. Measurement of the electrode potential of the stainless steel during this etching procedure shows that this potential is also constant throughout the
etching period, and, that therefore, such etches are equivalent
to etching under conditions of controlled potential.

Thus, simple electrolytic etching for examination of the
microstructures of stainless steels has provided a very sensitive method for the detection of chromium carbide precipitate
and sigma phase when present as a discrete phase. However,
depending on the electrolyte used, electrolytic etching may result in etching of boundaries which are free of any precipitates.
Conversely, in certain 18 Cr - 8 Ni stainless steels, low in
carbon content and containing molybdenum, grain boundaries
may be made susceptible to greatly accelerated preferential
attack in nitric acid by heat treatments without showing any

trace of intergranular precipitates when etched electrolytically.
As a result, such steels cannot be screened by electrolytic
etching when the nitric acid test is being used as the quantitative
standard for acceptability.

Acid corrosion of stainless steels in the various test
media, such as nitric acid and ferric sulfate-sulfuric acid,
also takes place at essentially constant electrode potential.
In the case of the cupric sulfate-sulfuric acid solution the
potential and rate of corrosion can be readily changed by adding metallic copper to the solution. Thus, an intergranularly
susceptible stainless steel may be corroded at any one of three
different potentials established under the following conditions:
(a) Immersion in cupric sulfate-sulfuric acid solution (boiling)
without metallic copper; (b) simultaneous immersion with
metallic copper, but not in contact with the stainless steel; and
(c) simultaneous immersion with contact between stainless
steel and copper. Under all three conditions the morphology of
intergranular attack, which is governed by the ratio of intergranular penetration to grain face corrosion, is identical.
Therefore, the use of metallic copper, i. e., shifting the potential of the stainless steel in the active direction, does not
change the type, but greatly accelerates the rate of corrosion.

D. R. TURNER

Bell Telephone
Laboratories

Electrolytic Etching
of Semiconductors

ABSTRACT

ANODIC DISSOLUTION REACTIONS at
semiconductor electrodes require electron holes.
If the hole concentration in the semiconductor
is relatively low, as in low resistivity n-type
germanium or silicon, the available holes in the
surface region are used up at low current densities and the etch rate is slow. The anodic current under these conditions can be increased by
providing additional holes at the surface. Holes
produced as a result of illuminating the semiconductor give uniform electrolytic etching on
n-type semiconductors. Germanium is electrolytically etched in several electrolytes while silicon can only be dissolved anodically in fluoride
solutions. A thick film of amorphous silicon
forms on silicon anodes in acid fluoride solutions
below a critical current density.

1. INTRODUCTION

Electrolytic etching of semiconductors is used to remove
damaged surface layers on single crystal material and/or shape

the semiconductor to a desired geometry. The term etching in semiconductor technology has come to mean semiconductor dissolution in general, regardless of the nature of the surface produced. Usually a polished surface is required but occasionally a matte or pitted surface is wanted. Either kind of surface can be produced by adjusting the conditions of the process. Germanium and silicon are the two semiconductors widely used today in solid state devices. Largely as a result of this use, most of the experimental work to date on electrolytic etching of semiconductors has been done on germanium and silicon.

Before any electrolytic treatment of a semiconductor can be made, an ohmic contact is required. The resistance of the ohmic contact should be low to avoid excessive heating when high current densities are used, such as in rapid etching and electropolishing. Oxide films, readily formed on the surface of most semiconducting materials, can result in high contact resistance and poor contact adhesion. Techniques have been developed to make satisfactory low resistance and adherent ohmic contacts to practically all semiconductors. For example a good ohmic contact can usually be made to germanium by simply abrading the surface and soldering with an ordinary lead-tin solder using an acid zinc chloride flux. Sullivan and Eigler (1) have shown that nickel deposited by chemical reduction (electroless process) provides a satisfactory ohmic contact on silicon. Electroless nickel has also been used as the initial step by Turner and Sauer (2) to make low resistance ohmic contacts to a number of other semiconductors, such as the intermetallic compounds GaAs and lanthanum-doped barium titanate ceramics. A detailed account of the various types of ohmic contacts and the techniques for applying them to germanium and silicon has been given by Sullivan and Warner (3).

2. EFFECT OF THE SEMICONDUCTOR ELECTRODE

The electrochemistry of the anodic etching of semiconductors is similar in most respects to the anodic dissolution of metals. The main difference in the electrolytic behavior of metals and semiconductors is in the electrode material itself.

The kinetics of an electrochemical reaction at a metal electrode
is determined entirely by phenomena occurring in the solution
or the solution-metal interface. If the electrode is a semiconductor, the rate determining process may also include phenomena that take place inside the surface of the electrode. It has
been shown quite conclusively by Brattain and Garrett (4) and
many others (5-11) that electron holes in the semiconductor are
required to carry out anodic reactions. In the case of etching,
presumably the holes are necessary to break the covalent bonding between surface semiconductor atoms and underlying atoms.
Since holes are required for anodic reactions at a semiconductor surface, the rate of the anodic process may be controlled
by the number of holes continuously available at the surface.
Holes consumed in the anodic reaction may be replaced by diffusion from the bulk or by the generation of hole-electron pairs
in the surface region. The limiting or saturation anode current
density without hole injection is related to the equilibrium hole
concentration (p), the lifetime for holes in the semiconductor
bulk (τ), and the surface recombination (generation) velocity
for holes (v_s) as follows (4):

$$i_s = qp\left[\left(\frac{D}{\tau}\right)^{1/2} + v_s\right]$$

where q is the electron charge and D is the diffusion constant
for holes in the semiconductor. Normally the saturation anodic
current density is determined primarily by the equilibrium hole
concentration and in a minor way by the bulk hole lifetime and
the surface hole recombination rate. In order to electrolytically etch semiconductors at a reasonable rate, anodic current
densities of the order of several hundred ma/cm^2 are necessary. The equilibrium hole concentration in low resistivity p-
type semiconductors is adequate to maintain anodic reactions
up to very high current densities (amperes per square centimeter). The surface of n-type semiconductors made anode becomes depleted of the necessary holes at relatively low current
densities thus limiting the anodic reaction rate. The depletion
produces a space charge region which only increases in width,
as shown by Bohenkamp and Engell (11), if more voltage is
applied to the electrolytic cell. Most of the increase in the

applied voltage appears across the space charge region.

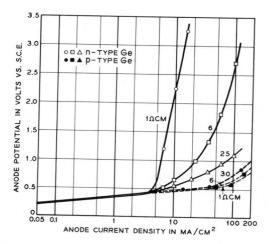

Fig. 1. Influence of resistivity on the anode potential-current
density relation in 0.1 N HCl at 20° C with N_2 atmosphere (5).

The data of Efimov and Erusalimchik (5) shown in Fig.1
give an example of the different current-voltage characteristics
obtained with various resistivity n- and p-type germanium electrodes made anode in 0.1 N HCl. Brattain and Garrett (4) and
others (7-10), however, found much lower saturation current
densities by one to two orders of magnitude with n-type germanium made anode in similar electrolytes. Similar curves for
n-type silicon would show saturation current densities in the
order of microamperes per square centimeter.

3. ELECTRO-ETCHING N-TYPE SEMICONDUCTORS

Germanium and silicon are electrolytically etched at
about the same rate, about $3x10^{-5}$ cm^3/coulomb. Thus at a
current density of 500 ma/cm^2, Ge and Si are dissolved at the
rate of about $1.7x10^{-5}$ cm/sec (0.0004 in/min). In order to
electrolytically etch n-type semiconductors at a reasonable rate,
some means must be found to increase the hole concentration at

the surface of the semiconductor. This can be done in several
ways: (1) illuminate the surface, (2) heat the semiconductor,
(3) inject holes close to the surface with a p-n junction, (4)
apply sufficient voltage to the electrode to cause avalanche
breakdown in the space charge region, (5) damage the surface
by abrasion or by high energy particle bombardment, or (6)
use a "chemical" etching electrolyte. Each of these methods
will now be discussed briefly.

   High intensity illumination provides the best means of
producing a large number of holes uniformly in the surface region for electropolishing. Schmidt and Keiper (12) have succes-
fully jet etched small areas of low resistivity n-type silicon
electrolytically up to a current density of 4 amp/cm^2 with intense light. Only light with wavelengths less than about 2μ for
germanium and about 1. 2μ for silicon can produce hole-electron
pairs. When high light intensities are used, the longer wavelengths are usually filtered out to avoid overheating the semiconductor and solution. Large area specimens present more of
a problem, but with adequate light and high hole lifetime material,
uniform anodic etching should be possible.

   The equilibrium hole concentration can be increased by
raising the temperature of the semiconductor. Uhlir (7) found
that the temperature variation of the saturation current density
across the barrier between anodic n-type germanium and 10%
potassium hydroxide solution is quite like that of a p-n junction.
About a tenfold increase in the saturation current density is obtained for each 30° C rise in temperature as shown in Fig. 2.
An extrapolation of the linear semilog plot to 100°C gives a
maximum saturation current density of about 100 ma/cm^2 which
is sufficient for only a moderate etching rate. The increase in
saturation current density with temperature for silicon is much
less, since silicon has a larger energy gap than germanium.
Thus fewer hole-electron pairs are produced in Si than in Ge
due to thermal generation. In general, increasing the temperature of the semiconductor is not a good way of increasing the
hole concentration in n-type Ge or Si.

   If a good hole-emitting p-n junction is positioned close
behind the n-type semiconductor to be etched anodically, an
adequate supply of holes can be injected for very rapid etching.

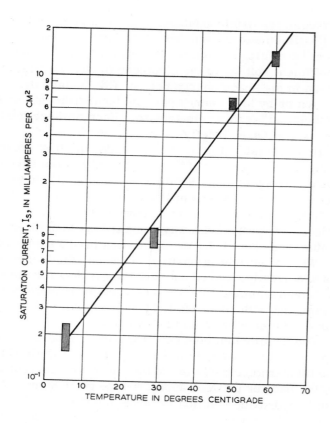

Fig. 2. Temperature variation of the saturation current of a
barrier between 5.5 ohm-cm n-type germanium and
10 percent KOH solution.

Ellis (13) has shown that the anodic etch will not be uniform,
however, if small-angle grain boundaries are present at the
surface. The dislocations that form the small-angle grain
boundaries are the sites of traps which permit hole-electron
recombination. The number of holes available for the anode
reaction at the dislocation is therefore reduced.

    Another source of additional holes for anodic etching of
n-type semiconductors is the avalanche breakdown. The break-

down occurs when the cell voltage is raised to a critical value at which holes diffusing from the semiconductor bulk are accelerated in the space charge region to kinetic energies sufficient to produce hole multiplication. Unfortunately this breakdown does not take place uniformly over the surface: it occurs first at defects scattered through the single crystal and non-uniform etching (pitting) results. Theoretically a perfect single crystal would exhibit uniform breakdown and there would be no surface pitting. Even if perfect crystals were available, however, avalanche breakdown still would not be a practical way of increasing the hole density for rapid anodic etching of n-type semiconductors since the power dissipated at the surface of the electrode would be large and require elaborate cooling.

If the surface of a single crystal n-type semiconductor is damaged by abrasion or by high energy particle bombardment, the generation (recombination) velocity for holes in the surface layer is increased to the extent that holes are readily available to carry out anodic reactions at a rapid rate. This condition lasts until most of the damaged surface material is removed. Then the anode current is limited as previously described due to hole depletion.

The saturation anode current density, i_s, on n-type Ge or Si electrodes is increased considerably in a "chemical" etching solution. Gerischer and Beck (9) have shown that holes are injected into Ge when the cathode reaction of the corrosion process is the reduction of an oxidizing agent. Turner (14) has found that i_s for n-type Si is linearly related to the rate of "chemical" etching in HNO_3-HF solutions. The i_s for a given "chemical" etch rate, however, was only about one tenth the local corrosion current on n-type Si. Using a "chemical" etching solution may not be a practical way of increasing the surface hole concentration. However, a measure of i_s in these solutions may provide a simple means of determining the "chemical" etch rate.

4. GERMANIUM

Germanium is electrolytically dissolved in most electrolytes. Jirsa (15) studied the anodic dissolution of germanium in aqueous solutions of KOH, HCl, H_2SO_4, and NH_4OH. He reported that germanates are the anode product in alkaline solutions while the corresponding germanium salts are formed in acid solutions. There is good evidence, however, that the stable form of germanium in acid solution is metagermanic acid, H_2GeO_3 (16-18). Anode efficiency measurements by Jirsa (15) showed that the electrolytic dissolution of germanium was tetravalent. At high anode current densities on prolonged electrolysis, an orange colored deposit of GeOis formed on the germanium. Turner (8) has confirmed these observations. Turner (8) and also Bardeleben (19) studied the nature of anodic films on germanium by a cathodic reduction techni que. They found that during anodic dissolution the germanium surface was always covered with about a monolayer of oxide or hydroxide.

Brattain and Garrett (4) demonstrated that holes were required for the anodic dissolution of germanium. In addition, they found that when holes were injected with light the total germanium dissolution current (in the saturated current region with n-type Ge) increased between 1.4 to 1.8 times the current due to hole injection. Uhlir (7) observed a current multiplication factor of 1.4. These studies assumed that the recombination rate for holes in n-type Ge in the vicinity of the Ge-electrolyte interface is the same as that near a solid state p-n junction. If only 10% more holes are recombined near the Ge-electrolyte interface, then an apparent current multiplication factor of 1.8 is really 2. Turner (8) has suggested that the mechanism for the anodic dissolution of germanium involves the diffusion of two holes to the surface with a return flow of two electrons. This would give a current multiplication factor of 2. In a single crystal of germanium, each surface atom is covalently bonded on the average to two underlying germanium atoms. It is proposed that a germanium atom goes into solution as a complex ion with the oxide or hydroxide radicals attached when the covalent bonds are broken by the arrival of at least one hole for each two-electron bond. This is shown schematically as follows:

$$
\begin{array}{ccc}
\overset{=}{\underset{\overset{++}{\underset{\overset{\bullet\quad\bullet}{Ge\ \ Ge}}{}}}{O}} & & \overset{\overline{=}}{\underset{\overset{++}{\underset{++}{}}}{O}} \\
Ge\ +\ 2\ e^{+} \rightarrow & +\ Ge & (1) \\
& \underset{Ge\ \ Ge}{\bullet\ \ \bullet} &
\end{array}
$$

(The dots represent covalent bonding electrons and e^{+} represents a hole). Dewald (20) has suggested that on the average the number of holes consumed for each germanium atom dissolved may be a fraction larger than 2 to conform more precisely to the current multiplication results obtained by Brattain and Garrett (4) and Uhlir (7). The flow of holes from the germanium bulk to the surface is accompanied by a proportionate return flow of electrons. This produces the observed current gain with hole injection. The source of these extra electrons is assumed to be the "dangling-bond" electrons that remain on the underlying germanium atoms after the surface atom goes into solution. It is suggested that these valence electrons are raised in energy to the conduction band when the monolayer of oxide or hydroxide is reformed by anodic oxidation:

$$
\overset{\bullet\quad\bullet}{Ge\ Ge} + H_2O \rightarrow Ge + \overset{=}{\underset{+}{O}} + Ge + 2H^{+} + 2e^{-} \qquad (2)
$$

Assuming that the stable form of germanium in acid or neutral solutions is metagermanic acid, the over-all reaction for the anodic dissolution of germanium can be written as follows:

$$
Ge + 2e^{+} + 3H_2O \rightarrow H_2GeO_3 + 4H^{+} + 2e^{-} \qquad (3)
$$

Beck and Gerischer (21) have proposed a more elaborate mechanism for the anodic dissolution of germanium in alkaline solutions on the basis of experiments which indicated that the reaction was first order with respect to the OH⁻ ions and the holes. They suggest that the presence of an OH⁻ ion at or near a Ge atom promotes the capture of a hole on the surface. The rate-determining step, according to their model, is the breaking of one of the two covalent bonds after the hole is captured. This same hole is largely responsible for breaking the remaining covalent bond allowing the complexed Ge ion to go into solution.

4.1 Nonaqueous Solutions

Germanium has been electropolished in a variety of non-aqueous electrolytes. Brouillet and Epelboin (22-23) employed fused salt baths of NaCl-KCl and NaF-KF mixtures. They found that germanium could be electropolished with a cell voltage of 2 volts for the chloride bath and 3 volts for the fluoride using a platinum cathode. Epelboin and Fromet (24) electropolished germanium in glycerine solutions containing chloride or fluoride ions. The conductivity of organic-type baths is generally low. Not only is a higher cell voltage necessary to pass the electropolishing current, but the power dissipated in the solution may produce enough heat to require cooling.

4.2 Cathodic Etching of Germanium

Bardeleben (19) studied the electrolytic formation of germane (GeH_4) on single crystal germanium cathodes. Up to moderate current densities (10 ma/cm^2), he observed no germane formation. Topfer (25), however, has found that germanium etches cathodically with almost 100% efficiencies by means of germane formation at very high current densities (~ 100 amp/cm^2). Mieluch (26) states that the evolution of gaseous germane occurs at Ge cathodic potentials more negative than about -200 mv on the hydrogen scale. He also suggests that holes may be consumed in the process of liberating Ge ions from the crystal lattice. Schmidt has reported that a-c etching of germanium is also possible. In order to obtain a polished surface, the electrolyte must be compatible with both anodic and cathodic d-c etching. Oxalic acid is recommended.

5. SILICON

Whereas germanium may be electrolytically etched in a large number of electrolytes, silicon has only been dissolved anodically in fluoride solutions. Strong alkaline solutions chemically attack silicon, forming a soluble silicate and hydrogen gas, and the rate of attack increases rapidly with temperature. However if a piece of silicon is made anodic in a hot strong alkaline solution such as 1N KOH, the chemical attack stops when the anode potential is greater than a critical value.

The passivating effect is attributed to the formation of an insoluble oxide film on the silicon. The chemical attack by the hot alkaline solution on the silicon does not resume immediately after the anodic bias is removed. Several minutes are required before the passive layer breaks down and chemical attack resumes. A brief cathodic treatment, however, reactivates the silicon immediately.

A number of different fluoride salts have been used as electrolytes for electropolishing silicon. Not only must the fluoride salt be sufficiently water soluble but the anode reaction product, the corresponding fluosilicate, must also be readily soluble in water. Potassium fluoride is highly water soluble but the fluosilicate is not. At a critical anodic etch rate silicon will passivate in KF solutions due to the precipitation of K_2SiF_6 on the surface. Ammonium fluoride and ammonium fluosilicate are both sufficiently water soluble. The acids HF and H_2SiF_6 are even more water soluble.

The initial work on electropolishing silicon by Uhlir (7) was done in largely nonaqueous solutions of HF in organic hydroxyl compounds such as alcohols, glycols, and glycerine. Faust (27) obtained electrolytic etching of silicon in similar largely nonaqueous solutions containing 2.5 to 15% by volume of 50% HF. Satisfactory etching is reported at current densities ranging from 20 to 800 ma/cm^2. Epelboin and Fromet (24) electropolished silicon in a solution of 66 grams of ammonium bifluoride (NH_4F-HF) per liter of glycerine at 800 ma/cm^2 and 80° C. An electrolyte composed of one part 49% HF and one part glacial acetic acid was used by Lesk and Gonzalez (28) for selective electrolytic etching of germanium and silicon. They found that this acid mixture worked the best of all electrolytes they tried.

The early work on electropolishing silicon was done in largely nonaqueous solutions because it was believed that silicon could not be polished in aqueous HF solutions. Uhlir (7), for example, anodized silicon in 24 to 48% by weight aqueous solutions of HF at current densities up to 500 ma/cm^2 and obtained only a matte black, brown, or red deposit. Later Turner (29) showed that silicon could be electropolished in aqueous HF solutions if a critical current density was exceeded.

This critical current density decreases linearly with a decrease in the HF concentration. Wang (30) also found that silicon was readily electropolished in dilute aqueous HF solutions. Schmidt and co-workers (12, 31) have electropolished small areas of both n- and p-type silicon using a jet of an aqueous electrolyte containing 8 gm NaF + either 5 cc 48% HF or 40 gm NH$_4$F per liter of solution. To electrolytically etch n-type silicon rapidly they have had to illuminate the surface with an intense light as described above.

5.1 Anode Potential-Current Density Relation

The anode potential-current density curves obtained for silicon in electropolishing solutions are similar to those observed for metals. A typical anode potential-current density curve for a horizontal p-type silicon electrode facing up in an aqueous solution of 5% HF at 25°C is shown in Fig. 3. This

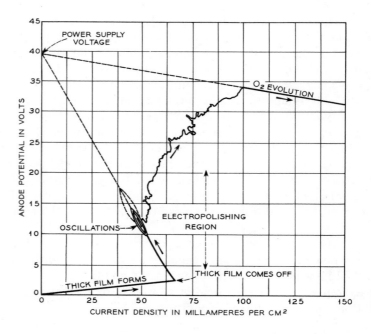

Fig. 3. Typical anode potential-current density curve for a horizontal p-type Si anode facing up in 5% HF at 25°C.

curve was obtained by slowly decreasing the resistance in series with a large 45-volt dry battery. The E-I curve for a vertical electrode (with considerable convection stirring) differs from Fig. 3 in that the transition into the electropolishing region is gradual.

There are three distinct parts to the E-I curve shown in Fig. 3. In the initial section the thick film* which Uhlir (7) observed is formed and there is considerable gassing. The second part of the E-I curve begins at the critical current density where the thick film comes off and electropolishing starts. In this region virtually no gas is evolved. Oscillations in the cell current and potential frequently occur in the electropolishing region; some authors contend that these oscillations are essential for the best polishing, but others dispute this contention. Experimental conditions which give a maximum cell impedance are generally considered to give optimum electropolishing on metals (32). Epelboin and Fromet (33) have found that this criterion may not be applicable for electropolishing semiconductors since the resistance of the semiconductor electrode may not be negligible. However they have found that microscopic examination of the surface using phase contrast polarized illumination can be used to determine the optimum condition for electropolishing Ge and Si. A simple procedure for electropolishing silicon is to apply about 15 volts directly to the cell. The initial current will be large and exceed the critical current density. As the high resistance electropolishing film forms, the current drops and in a short time practically all of the applied cell voltage appears across the polishing film. The potential between the silicon anode and the electrolyte thus automatically stays in the electropolishing region.

The third part of the E-I curve shown in Fig. 3 begins with the onset of continuous oxygen evolution. This section is generally considered to be outside the electropolishing region. In addition, excessive heating may be encountered due to the

---

*This will be called the thick anode film throughout this paper to distinguish it from the thin film which is present during electropolishing silicon. The thick film can grow to a thickness of as much as several tenths of a millimeter, whereas the thin film is probably less than 100 Å in thickness.

amount of power dissipated at the anode surface.

5.2 Nature of the Thick Anode Film

Uhlir (7) suggested that the thick anode film which forms on silicon in aqueous HF solutions below the critical current density is a suboxide of silicon. Faust (27) and Wang (30) also assumed it to be some kind of oxide layer. On the basis of experimental results which indicated that the critical current density was determined by the rate of mass transfer of HF to the silicon, Turner (29) presumed the anode film to be $(SiF_2)_x$.

Uhlir (7) found an effective valence of 2.0 ± 0.2 for silicon dissolution during thick film formation. He also observed that the film reacted with water, alcohol, and even toluene with gas evolution after being dried and stored in air for as long as one year. The gas evolved has been identified as hydrogen. Turner (29) observed that pieces of the film react with explosive violence when put in contact with a strong oxidizing agent such as concentrated nitric acid. These results all indicate that the silicon in the anode film exists in some reduced form.

Additional studies were carried out on the nature of the thick anode film. Thick specimens of the film were prepared by anodizing an electropolished p-type silicon electrode in 48% HF at 200 ma/cm^2 for 1/2 hour. Then the electrolyte was changed to 5% HF and the critical current density required for electropolishing was exceeded. As a result, the thick anode film lifted off in pieces and floated to the surface of the electrolyte. The large pieces were lifted from the surface of the solution with strips of filter paper and placed on more filter paper until dry. The small pieces not removed dissolved in the HF solution overnight. Chemical analysis of the anode film prepared in the manner just described showed that it was neither an oxide or a fluoride as previously supposed but almost all silicon, about 96% by weight! Archer (34), using an oxidation technique, has found that the dark deposit formed on the p-type side of a silicon p-n junction in 48% HF plus a few drops of nitric acid was also mostly silicon. He has confirmed that the thick film anodically grown on silicon in 48% HF is largely pure silicon.

The following series of electrochemical and chemical equations are proposed to explain all the observed facts concerning the thick anode film formed on silicon in HF solutions. The initial process is silicon dissolution:

$$Si + 2HF + (2\text{-}n)\, e^+ \xrightarrow{\text{rapid}} SiF_2 + 2H^+ + ne^- \qquad (4)$$

where n < 2, assuming that holes are required to carry out anodic processes on semiconductors, and e^+ represents an electron hole. The electrochemical reaction as written assumes that silicon dissolution is divalent, as suggested by Uhlir's results. The subsequent chemical reactions which are believed to take place are shown schematically:

$$2SiF_2 \xrightarrow{\text{rapid}} \underline{Si} + SiF_4\uparrow \qquad (5)$$

$$\xrightarrow{2HF} H_2SiF_6 \qquad (6)$$

$$\xrightarrow[\text{slow}]{2H_2O} SiO_2 + 2H_2\uparrow \qquad (7)$$

$$\xrightarrow[\text{rapid}]{6HF} H_2SiF_6 + 2H_2O \qquad (8)$$

The thick amorphous film of silicon on silicon forms only because the reaction between silicon and water is slow. In strong HF solutions, the "mass transfer" of water molecules to the silicon may also be a factor. This is indicated to some extent by the fact that the maximum silicon film thickness which can be formed decreases with HF dilution; i.e., thick films on the order of tenths of a millimeter are obtained in 48% HF, but only very thin films, between 0.01 and 0.001 mm, are formed in 5% HF.

5.3 Conditions for Electropolishing Silicon

Turner (29) studied the effects of temperature, HF concentration, viscosity, and fluosilicic acid concentration on the

critical current density required to start electropolishing a
horizontal silicon electrode (facing up) in unstirred solutions.
The critical current density, i_c, is defined as that at which the
thick film comes off and the transition to the electropolishing
condition takes place.

The E-I curve in Fig. 3 was obtained at 25° C. If the
temperature of the silicon is varied, the critical current density also changes. The realtion between i_c and temperature in
5% HF aqueous solutions is shown in Fig. 4. The critical current

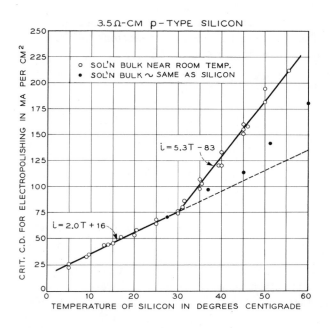

Fig. 4. Effect of temperature on the critical current density
required to start electropolishing silicon in 5% HF.

density increases linearly with temperature. The break in the
straight line near room temperature is attributed to the onset
of convection stirring due to a thermal gradient between the
silicon and the solution. Attempts were made to thermostat the
solution to the same temperature as the silicon. The solid
points are these data. The results were in the right direction,

but apparently thermal gradients were not eliminated entirely.

At a constant silicon temperature, the i_c was found to be directly related to the HF concentration. Data obtained at four temperatures, two below and two above 30° C, are shown in Fig. 5. The practical range of HF concentration for electro-polishing silicon is 2 to 10% by weight HF. Below 2% HF the

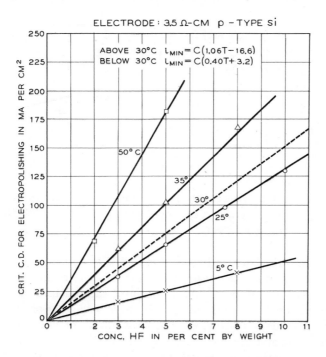

Fig. 5. Effect of HF concentration on the critical current den-sity required to start electropolishing silicon at vari-ous temperatures.

solution conductivity decreases rapidly both in aqueous and non-aqueous solutions. When the cell conductivity is low, the power dissipated as heat can be large even at moderate currents. Above 10% by weight HF the critical current density required to start electropolishing becomes high and the power dissipated in the silicon can heat the silicon so that an even higher current

density is required. For most applications, 5% HF is a satisfactory concentration for electropolishing silicon.

The effect of viscosity on the critical current density
required to start electropolishing a horizontal silicon electrode
in 5% HF solutions at 25° C is presented on a log-log plot in
Fig. 6. Glycerine was used to increase the solution viscosity.

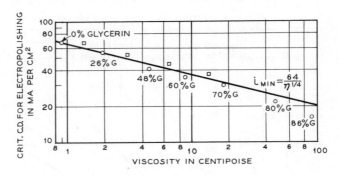

Fig. 6.   Effect of viscosity on the critical current density required to start electropolishing silicon in 5% HF and
glycerin at 25° C.

The straight line drawn has a slope of -1/4 and is a reasonable
fit to most of the data. Large deviations occur only at the highest viscosities. Fig. 6 also shows how the critical current
density changes in the transition from an aqueous solution to a
largely nonaqueous solution. The advantage of being able to
achieve a lower current density to electropolish silicon by increasing the solution viscosity with nonaqueous materials is
offset by a corresponding increase in the solution resistance
and therefore solution heating.

Some workers (35) have reported that the critical current density for electropolishing certain metals is decreased
when the concentration of the metal in the solution is increased.
Fluosilicic acid is the final anode reaction product during the
electropolishing of silicon in HF solutions. Turner (29) found
no change in i_c, within the limits of experimental error, with
additions of up to 25% by weight H_2SiF_6 in 5% aqueous HF.

Turner (29) has shown that the observed effects of HF

concentration, viscosity, and temperature on i_c are of the right order of magnitude to conclude that i_c is the current density at which the supply of HF at the silicon anode becomes limited by its rate of "mass transfer, " i. e. , by diffusion, convection, and migration from the solution bulk to the electrode surface.

6. OTHER SEMICONDUCTING MATERIALS

Very little has been published on the electrolytic etching of semiconducting materials other than germanium and silicon. There probably have been many unpublished small experiments carried out to determine a suitable electropolishing process for many of the intermetallic semiconductors. Uhlir (36) for example, found that a largely nonaqueous HF solution suitable for electropolishing silicon would also electropolish GaSb.

Dewald (37) electropolished InSb successfully in a Jacquet type perchloric acid bath containing 10 parts $HClO_4$, 40 parts acetic anhydride, and 2 parts water.* Electropolishing was done at about 5^0 C with a current density of about 50 ma/cm². A solid black film of oxidation product was produced on the surface but this was readily stripped off under a stream of water, leaving a mirror bright surface.

Harper and Astor (38) also used the Jacquet perchloric-acetic acid bath for electrolytic polishing and etching of gallium arsenide. They observed four distinct regions in the E-I curve where different kinds of surfaces were obtained. Below 250 ma/cm² the microstructure was made visible and twin boundaries and grain boundaries were attacked preferentially. In the second region, from 250 to about 300 ma/cm² etch pits were formed; they were better defined in shape than those produced by chemical etching. Electropolishing occurred in the third region from 300 to 400 ma/cm². Above 400 ma/cm², etch pits were formed in the first 30 seconds. These were then removed quickly by polishing. The surface, however, became quite irregular in this region after one minute.

---

*For safe practice it is best to add the acid slowly to the anhydride while stirring and cooling.

7. SPECIAL TECHNIQUES FOR SELECTIVE ETCHING

Many special techniques have been developed for selective electrolytic etching of semiconductors. Tilley and Williams
(39) adopted a jet etching technique to reduce the thickness of a
germanium wafer prior to making transistors by plating a metal
emitter and collector on opposite sides of the wafer. Two jets
of solution were directed at the germanium, one on each side
of the wafer, positioned so that concentric circular areas were
drilled into the germanium. Since germanium dissolves anodically in practically all aqueous electrolytes, the etching
electrolyte can be a standard plating solution. When the desired germanium thickness is reached by electrolytic polishing,
the current is simply reversed, making the germanium cathode,
and the metal spots are plated in place. A similar process for
jet etching and plating on silicon was described by Wurst and
Borneman (40). Since silicon is anodically etched only in fluoride solutions, they found it necessary to use a separate fluoride
etching solution prior to plating most metals.

Uhlir (41) described a method of micromachining germanium and silicon using a "virtual" cathode. Instead of con-
fining the area to be etched by a narrow jet of solution, he used
a glass tube with the end drawn down to a tip as small as one
micron diameter and positioned close to the germanium. The
cathode and a 10% KOH etching solution were placed inside the
tube. A variety of shapes were produced by moving the tip with
respect to the germanium. Holes were drilled by slowly ad-
vancing the glass tip into the germanium. Uhlir (41) obtained
good results with only a gravity flow of solution from the tiny
orifice. A more rapid flow of solution might be desirable for
a higher maximum rate of etching but a larger etch pattern
would be produced. Whenever small orifices are used, it is
necessary to filter the electrolyte very carefully to avoid clog-
ging by fine particles.

Uhlir (7) also explored methods of shaping germanium
by means of injecting holes near where etching is desired.
This method is most effective with n-type germanium where
the equilibrium hole concentration is low. Selective etching
was produced either by focusing light on the surface to create

hole-electron pairs or by hole injection from a forward-biased p-n junction.

Sullivan and Eigler (42) developed a technique for removing the damaged surface layer from the p-n junction area of germanium diodes without masking. The germanium diode is placed inside a hairpin-shaped platinum cathode and a stream of 0.1% KOH is allowed to flow down between the cathode and the germanium. Surface tension confines the electrolyte to the junction area. A polished surface is usually completed in 1 to 2 min at 1.5 amp/cm^2.

Electrolytic etching has been used to reveal p-n junctions (43) as well as to remove n- or p-type material preferentially from diodes and transistors (28). These processes make use of the rectifying barrier of p-n junctions as well as the hole depletion effect at the surface of n-type germanium and silicon.

References

1. M. V. Sullivan and J. H. Eigler, J. Electrochem. Soc., 104, 226 (1947).
2. D. R. Turner and H. A. Sauer, J. Electrochem. Soc., in press.
3. M. V. Sullivan and R. M. Warner, Jr., in F. J. Biondi, ed., Transistor Technology, Vol. III, p. 163, D. Van Nostrand Co., Inc. 1958.
4. W. H. Brattain and C. G. B. Garrett, Bell System Tech. J., 34, 129 (1955).
5. E. A. Efimov and I. G. Erusalimchik, Zhur. Fiz. Khim., 32, 413 (1958).
6. E. A. Efimov and I. G. Erusalimchik, Zhur. Fiz. Khim., 32, 1103 (1958).
7. A. Uhlir, Jr., Bell System Tech. J., 35, 333 (1956).
8. D. R. Turner, J. Electrochem. Soc., 103, 252 (1956).
9. H. Gerischer and F. Beck, Z. physik. Chem. (Frankfurt), 13, 389 (1957).
10. J. B. Flynn, J. Electrochem. Soc., 105, 715 (1958).
11. K. Bohnenkamp and H. J. Engell, Z. Elektrochem., 61, 1184 (1957).

12. P. F. Schmidt and D. A. Keiper, J. Electrochem. Soc.,
    106, 592 (1959).
13. S. G. Ellis, Phys. Rev., 100, 1140 (1955).
14. D. R. Turner, unpublished results.
15. F. Jirsa, Z. anorg. u. allgem. Chem., 268, 84 (1952).
16. O. H. Johnson, Chem. Revs., 51, 431 (1952).
17. M. Lourijsen-Teyssèdre, Bull. soc. chim. France, 1955,
    1118.
18. N. de Zoubov, E. Deltombe, and M. Pourbaix, CEBELCOR,
    Rappt. tech., No. 27, (1955).
19. J. Bardeleben, Z. physik. Chem. (Frankfurt), 17, 39 (1958).
20. J. F. Dewald, in N. B. Hannay, ed., Semiconductors,
    p. 727, Reinhold Publishing Corp., 1959.
21. F. Beck and H. Gerischer, Z. Elektrochem., 63, 500 (1952).
22. P. Brouillet and I. Epelboin, Compt. rend., 237, 895 (1953).
23. P. Brouillet, Métaux Corrosion-Inds., 30, 243 (1955).
24. I. Epelboin and M. Fromet, Métaux Corrosion-Inds., 33,
    1 (1958); I. Epelboin, French pat. 1, 107, 706 (1956)
    (C. A., 53, 4977g (1959)).
25. A. Topfer, personal communication.
26. J. Mieluch, Bull. acad. polon. sci., Ser. sci. Chim.,
    géol. et géograph., 7, 151 (1959).
27. J. W. Faust, Jr., U. S. pat. 2, 861, 931 (1958) (C. A., 53,
    3944i (1959)).
28. I. A. Lesk and R. E. Gonzales, J. Electrochem. Soc., 105,
    469 (1958).
29. D. R. Turner, J. Electrochem. Soc., 105, 402 (1958).
30. P. Wang, oral presentation, Electrochem. Soc. Meeting,
    Oct. 1957.
31. P. F. Schmidt and M. Blomgren, J. Electrochem. Soc.,
    106, 694 (1959).
32. I. Epelboin, J. chim. phys., 49, C214 (1952).
33. I. Epelboin and M. Fromet, J. phys., radium, 18, 60A
    (1957).
34. R. J. Archer, personal communication.
35. A. Hickling and J. K. Higgins, Trans. Inst. Metal Finishing,
    29, 274 (1953).
36. A. Uhlir, Jr., unpublished results.
37. J. F. Dewald, J. Electrochem. Soc., 104, 244 (1957).

38. J. G. Harper and M. S. Astor, oral presentation, Elec-
     trochem. Soc. Meeting, May 1959.
39. J. W. Tilley and R. A. Williams, Proc. I. R. E., 41, 1706
     (1953).
40. E. C. Wurst, Jr. and E. H. Borneman, J. Appl. Phys., 28,
     235 (1957).
41. A. Uhlir, Jr., Rev. Sci. Instr., 26, 965 (1955).
42. M. V. Sullivan and J. H. Eigler, J. Electrochem. Soc.,
     103, 132 (1956).
43. E. Billig and J. J. Dowd, Nature, 117, 115 (1953).

DISCUSSION

J. SPRAGUE (Sprague Electric): I have a comment to
make on your mechanism for the formation of thick anodic
films on silicon. We obtained similar results except that in
certain cases the silicon layer was found by x-ray diffraction,
to be polycrystalline rather than amorphous.

D. R. TURNER: I should have mentioned some work by
Dr. Archer of our Laboratory. He studied the dark stain pro-
duced on p-type silicon by the technique given by Fuller [U. S.
Patent 2,740,700, May 14, 1954] to reveal p-n junctions.
Dr. Archer found this stain to be pure silicon; perhaps, he
could make some comments on its structure.

R. J. ARCHER (Bell Telephone Laboratories): Of the
six diffraction patterns we have taken, three showed single
crystal material, one amorphous, one single crystal with a
polycrystalline ring superimposed on it, and one single crystal
with a second interpenetrating single crystal lattice. We are
not sure whether or not the single crystal pattern comes from
the structure of the subphase of the layer.

A. POE (General Electric): You showed that oxygen
evolution starts at approximately 40 volts. Certainly, oxygen
is evolved at a lower potential than this. I also have a question
concerning the amorphous or polycrystalline silicon layer; if
it is silicon, then how does it dissolve in nitric acid if no hydrogen fluoride is present?

D. R. TURNER: As I mentioned, the silicon electropolishing film has a high resistance; thus, most of the 40 volt potential drop is across the film. Oxygen evolution takes place when the potential between the outer edge of this film and the solution reaches the value at which oxygen deposition takes place. In answer to your second question, I stated that the reaction between the silicon film and nitric acid was violent. This reaction is an oxidation process, not dissolution.

H. SELLO (Fairchild Semiconductor): You state that p-type silicon and germanium etch at the same rate electro- lytically. In light of the different mechanisms, how do you account for this?

D. R. TURNER: The difference between the two mater- ials lies in the formation of a thick anode film on silicon. Once this film is removed and electropolishing occurs, the mechan- ism of dissolution is, I believe, quite similar. The amount of material etched electrolytically per coulomb of electricity is related to: electrochemical equivalent/density. The electro- chemical equivalent for Ge is about twice that of Si, but the density of Ge is about 2 times that of Si so etch rates are about the same.

H. GERISCHER (Max Plank Institute): Concerning your mechanism for the dissolution of silicon, can you be sure that the product you analyze by x-ray diffraction is the same as that present during electrolysis? If it is a film of silicon it must be insulated from the electrode or else it would undergo disso- lution again.

D. R. TURNER: When the critical current density is exceeded, the film that has built up comes off almost immediately This suggests that during the growth of the film the reaction takes place at the single crystal electrode surface, and thus the film must be very porous.

G. A. WOLFF (U. S. Army Signal Research and Develop- ment Laboratory): We have studied the etching of silicon using chlorine at elevated temperature as an etchant. We found un- der certain conditions that a sub-halide layer was formed on the surface inhibiting further reaction. When these samples were placed in water or an ammonia solution, hydrogen was evolved leaving a black residue on the surface which may be silicon.

H. SELLO: You showed a dependency of the ratio on the fourth root of the viscosity of a mixture of 5 percent HF in glycerine. Is there any possibility that the activity of the HF or possibly some HF-glycerine complex could be responsible for this effect on the rate?

D. R. TURNER: For a vertical electrode, one can derive the dependency of i_c, on the viscosity; i_c varies as one over the viscosity to the $1/4$ power. I have, however, used a horizontal electrode; no one has to the best of my knowledge, succeeded in deriving a theoretical equation for this dependency for a horizontal electrode. Experimental work in heat transfer and in cathodic reduction processes give the viscosity to the $1/3$ power for the horizontal case. For our case, we obtain a $1/4$th power instead of $1/3$rd but feel that this is a good enough agreement to say that the effect of viscosity is as it should be.

H. SELLO: Your graph of i_c versus temperature exhibited a break near room temperature which you attributed to convective currents. Wouldn't you expect mixing to affect the rates even below this break?

D. R. TURNER: In the case of a vertical electrode, this is certainly true because of the streaming of either more dense or less dense anode products across the face of the electrode. This was one reason why we used horizontal electrodes. In this case anode films leave the surface by a normal diffusion process. You, of course, still have a natural convection effect, but it is reduced considerably. The potential current curve is different for the two cases; the horizontal electrode gives a sharp change in the curve at the critical current density while the vertical electrode does not give a sharp change.

C. V. KING (New York University): Should you not be using the kinematic viscosity, that is, the viscosity divided by the density, for your work with glycerine solutions?

D. R. TURNER: That is true, we have taken this into account in our work.

H. GERISCHER: I do not think that a stoichiometric formulation should be used for the consumption of holes and electrons in the dissolution of germanium. We found no constant relation between the holes and electrons in our studies. For a very high injection current, practically all of the holes are used for dissolution, and the multiplication factor is close to one. For low injection, one finds a multiplication factor of about two. I am not sure if there is a chemical reason for this or if it is more like a statistical average over several steps with electron transfer.

D. R. TURNER: That is very interesting.

SURFACE REACTIONS

IN

LIQUID MEDIA

N. HACKERMAN
University of Texas

Kinetics
of Dissolution Processes

ABSTRACT

THE KINETICS OF DISSOLUTION of
solids is governed in general by transport phenomena, or by whatever process is required to dis-
rupt the primary aggregating forces in the solid,
or by some combination of both. In principle the
steps can be separated experimentally and studied
individually. For processes controlled by transport, the problems, both theoretical and experimental, are those of fluid dynamics and of the diffusion layer in nonturbulent systems. For processes in which the rate depends on bond disrup-
tion the principal step may be one of solvation, or
it may involve an oxidation-reduction system. The
latter is predominant in most cases involving
metals, in which case it becomes necessary to
determine which, if either, of the electron transfer processes is limiting.

1. INTRODUCTION

Reaction rates of metals with aqueous solutions, as in
any heterogeneous reaction, are controlled by one or more of

several sequential steps. In principle each of these steps can be described satisfactorily, whether the reaction is spontaneous as in corrosion processes or induced as in anodic processes. In general terms, the steps are those involving transport and those involving activation. To these may be added the role played by contaminants in the liquid phase, added either purposefully or adventitiously. This is itself a large and complex field which depends ultimately on the subject of interest considered herein, but it will not be pursued further at this point.

2. TRANSPORT

The transport steps may be controlling either in bringing reactant material to the reaction site (the metal-solution interface) from either phase, or in removing products from the site into the liquid phase. Accepting the fact that metal reactions in conducting solutions are electrochemical in nature, it follows that control may reside in transport with respect to the cathodic process, or with respect to the anodic process, or with respect to both simultaneously - a much less likely possibility. In metal dissolution reactions, the steps can be described still less equivocally: for the first case, the transfer of reducible species from the solution to the electrode is involved; for the second case, the removal of oxidized species from the electrode is involved. In the latter instance complications are usually caused by the formation of solid reaction products. Since these solid products are often somewhat adherent to the metal, the rate of transport of either reducible or oxidizable substances through the scale to the metal must be considered. Thus the coherent character of the covering product becomes important, and this in turn is certainly related to the kinetics of dissolution of the solid compound itself.

3. FILMS OR SCALE

The role of adherent, coherent solids on the metal surface in metal dissolution rates is fairly obvious: they act largely as barriers to the approach of the reactants to one another. In some instances, such as for the oxides on tantalum

or titanium under proper conditions, the movement is mainly
of charged particles through the lattice itself. This requires
a flux which can be provided by adsorbed ions on the external
surface of the oxide or by potentials, either self-induced or
applied. Very low corrosion rates normally prevail under these
circumstances and it is likely that mechanisms postulated for
metal-gas reactions (e. g. , Wagner-Mott-Cabrera) are applicable here. In this connection, one apparently fruitful approach
to rates of thin film formation uses the ellipsometer for direct
measurement of film thickness (1). For grosser systems the
use of extrapolated rates at zero time is often helpful in un-
ravelling the kinetics of bare metal dissolution reactions.

        For thicker scale, the nature of the packing of the ad-
herent precipitate is sometimes determining. For instance,
rapidly formed precipitates are apt to be finely divided and may
provide a more densely packed coating than does a solid formed
more slowly to give coarse grains (2). It is clear that if transport through the grains from or to the metal surface is not
rapid, the more densely packed material will provide more of
an impedance to the reaction. The question of scale thickness
and probability of spalling is also raised. It must be concluded
that with few exceptions (3) there is little good, elementary
scientific work available on detailed effects of reaction-produced
coatings on reaction rates.

4. ACTIVATION

        Activation control of an overall dissolution rate can, of
course, reside in the reduction process, in the oxidation process, in a mixture of both, or in a mixture including some transport control. The reduction process is usually more influential
in determining the overall rate. Thus, in the absence of transport control, the kinetics of the electrode process for reduction
of hydrated protons, or water molecules, or dissolved molecular
oxygen plays the major role in metal dissolution kinetics. Indeed the literature confirms the conclusion that many of the
systems seen in experiment or in practice are diffusion controlled; that most of the rest are under mixed diffusion and
activation control; and that those with some activation control

are primarily under the influence of the cathodic reaction.

There are many examples to support the statement above and some are given in reference (4). In this group, for instance, Sekerka states that metals reacting with acids or alkalis less concentrated than 0.1 M dissolve under control of diffusion processes, whereas in acids more concentrated than 0.5 M, the control resides in the hydrogen evolution reaction. Between these concentrations the control is mixed. Loshkarev studied the dissolution of steels and low alloys in 6.5N HNO_3 and concluded that the rates were determined by the rate at which solvent was brought to the surface. Ammar and Riad believe that an electrochemical desorption step in the hydrogen reaction is limiting in metal-acid solution systems. Makrides et al describe the effect of pH change on rates, as does Stern. Georgi showed the effect of a cathodic depolarizer like ferric ion on the reaction between nickel and HCl. There is a vast literature in the areas of transport control and of cathodic control. Both aspects are to be considered in detail in the following sections by J. V. Petrocelli and C. V. King.

5. METAL-CONTROLLED RATES

Reactions in which the rate is governed wholly or largely by the process

$$metal\text{-}ion\text{-}in\text{-}lattice \rightleftharpoons metal\text{-}ion\text{-}in\text{-}solution$$

are not very numerous, or at least not very well defined. Such reactions require that the reaction products be soluble, or, if insoluble, non-adherent; e.g., they must precipitate at some point distant from the interface. A second requirement is that the reduction reaction be very fast. The potential of the dissolving metal presumably should be at or near that of the cathodic reaction since this must be polarized little or none at all. However, in most cases in which the potential becomes markedly cathodic, as in passivated metals, the corrosion rate is actually low, probably due to impeding surface barriers. The question of whether such a system is under activation control or diffusion control is still being debated and it cannot be used here as a clear-cut example. Another possibility with regard to reaction potential is that it depends wholly on the character of ohmic resistances in the reaction cell circuit.

It appears that most reactions controlled by the equation above are rapid, although this is not a hard and fast requirement. Again, a somewhat random sampling of the literature provides some illustrations (5). Bond, Hill, and Tennison followed the reaction of copper in persulfate solutions. Their work indicates the importance of complexing agents for the metal ion in dissolution processes generally and processes controlled by activation steps in the anodic reaction in particular. Scott and Shell were not interested in dissolution rates but simply in dissolving various metals: they found a 90 percent H_2O_2 in concentrated trifluoroacetic acid solution effective and fast for such metals as iron, manganese, magnesium, indium, and lead. Vander Wall and Whitener studied the system zirconium in nitric acid-hydrofluoric acid mixtures and concluded that the rate was first order with respect to molecular HF, which indicates either a film dissolving process or direct metal dissolution as rate controlling. Hackerman, Hurd, and Snavely followed the extremely rapid rate of uniform dissolution of stressed steel in a very concentrated solution of ammonium nitrate and ammonia in water. In this case the reaction potential was nearly that of the anodic process but still the cathodic reaction did not appear to be limiting. This suggests that the reaction was controlled mainly by ohmic resistances or that the electrochemical concept of corrosion reactions requires some modification for these systems (6). An interesting instance of very high metal dissolution rates is that produced by imposing anodic current on a metal in acid solution, at current densities high enough to suggest that they might be considered as a "solution plasma" (7).

Even if systems under pure anodic control were to be found in plentiful amounts, the kinetics could not yet be clearly worked out because of the variables resident in the metal itself. In general, the thermodynamic concept of the solid being in its standard state has been used in kinetic reasoning, only the surface area being considered as a variable. In other words, the effect of crystal imperfections and the quantitative relationship between their concentration and location with reaction rate remains to be discovered. It appears quite evident that vacancies, dislocations, terraces, and the like are nuclei for surface reactions if preferential etching and decorating procedures may be cited as evidence. For silver halide single crystals the dislocation density seems to be pertinent to the rate of reaction nucleation and to initial reaction rates (8). However, in a study of the reaction between single crystal copper and aqueous ethylenediammine solutions, Jenkins (9) reports that there is no clear relationship between dislocations and reaction nucleation. Nevertheless, it is highly important to make such studies for as many systems as possible because the possibility does exist. Certainly the experience with halides ought to be transferable to oxides and to other solid reaction products.

In spite of the fact that no good answers are yet available, a few pertinent and leading questions are possible. Are nucleation sites common (i. e., in high concentration) for fast, uniform dissolution reactions and uncommon (in low concentration) for localized reactions? Are experiments with single crystal, pure metal samples likely to give information applicable to multicomponent, polycrystalline aggregates? Are bare metal reaction rates best studied by using appropriate complexing agents to remove reaction debris continuously? There is some reason for optimism in spite of the sub-embryonic character of our knowledge at this point. A number of studies have added information of consequence. By way of illustration, equations have been developed for unimpeded anodic reactions, among others, on the basis of electrochemical theory (10). Also the study of corrosion of whiskers (11) and of single crystal metals (1, 9) has become somewhat more common. Studies on electrodeposition on whiskers (12) and on dissolution and electrodeposition in copper-copper sulfate solutions (13) are sure to be pertinent. Certainly the recent Faraday Society Discussion on "Crystal Imperfections and Chemical Reactivity" (14) should prove very useful. Although it may not be especially pertinent to the metal-solution systems, the general trend of work and the tentative principles evolved should show the way to significant experiments in this field.

In summary, this paper provides no solutions to the

problems of metal dissolution reactions controlled by the anodic reaction itself because the state of knowledge is still at too low level. However the problems are beginning to emerge in sharper focus, and this is always a precursor to obtaining firm knowledge in a reasonably short time.

Acknowledgment

The author takes this opportunity to acknowledge financial support of work in his laboratory in this field by the Welch Foundation, Houston and by the Office of Naval Research. This support has been instrumental in providing for some of the work cited here, as well as other researches, and in providing background for speculation with respect to these problems.

References

(Aside from reference 14 this list is used for illustrative purposes only, and it is not intended to be either exhaustive or typical).

1. J. Kruger, J. Electrochem. Soc., 106, 847 (1959).
2. N. Hackerman and E. E. Glenn, Jr., J. Electrochem. Soc., 100, 314 (1953).
3. W. Feitknecht, Chem. & Ind. (London), 1959, 1102.
4. I. Sekerka, Werkstoffe u. Korrosion, 10, 383 (1959); H. R. Froning, and J. H. Jones, Ind. Eng. Chem., 50, 1737 (1958); A. G. Loshkarev, J. Appl. Chem., U. S. S. R., (English Translation), 31, 1165 (1958); I. A. Ammar and S. Riad, J. Phys. Chem., 62, 150 (1958); H. C. Gatos, J. Electrochem. Soc., 103, 286 (1956); A. C. Makrides, N. M. Komodromos and N. Hackerman, ibid., 102, 363 (1955); M. Stern, ibid., 609; K. Georgi, Z. Elektrochem., 39, 736 (1933).
5. G. C. Bond, B. M. Hill and R. Tennison, J. Chem. Soc., 1959, 33; J. Halpern, M. Milants and D. R. Wiles, J. Electrochem. Soc., 106, 647 (1959); A. F. Scott and Jane G. Shell, J. Am. Chem. Soc., 81, 2278 (1959); E. M. Vander Wall and E. M. Whitener, Ind. Eng. Chem., 51, 51 (1959).
6. C. Wagner and Z. Traud, Z. Elektrochem., 44, 391 (1938).

7. A. Uhlir, Jr., Rev. Sci. Instr., 26, 965 (1955).
8. T. Evans and J. W. Mitchell, in Defects in Crystalline Solids, p. 409, Physical Society, 1955.
9. L. H. Jenkins, J. Electrochem. Soc., in press.
10. F. A. Posey, J. Electrochem. Soc., 106, 571 (1959).
11. J. F. Green and A. A. Woolf, Research (London), 11, 38 (1958).
12. P. B. Price, D. A. Vermilyea and M. B. Webb, Acta Met., 6, 524 (1958).
13. E. Mattson and J. O'M. Bockris, Trans. Faraday Soc., 55, 1586 (1959).
14. Discussion of the Faraday Society on "Crystal Imperfections and the Chemical Reactivity of Solids" held at Queen's University, Kingston, Ontario, Canada, to be published; see also Discussions Faraday Soc., 5, (1949).

DISCUSSION

H. J. ENGELL (Max Planck Institute): As already explained by Prof. Hackerman, two limiting mechanisms can be expected for the dissolution of a solid: (a) Equilibrium exists at the phase boundary of the solid and the solution, and the transport of the dissolved solid into the interior of the solution is rate determining. (b) The rate determining step of the solution process is the transport through the phase boundary solid-solution; then the transport of dissolved particles from the interphase into the solution can be assumed to be fast enough to be without influence on the overall rate of the dissolution.

In the case of dissolution of a number of semiconducting metal oxides in acid aqueous solutions, it can be calculated from the rate of solution, that a phase boundary reaction must be rate determining. Moreover, it can be shown, that this reaction is electrochemical in nature, for its rate depends on the potential of the dissolving oxide. As an example, Fig. 1 shows the influence of the electrode potential on the rate of dissolution of $Fe_{0.94}O$ in sulfuric acid and hydrochloric acid. The rate of dissolution is expressed in terms of a dissolution current. A linear relation exists between the electrode potential and the logarithm of the dissolution current. The rate of dissolution increases, as the electrode potential changes in the cathodic (less noble) direction. Fe_3O_4 shows the same behavior with the exception that a maximum dissolution rate occurs at

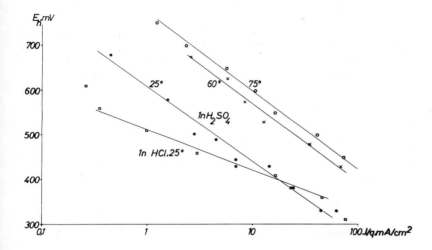

Fig. 1. Electrode potential of $Fe_{0.94}O$ as a function of dissolution rate (expressed in current density) in sulfuric acid and hydrochloric acid [Engell, Z. physik. Chem. N. F. , 7, 158 (1956)]

+ 200 mV (hydrogen scale) (Fig. 2). In the case of CdO, a super-position of both limiting mechanisms (a) and (b) cited above is to be assumed, for the rate of dissolution depends on the electrode potential as well as on the rate of stirring of the solution. The dissolution current does not show a logarithmic dependence on the potential (Fig. 3).

The logarithmic dependence of the dissolution rate on the electrode potential can be explained in the case of ionic crystals under the following assumptions: (a) The dissolution process is far from equilibrium. (b) The passage of cations and anions can be treated as independent electrochemical reactions. The rate of each of them depends logarithmically on the electrode potential and on the chemical potential of the species in question in the solid phase. (c) According to the

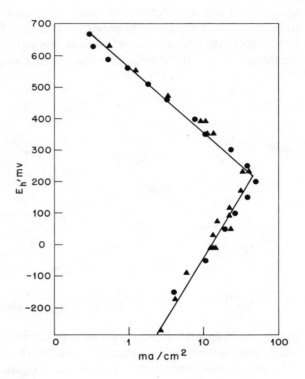

Fig. 2. Electrode potential of Fe_3O_4 (two samples) as a function of dissolution rate in $1N H_2SO_4$ at 75^oC [Engell,
Z. physik. Chem. N. F., 7, 158 (1956)]

Duhem-Margules equation for compounds with a small deviation from the stoichiometric composition [Schottky, Ulich, and
Wagner, Thermodynamik, p. 375, Berlin 1929], the sum of the
chemical potentials of anions and cations is constant in the
crystal (and in its surface). (d) In the steady state of the dissolution process, equivalent numbers of anions and cations have
to pass through the phase boundary per unit time.

Under these assumptions we obtain [Z. physik. Chem.
N. F., 7, 158 (1956)],

$$\frac{d\ln I}{dE} = (\alpha_c |z_c| - \alpha_a |z_a|) \frac{F}{2RT} \quad ,$$

where I is the dissolution current, E the electrode potential, α_c and α_a the transfer factor (Durchtrittsfaktor) of the cations and anions, respectively, z_c and z_a the valencies, and F the Faraday constant.

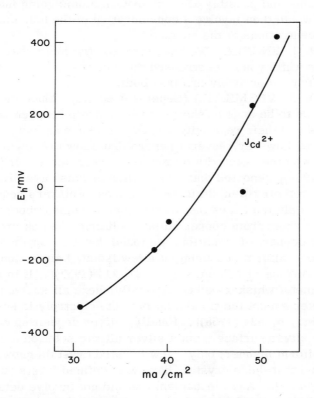

Fig. 3. Electrode potential of CdO as a function of dissolution rate in $1N H_2SO_4$ at 25°C [Engell, Z. Elektrochem., 60, 905 (1956)] .

J. F. DEWALD (Bell Telephone Laboratories): Dr. Engell's comment is very interesting; however, I would like to bring out one point. He treats the metal oxides, for example cadmium oxide, as ionic compounds. ZnO which we have been studying [this volume] would usually be considered as ionic; however, it has a Wurtzite structure and is tending strongly toward covalent bonding. Thus another explanation could be based on considering the metal and oxygen atoms as being covalently bonded to the surface, rather than ionically. The metal atoms and possibly also the oxygen atoms going into solution would then involve a consideration of the hole and electron concentrations at the surface.

H. J. ENGELL: We have stressed the ionic character of the bonds while you have stressed their covalent character; the actual situation probably involves both.

D. A. VERMILYEA (General Electric): Much more work needs to be done to show the relationship between defects in metals and their reactivity as Prof. Hackerman has stated. There are, however, several papers that show the importance of defects on the reactivity of metals. Green and Woolf [Research 11, 38 (1958)] reported that silver whiskers dissolve preferentially from their tip in nitric acid. Copper whiskers require approximately ten times the overvoltage to cause copper to deposit on them from copper sulfate solutions than on ordinary pieces of copper. In addition, we found that the copper deposition is non-uniform, occuring at a few isolated sites along the whisker surface [J. Chem. Phys. , 27, 814 (1957)]. It is possible to grow metal whiskers electrolytically; here all surfaces of the whisker except the tip are inert in the electrolytic solution [Acta Met. , 6, 524 (1958)]. Finally, silver depositing on an ordinary silver surface from a silver nitrate solution does so in a non-uniform manner; only a few isolated crystals grow. We have found that these crystals have well defined facets [unpublished results]. Any mechanism that did not involve defects in the metal would lead to a sphere or some other smooth shape rather than a faceted crystal.

N. HACKERMAN: That is correct, there is evidence in the literature showing the importance of defects in the reactivity of metals. My statements referred to quantitative data on the influence of dislocation density on reaction rates.

A. DRAVNIEKS (Standard Oil of Indiana): The dissolution rates of metals are different for each acid; in other words, the anion of the acid is an important factor in dissolution rates. If the rate determining step is the anodic process, how can you explain the great influence of the anions.

N. HACKERMAN: This is what I meant by removing reaction debris or complexing the metal ion; the effects are related to the character of the anion.

M. O. BLOOM (Naval Research Laboratory): You mentioned that the dissolution rate of iron was high at approximately room temperature, and low at more elevated temperatures. At room temperature $Fe(OH)_2$ was the reaction product. It has recently been shown [Linnenbom, J. Electrochem. Soc. , 105, 323 (1958)] that the transformation from $Fe(OH)_2$ to Fe_3O_4 as the reaction product of iron in oxygen-free water takes place at relatively low temperature (60°C). May this not have a major effect on the overall mechanism?

N. HACKERMAN: The products from this system are very hard to handle; they change rapidly in air and thus must be analyzed in a closed system. If the transformation from $Fe(OH)_2$ to magnetite can occur readily at 60°C, magnetite would be present, but we have not found it.

J. V. PETROCELLI

International Nickel Company
Research Laboratories

Electrochemistry
of Dissolution Processes

ABSTRACT

THE BASIC ELECTROCHEMICAL con-
cepts and ideas underlying the phenomena of metal
dissolution are reviewed. The emphasis is on the
electrochemistry of metallic corrosion in aqueous
solutions. The role of oxidation potentials as a
measure of the "driving force" is discussed and
the energetic factors which determine the relative
electrode potential are described. It is shown
that a consideration of electrochemical kinetics,
in terms of current-voltage characteristics, allows
an electrochemical classification of metals and
leads to the modern views of the electrochemical
mechanism of corrosion and passivity.

1. INTRODUCTION

A consideration of the nature of this volume and its
objectives seem to dictate some discussion of general principles. Therefore an attempt will be made to present the ideas
and concepts underlying the electrochemical approach to the
dissolution process.

326

Although this treatment will be restricted to the dissolution of metals in aqueous solutions, particularly metallic corrosion, the ideas should be partially applicable to the behavior of semiconductors. As discussed in part III of this volume, semiconductors have a low and variable electron density and a rather wide energy gap between the valence and conduction electrons. These and other factors allow the existence of "surface states" and the presence of electric fields within the surface layers which may affect their electrochemical behavior.

Considerable progress has been made during the past decade toward a better insight into the basic concepts and mechanism involved in metallic dissolution and corrosion. More emphasis has been placed on the "fundamental particles" (metallic ions, electrons, and electron acceptors) and on the use of current-voltage characteristics. The wide recognition of dissolution and corrosion as electrode processes, and the idea of a polyelectrode exhibiting a mixed potential, have augmented the use of electrochemical techniques in the study and interpretation of corrosion phenomena. There is even some evidence that the phenomenon of passivity may soon be clarified.

2. ENERGETICS

2.1 The Reversible Electrode

The fundamental causative factor for the dissolution of metals and the mechanism of the process are identical to those pertinent to the establishment of an electrode potential. We may begin consideration of the dissolution process with a discussion of the thermodynamically reversible electrode potential, E_{eq}^{M}, of a metal, M, and proceed to show that the dissolution reaction is a departure from the equilibrium conditions. With this approach we can appreciate the role played by the electrode potential in corrosion and gain an insight into the true nature of the process.

Several investigators have shown that the electrode potential, sometimes referred to as the oxidation-potential, and the overpotential are a measure of the electrochemical affinity for the corrosion process (1, 2).

When a metal is immersed in a solution containing ions of that metal, the electrochemical potential of the ions in the metallic lattice and in the solution will usually be unequal. The same will be true for the free electrons (near the Fermi level) in the metal and electrons in the energy levels of electron acceptors in the solution.

Let us assume for the present that only the metallic ions can cross the metal-solution interface. These ions will make transitions from the metal to the solution and in the opposite direction. The rate per unit area at which ions leave the metal may be designated as an anodic current density $(i_a)_M$, and the rate in the opposite direction - the deposition reaction - as a cathodic current density $(i_c)_M$. At the beginning the two rates will not be equal and the ions will attempt to redistribute themselves until the electrochemical potential of the ion is equal in both phases.

During the time that the unequal currents exist, the metal and the solution become electrically charged, one positively and the other negatively. This charge gives rise to an electrical double layer at the interface which produces an electric field normal to the surface of contact and in such a direction that the net current is very rapidly reduced to zero and

$$(i_c)_M = (i_a)_M = (i_o)_M \tag{1}$$

where $(i_o)_M$ is the exchange current density of the metallic ions (3).

When equilibrium has been established, the emf, $_M\mathcal{E}_S$, at the metal-solution interface has been exactly counterbalanced by the electrical potential difference formed between the phases as a result of the double layer, and

$$_M\mathcal{E}_S = V^S - V^M \tag{2}$$

where V^S and V^M are the electrical potential of the solution and the metal, respectively (4). Since we shall be primarily concerned with the experimentally determined electrode potential,

E, the reader is referred to the article by Parsons (5) for a comprehensive discussion of the various potentials and their significance.

The experimentally measured reversible electrode potential, E_{eq}^M , includes not only the above emf but also the potential difference at the metal-platinum contact. The electrons are the electromotively active particles at this junction, and it may be assumed that at equilibrium an electrical potential difference exists between the two metals which equalizes the electrochemical potential of the electrons in the two phases. As is well known, it is equivalent to the Volta potential difference and is given by the following:

$$V^{Pt} - V^M = (\alpha_\epsilon^M - \alpha_\epsilon^{Pt}) / z \mathcal{F} \qquad (3)$$

where α_ϵ is the electronic work function - Langes' real potential - for the electron in the metal (3, 5, 6) and $\mathcal{F}$ is the Faraday constant.

The single thermodynamically reversible electrode potential as measured against the standard hydrogen electrode is equal to the emf of the cell,

$$Pt \mid M \mid M^+ \mid\mid H^+ \mid H_2 \mid Pt \qquad (4)$$

and given by

$$E_{eq}^M = {}_M V_S + (\alpha_\epsilon^M - \alpha_\epsilon^{Pt}) / z \mathcal{F} + {}_{Pt} V_S^o \qquad (5)$$

where the potential at the platinum-solution interface, ${}_{Pt} V_S^o$, is arbitrarily assigned the value zero. In the case where the metallic ions in the solution are at unit activity, we have the standard electrode potential, $(E_{eq}^M)^o$.

The various energetic factors which determine the value of E_{eq}^M are the sublimation energy of the metal, the ionization potential of the atom, the electronic work function and the hydration, or other complexing energy of the ion. These factors have been discussed extensively by Kieffer (7), Piontelli (8) and

and Latimer (9). It appears that none of the factors can be singled out as the one responsible for the relative electrochemical activity of the metal.

The concept of "work functions," the values of which are either equal to or derivable from the above energetic factors, are used below. These lend themselves more readily to considerations of mechanisms and kinetics.

The kinetic treatment for electrode processes yields the following well known expressions for the anodic and cathodic current densities (3, 10, 11):

$$i_a = k_a \, a_{(M^+)_M} \, \exp\left[-\overline{\Delta F_a}/RT\right] \exp\left[z\mathcal{F}\beta_M V_S/RT\right] \quad (6)$$

$$i_c = k_c \, a_{(M^+)_S} \, \exp\left[-\overline{\Delta F_c}/RT\right] \exp\left[z\mathcal{F}\alpha_M V_S/RT\right] \quad (7)$$

where k includes the frequency factors, ΔF is the activation energy, a_{M^+} the activity of the ions at the interface, and α and β are the fraction of the potential difference acting in the cathodic and anodic direction, respectively.

The rates may also be given in terms of the exchange current density, $(i_o)_M$, and the activation overvoltage, η, as follows:

$$i_a = i_o \, \exp\left[z\mathcal{F}\beta\eta_a/RT\right] \quad (8)$$

$$i_c = i_o \, \exp\left[z\mathcal{F}\alpha\eta_c/RT\right] \quad (9)$$

where it is assumed that the activities - or concentrations - of the ions remain constant. These are known as the Tafel relations.

Throughout this paper the assumption will be made that the concentration of the ions will remain constant. Therefore any effects due to concentration polarization will be excluded.

The energetic relationships are shown schematically in Figs.1(a) and 1(b) where we assume unit activity for the ions. In Fig.1(a) Y_+ is the ionic work function for the metallic ion in the metallic lattice, and W_+ the ionic work function for the ion in the solution. When the two phases come in contact, the potential energy curves - Morse type functions - will overlap and cross at some point x. The activation energy for the anodic reaction, $\overline{\Delta F_a}$, and for the cathodic reaction, $\overline{\Delta F_c}$, will usually not be equal. After the electrical double layer has formed and equilibrium has been established, the situation will be as shown in Fig.1(b). For unit activities of the ions the activation energy will have about the same value in both directions, $\overline{\Delta F}$, and the values of α and β will depend upon the shape of the curves and where they cross (11, 12, 13, 14). An analogous treatment yields similar expressions for the exchange of electrons between an inert electrode and a redox system such as $H_2 | H^+$, $Fe^{+3} |$ Fe^{++}, etc. (13, 14, 15).

It should be noted that in the case where only electrons are exchanged with the metal the value of the reversible electrode potential, E_{eq}, is independent of the electrode material. The value of the exchange current, however, depends on the metal in question. Although this kind of a reversible potential can only be measured on an inert electrode, in principle the potential and the exchange current may be established on any electron conductor.

The rate equations may be expressed in the more practical form as functions of the measured electrode potential, E, as follows:

$$i_a = i_o \exp \left[-z\mathcal{F}\beta E_{eq}/RT \right] \exp \left[z\mathcal{F}\beta E/RT \right] \qquad (10)$$

$$i_c = i_o \exp \left[-z\mathcal{F}\alpha E_{eq}/RT \right] \exp \left[z\mathcal{F}\alpha E/RT \right] \qquad (11)$$

Typical curves schematically showing the current-voltage characteristics of a redox system are shown in Fig. 2. Curves A and C are the polarization curves for the anodic and cathodic reaction, respectively. E_{eq} is the reversible potential for the various concentrations of the cathodic reactant - the metal ion in the case of a metal - and C_1, C_2 and C_3 the polarization curves for decreasing concentration.

It should be noted that E_{eq} is not necessarily the stand-

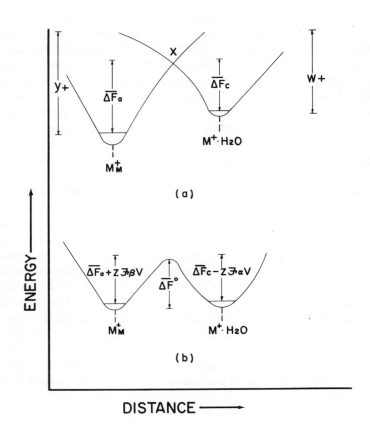

Fig. 1.   Schematic potential energy-distance relations for the
ions in the metal and in the solution. (a) On immediate immersion.(b) After ionic equilibrium has been
established.

ard electrode potential but depends upon the particular solution
under consideration.   When the solution is originally free of
the metallic ions - usually true in corrosion - we may assume
a metallic ion concentration of about 10^{-6}M.   If some insoluble
compound of the metal, such as the hydrated oxide, is stable,
the ion concentration may be obtained from its solubility product.

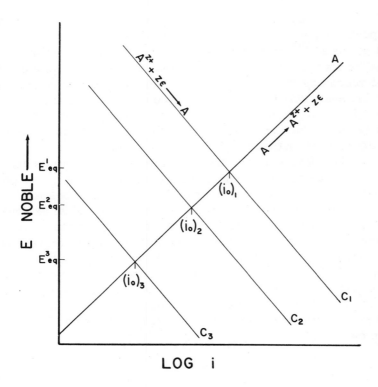

Fig. 2. Schematic polarization curves - Tafel lines - for a
         redox system.

      Although E_{eq} may not be attained experimentally, the
calculated value will yield a measure of the relative tendency
for the metal to react and in many cases may serve as the
"open circuit" potential on a corrosion diagram. This quantity is a good measure of the solution potential - a term often
used in corrosion. When different metals or different portions
of the same metal are compared as to their relative tendency
to corrode, E_{eq} is significant because it is a measure of the
relative electromotive activity of the ions in the given situation.
In many cases, however, the mixed potential - discussed later -
may be pertinent.

The energetic factors Y_+, W_+, and α_ϵ focus attention on the particle dynamics. The driving force of the reaction - the seat of the emf - resides in the escaping tendencies of the metallic ions and electrons across the interfaces. The electric field which controls the rates by changing the activation energies acts perpendicular to the surface of contact, across the interface. It should be noted that the currents $(i_c)_M$, and $(i_a)_M$ flow as a result of the above factors and not because of any "potential difference" between various points on the surface.

The above interpretation and concepts of currents and electrical potential differences form the basis of the mixed potential - polyelectrode theory or concept discussed below.

If for any reason, such as the application of an external current, the electrode potential of the metal is changed from the equilibrium value, or cannot assume this value, there will be a net anodic or cathodic current density according to the value of E. A change in the noble direction (more positive) will cause a net ionic current in the anodic direction, $(i_a)_N$, equal to the difference between the total anodic and cathodic current. According to Eqs. (8) and (9) this change will be given by

$$(i_a)_N = i_a - i_c = i_o \left\{ \exp\left[z\mathscr{F}\beta\eta/RT\right] - \exp\left[-z\mathscr{F}\alpha\eta/RT\right]\right\}$$

(12)

where the resulting dissolution reaction is a result of a variation from the equilibrium conditions.

3. THE MIXED POTENTIAL

3.1 Polyelectrodes

The transition of electrons across the metal-solution interface will actually occur whenever there is an electron acceptor in the solution with energy levels of appropriate value. This transition will be true, for example, when the reversible electrode potential for the oxidizing system E_{eq}^0 is more noble than E_{eq}^M. In this case electrons will make transitions predominately from the metal to the solution at a rate given by

Eq. (11) with the appropriate values of E_{eq}, i_o, and α.

We shall assume that the solution is a good conductor and that conducting films are not present at the surface of contact. If we have a metal such as zinc in a deaerated solution of sulfuric acid where $P_{H_2} = 1$ atmosphere, the following reactions are possible:

$$(M^{z+})_M \;\rightarrow\; (M^{z+})_S + z\epsilon(M) \;;\; (i_a)_M \tag{13a}$$

$$(M^{z+})_S + z\epsilon(M) \;\rightarrow\; (M^{z+})_M \;;\; (i_c)_M \tag{13b}$$

$$H_2 \;\rightarrow\; 2(H^+)_S + 2\epsilon(M) \qquad ;\; (i_a)_{H_2} \tag{14a}$$

$$2(H^+)_S + 2\epsilon(M) \;\rightarrow\; H_2 \qquad ;\; (i_c)_{H_2} \tag{14b}$$

The separate anodic and cathodic processes will occur simultaneously but statistically independent of one another. The rate of each reaction will be governed by the electrical potential difference which exists across the metal-solution interface and the appropriate values of i_o, α and β for each system. In the absence of an external disturbance, for instance an external current, a steady state will usually be reached where the sum of the rates of the cathodic reactions will equal the sum of the rates of the anodic reactions, viz., $\Sigma i_a = \Sigma i_c$. The electrode potential will assume some value, E_{MP}, which is designated the mixed potential, and the electrode is considered as a poly-electrode (11, 16, 17, 18).

The situation is depicted schematically in Fig. 3. When the metal exhibits the electrode potential E_{MP}, there is a net dissolution current i_{cor} which is given by:

$$i_{cor} = (i_a)_M - (i_c)_M = (i_c)_{H_2} - (i_a)_{H_2} \tag{15}$$

If only reactions (13a) and (13b) were possible, the reversible potential for the metal, E_{eq}^M, would be established; if only reactions (14a) and (14b) were possible, the reversible potential for hydrogen would be established. Since, however, both systems are able to react, dissolution will take place at the potential E_{MP}. The back reactions $(i_c)_M$ and $(i_a)_{H_2}$ are very low in most practical cases so that the curves B and D in Fig. 3 are usually omitted. The conventional corrosion diagram, introduced by U. R. Evans, results.

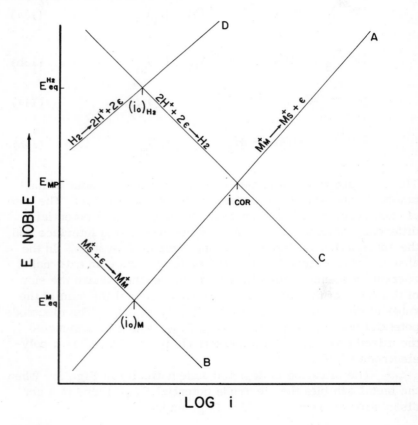

Fig. 3.   Mixed potential diagram for dissolution of a metal in an air free acid solution (schematic).

In more complicated cases several different electrode processes may occur simultaneously; the general principle, however, remains the same. The polyelectrode will exhibit a single mixed potential, E_{MP}, and the sum of all the rates for the anodic reactions will equal the sum of the rates for all the cathodic reactions (19).

The mixed potential-polyelectrode concept may be summarized as follows: there exists on the metal surface, which is undergoing dissolution, two or more statistically independent electrode reactions which are only related by the common electrical potential difference which exists between the metal and the solution. The emphasis is on currents flowing across the interface and the potential difference across the interface. Thus in many cases we need not assume the existence or the location of separate cathodic and anodic areas, as is usually true in the theory of local elements. However no distinction should be made between the mixed potential concept and the theory of local elements. The latter may be considered a special case under the former more general theory (20). It is not necessary to have separate macroscopic areas which are exclusively cathodic or anodic on a metallic surface in order for the dissolution process to proceed by an electrochemical mechanism, either operationally or conceptually. Any one site may be anodic during one instant of time and cathodic during another instant, and/or anodic and cathodic processes can occur simultaneously on atomically adjacent sites. The sites may also shift about the surface rapidly. These things must occur during uniform dissolution. The various surface sites may have atomic, microscopic and/or macroscopic dimensions. It is doubtful that any given part of a metallic surface is entirely anodic or cathodic on an average time basis unless some special condition exists such as a rectifying film or lack of a necessary reactant at the site in question.

As is well known, however, non-uniform corrosion under uniform or homogeneous solution conditions does occur so that the values of $(i_a)_M$ and/or $(i_c)_O$ can be larger at some surface sites than at others (21). These differences may arise from variations in composition and structure; heterogeneities due to composition may supply areas which are predominately cathodic or anodic depending upon the values of E_{eq}, i_o, α and β of the different reacting systems at the particular sites.

Galvanic couples is an extreme case. It has been suggested
that even on an apparent homogeneous surface of a pure metal
the Tafel constants i_o, α and β for a cathodic reaction will
vary over the surface (22).

This subject will be resumed in the discussion of anodic reactions. It should be emphasized here, however, that
the existence of separate macroscopic cathodic and anodic
areas is not the primary cause of corrosion, nor a requirement for the use of electrochemical concepts to describe the
process. The primary cause is the thermodynamic instability
of the metal in the solution; the mechanism involves the futile
attempt of the metal to establish an equilibrium potential for
the metal-metal ion reaction.

This more generalized theory has some important experimental and practical implications. In particular it allows
greater use of polarization data for the interpretation of corrosion phenomena and for the determination of the rate of corrosion during the corrosion process. For purposes of discussion we may designate this as the mixed potential technique.

Although the author believes that the generalized concept was originally responsible for the electrochemical treatment of corrosion processes by the early workers, it appears
that Hammett and Lorch (23) and Frumkin (24) were among the
first to specifically describe metallic dissolution according to
this concept. Wagner and Traud (16) showed that the electrode
kinetics for hydrogen evolution are not affected by the simultaneous dissolution of the metallic ions.

Frumkin and Kolotyrkin (25) have applied the concept
and techniques successfully to the dissolution of lead and
nickel in acids and iron in alkalies. The author (18, 26) has
shown that the dissolution of aluminum in acid and alkaline
solutions containing various oxidation-reduction systems behaves according to this principle. He also showed that the
rate of dissolution of aluminum, zinc and their alloys in various acid, neutral, and alkaline solutions may be obtained from
polarization data (27).

Stern (28) has given a detailed treatment of mixed potential techniques and has applied them to determine the corrosion rate of iron in acid solutions. Makrides et al (29) and

Gatos (30) have also used the methods for studying the dissolution of iron in acid media.

Heumann and Roschenbleck (31) have shown that the dissolution of active chromium and iron-chromium alloys follows the behavior predicted by the generalized theory and accounts for the dependence of the potential on pH.

3.2 Electrochemical Activity

The basic factors which determine the dissolution process may now be enumerated as follows:

(1) The thermodynamically reversible electrode potential, E_{eq}, for all possible electrode processes for the given conditions.

(2) The exchange current density for each redox system.

(3) The current-voltage characteristics, the polarization curve, for each possible reaction.

The first factor determines the tendency for dissolution to occur while the second and third, which are closely related, determine the rate of dissolution. The use of the standard electrode potentials as a measure of nobility is well known. The recognition that the exchange current density is a measure of the reversibility of a process and therefore a quantity characteristic of the reactivity of the system is more recent (13, 32). As indicated by the Tafel relations, the exchange current density is a direct measure of the rate of the electrode reaction for any given value of the activation overvoltage (33). The values of i_o may then be taken as a criterion for the electrochemical activity of a system.

The effect of $(i_o)_{H_2}$ on a given metal, M, is shown schematically in Fig. 4.   Curves A and B represent the anodic and cathodic Tafel lines for the metal, respectively. The curves C and D, and E and F show two possible sets of Tafel lines for the hydrogen reactions on the metal M. The former set corresponds to a lower value of $(i_o)_{H_2}$ than the latter. It will be seen that the value of the mixed potential and the corrosion current depend on the value $(i_o)_{H_2}$ and that i_{cor} increases as $(i_o)_{H_2}$ increases while the mixed potential becomes more

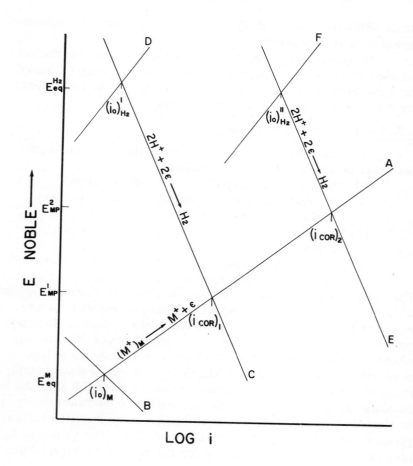

Fig. 4.   Effect of the exchange current on the mixed potential
          and corrosion current (schematic).

noble. A similar argument will readily show the effect of
$(i_o)_M$ on a corrosion process. Bockris (11) has presented analytical expressions for these effects.

Since aqueous solutions contain hydrogen ions, water
molecules, and generally oxygen, the measured electrode potential of metals will usually be a mixed potential. Taking the

reaction with hydrogen ions as a typical case, we find that the smaller the ratio $(i_o)_{H_2}/(i_o)_M$ the more nearly will the mixed potential correspond to the reversible potential of the metal in the given solution. Conversely the larger the ratio, the closer will the mixed potential correspond to the reversible hydrogen potential. In cases where both $(i_o)_{H_2}$ and $(i_o)_M$ are extremely small, the electrode potential may be predominately due to adsorbed ions, dipoles, etc., and will have no appreciable electromotive character.

If we neglect the back reactions $(i_a)_{H_2}$ and $(i_c)_M$, the curves in Fig. 5 show some possible mixed potential relations (34).

Piontelli (35) has classified metals according to three groups. The "normal" metals such as Pb, Hg, Tl, Cd, Zn, Sn; The "intermediate" metals such as Ag, Au, Cu, Bi, As, Sb; and the "inert" metals (Fe), Ni, Co, Rh, Pd, Pt, Cr, (Mn), (Ti).

The normal metals exhibit ionic exchange currents of about 10^{-3} amp/cm^2 or greater and a low hydrogen exchange current of about 10^{-12} amp/cm^2 or less. They yield fairly well defined reversible electrode potentials and in solutions 0.1M to 1.0M with respect to their ions, they behave according to Fig. 5(a).

The normal metals have low melting points and a predominately electrostatic type of bonding (long range and weak) and a large atomic volume. These factors may lead to a low and flat energy curve for the ionic work functions, Y_+ and W_+; hence to a low activation energy for ionic transitions.

The inert metals show very low ionic exchange currents (on the order of 10^{-10} amp/cm^2) but relatively high exchange currents for electron transitions. They behave therefore according to Fig. 5(b) and act as good reversible electrodes for many redox systems. Their electrode potential in many solutions is a function of the hydrogen ion concentration rather than of their own ions; $(i_o)_{H_2}$ is about 10^{-6} amp/cm^2 on these metals.

The inert metals have predominately a covalent type of bonding (strong but short range) a small atomic volume and a high melting point. These characteristics may well dictate a rather steep potential energy curve for ionic transitions with a resulting high activation energy.

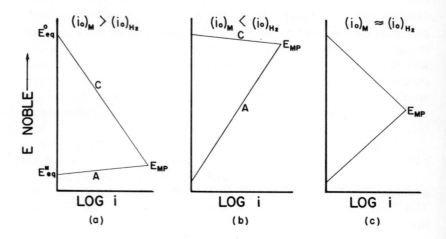

Fig. 5. Various types of mixed potential diagrams (schematic).

Fig. 6 shows schematically the two types of energy curves suggested here. It should be noted that the physical characteristics discussed above may affect the W_+ function as well as the Y_+ function. This is borne out by the experimentally observed high activation energy for both dissolution and deposition of the ions.

The intermediate metals fall into an intermediate position with respect to the factors discussed.

The electrochemical inertness (low values of $(i_o)_M$) seems to correlate with an incomplete electronic sub-shell in the free atom, high values of heat of solvation of the ions, small interatomic spacing in lattice, and high coordination numbers.

The discussion so far should have indicated the great importance of the polarization curves in determining the corrosion characteristics of metals. LaQue (36) has stressed this fact and reports extensive data on the deviation of corrosion potentials from the standard values. His values should correspond to the mixed potential discussed above. The important role of polarization functions has also been treated by Evans (34), Brown (37), Wesley (38), and Muller (39).

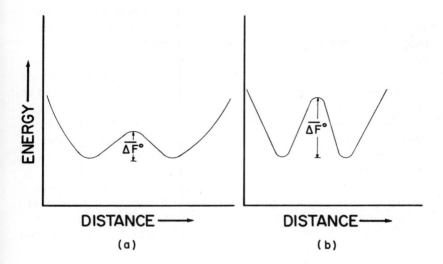

Fig. 6. Schematic potential energy-distance functions. (a)
"Shallow" work functions intersecting at a low point.
(b) "Steep" work functions intersecting at a high
point.

4. THE CATHODIC REACTION

The cathodic reactions for a given system are of major
importance in determining the extent and the course of dissolution. The most commonly encountered reactants are oxygen,
hydrogen ions, and water molecules. In some cases foreign
metallic ions and/or oxidizing agents such as ferric ion, nitric
acid, etc., may be present (30). These agents are of particular
importance in some accelerated corrosion tests (40).

The effect of oxidizing agents on metallic dissolution has
been studied rather extensively in recent years, particularly
with respect to passivity phenomena. Streicher (41) has made
a detailed study of such reactions on stainless steels. Evans
(42) has shown that metals such as Mg and Zn yield only hydrogen in dilute nitric acid but also nitrogen oxides in concentrated
acid. The noble metals yield chiefly the nitrogen oxides.

Hoar (43) discussed the important role of the cathodic reduction of oxygen in corrosion. Tomashov (44) and Delahay (45) have obtained the overvoltage characteristics for the reaction on a number of metals.

The reversible potential for the oxygen system in an air saturated solution varies from about +1.23v (hydrogen scale) at pH= 0 to about +0.40v in strong alkaline solutions. In neutral solution the potential is about +0.81v. It should not be necessary to consider reactions at more noble potentials than the above for most metals since $(i_o)_{O_2}$ is about 10^{-8} amp/cm^2 or less on their surface.

Although the effects of concentration polarization are not being considered in this discussion, it should be noted that the concentration of oxygen in air saturated solutions is very low and that the cathodic reaction may be subject to pronounced concentration polarization (46).

The kinetics of the hydrogen reduction reaction have received a great deal of attention by many investigators. It may be noted, however, that - as in the case of oxygen - the exchange current density $(i_o)_{H_2}$ is very low on most metals so that reactions at more noble values than the reversible potential may usually be neglected.

5. THE ANODIC REACTION

5.1 Activation Overvoltage

The anodic reaction, except for studies on passivity and the formation of thick anodic films, has hardly been studied. The actual mechanism of the anodic reaction prior to the onset of passivity demands greater attention. The electrochemical activity of the metallic ions may differ on different parts of a pure metal surface. The variations may be due to varying values of the ionic work function Y_+ and/or different shapes of the Morse-type functions of Y_+ and W_+. The activation energies ΔF_a and ΔF_c depend not only on the values of Y_+ and W_+ but also at what point the work functions cross. Therefore the "geometric" or steric relationship between the surface ions and the water molecules or other complexing agent are important.

It has been reported that the rate of dissolution and the reversible potential may differ for the various crystallographic planes (47, 48). It is very likely that local imperfections, zones of disarray (such as edges and corners of incompletely packed planes, emergent dislocations, etc.) may also be sites of higher activity (49, 50, 51).

Randles (13) has determined the activation energies for the metal-metal ion reaction for Tl, Cd, Pb, Zn, and Cu as amalgamated electrodes. He found values of about 6 to 10 kcal/mol, in general agreement with Piontelli's classification given above. These low values indicate that the potential energy curves for Y_+ and W_+ must be flat and cross at a low point as shown schematically in Fig. 6(a).

The effect of some anions in accelerating the anodic reaction may be due to their influence on the potential energy curves. In the work cited above Randles reports significant increases in the exchange currents in the presence of the halogen ions. For zinc the increase was in the order $Cl^- < Br^- < CNS^- < I^-$. He suggests that the increasing covalency of bonding between the surface metal ions and the adsorbed anion lowers the activation energy. This important anion effect, particularly the effect on selective surface sites as in pitting type corrosion, has also been studied by Streicher (52).

Piontelli (53) in discussing the effect of anions suggests that the deformable anions are drawn into the electric field at the surface and participate catalytically by forming a more reactive "activation complex."

Wesley (54) has suggested that the large overvoltage required for the dissolution of nickel, and perhaps other transition metals, may be due to the necessity for the electrons in the d-band of the metal to undergo rearrangement in order to form the complex aquo-ion in the solution.

5.2 Passivity

The adsorption of hydroxyl ions, oxygen ions, and oxygen atoms has an inhibitive effect on the anodic reaction. This effect is especially true when the metal oxide or hydroxide is insoluble under the given conditions. These ions and atoms tend to form tenacious bonds with the surface atoms of some metals and in many cases will grow as three dimensional films. The latter process is known to occur in many cases of "anodization" at relatively high potentials.

It is likely that a monolayer of such ions and/or atoms has the effect of increasing the ionic work function Y_+. Three-dimensional films, however, introduce a third phase and one must now consider transfer of ions from the metal to the film, through the film, and from the film to the solution. In some cases it is possible that the anodic current is primarily due to the transfer of anions in the reverse direction.

The potential energy-distance relations are shown schematically in Fig. 7. The three possibilities for the slow, rate controlling step may occur at the metal-film contact (A), in the film (B), or at the film-solution contact (C).

The Mott-Cabrera theory (55) or some modification of it (56) has apparently been successful in describing the mechanism of anodic formation of thick oxide films on the "valve-metals," Al, Ta, Nb, Zr, etc. The recent works of Johansen et al (57) and Petrocelli (58) are pertinent to this field.

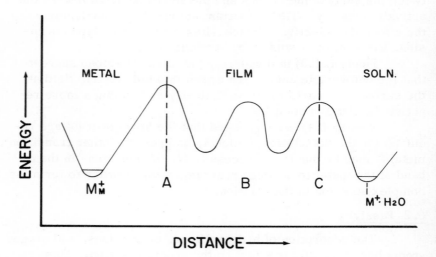

Fig. 7.   Schematic potential energy-distance curves for ionic transitions when film is present on metal surface.

In general the anodic reaction consists of the transfer of ions - in most cases the metallic ions - from the metal into the film and on through the film to the film-solution interface. The slow step postulated in the original theory was the transition from the metal into the oxide. The kinetic treatment accounted for the relation experimentally found between the current and voltage, e. g. :

$$i_a = \alpha \, e^{-\beta \, \Phi} \tag{16}$$

where Φ is the electric field which exists between the metal surface and the outer surface of the oxide.

It is very likely that the anodic process in the very thin passive films is of the same nature as that postulated in the Mott-Cabrera theory. Although the exact nature of the films responsible for passivity is still a controversial subject (59), there does appear to be ample evidence that the film is very thin (in the range 10-200 Å), compact, and non-porous (18, 57, 58, 59, 60, 61, 62).

Bonhoeffer, Vetter, and others (63) have made extensive studies on iron which indicate that the passive film is composed of one or more oxides of iron. Young (64), Vermilyea (65) and Johansen et al. (57) have shown that the Mott-Cabrera concepts are applicable for the thin films on Ta, Ti, Hf, and Hb. Petrocelli (58) has shown evidence that the dissolution of aluminum in sulfuric acid takes place through a thin film and that the process appears to follow the Mott-Cabrera theory. Stern (66) reports data indicating that the kinetics for the anodic oxidation of stainless steel are similar to those for aluminum and tantalum (67). Pryor (68) has recently reviewed the work on passive films on iron and suggests a single passive film of γ Fe_2O_3 which contains non-uniform defect concentrations. Cretella and Gatos (69) have shown that an oxide film (very likely GeO_2) is associated with the passivity of Ge in HNO_3.

The "Flade potential," the limiting potential at which film formation occurs, is discussed below; it appears to correspond to the thermodynamic reversible potential of the stoichiometric oxide in the case of several metals such as silver, platinum, and gold (70). In the case of iron and some other metals the differences are significant (63).

It is suggested that in many cases the film formation and subsequent ionic transfer are highly irreversible processes; the film is not a stoichiometric oxide but perhaps a quasi-oxygen-lattice with vacant interstitial positions for the metallic ions as suggested by Verwey (71). The slow step is perhaps the one originally postulated by Mott, the transfer of metallic ions into the film. That the metal dissolves in a higher valence state at the higher potentials (see below) may be due to the smaller radii of this ion, which allow it to penetrate more easily through the more resistant film present at these voltages.

The elucidation of the composition and physical properties of these films should continue to be a major objective in future investigations. The mechanism of formation - initiation and growth - deserves special attention. This area should be of particular importance in efforts to devise alloys which may be rendered passive in various environments.

Imperfections and crystallographic orientation at or near the metal surface must be influential in determining the properties of the film. It is highly probably that dislocations in the metal will cause imperfections in the film and/or influence the initiation and growth of the film. It is possible that the metallic dislocations are continued through the film and create active sites which may be responsible for pit initiation in the passive state. The formation of a compact and non-porous film may not be possible over some sites of disarrays. Since pitting type corrosion presents a very important problem, studies on pit initiation and pit growth deserve a great deal more investigation (52).

Some experimental data obtained in high temperature oxidation studies indicate that the above might be a fruitful field of investigation. Harris et al (72) have shown that the nucleation and growth of cuprous oxide on copper are closely related to dislocations in the metal. Gulbransen and Andrews (73) report data which indicate that the growth of oxide nuclei on iron is related to the number and arrangement of dislocations in the metal crystal.

In its simplest form the "modern" theory of passivity

is based on the following concepts. As may be deduced from the mixed potential-polyelectrode theory, the mechanism of the process of self-passivation is identical to that which occurs when a metal becomes anodically passive by the application of an external current. In the former case some electron acceptor in the solution removes electrons from the metal, while in the latter case an external battery removes them (58, 74, 75, 76, 77). It is interesting to note that this particular aspect of the theory was recognized as early as the late twenties (78).

A system composed of a given metal and solution at constant temperature has a limiting anodic current density, $(i_a)_L$, and a limiting electrode potential, E_L. When these are exceeded (potential becoming more noble) an insoluble film forms on the metal surface. The film allows the passage of a very low dissolution current and is maintained by a portion of this current. Fig. 8(a) shows a schematic anodic polarization curve obtained potentio-statically for the metal, M, in a given solution where the metallic deposition reaction is assumed to be negligible; E_{eq}^M is the reversible electrode potential and along the portion of the curve $\overline{AB}$ metal dissolves according to the usual activation overvoltage (Tafel line) behavior. At the limiting current density, $(i_a)_L$, and potential E_L, the film starts to form and the current density decreases to some low value at C.

The behavior along $\overline{CDE}$ varies according to the metal. The current density along $\overline{CD}$ remains fairly constant for metals such as iron, chromium and stainless steel as the potential increases; the metal continues to dissolve at 100 percent efficiency. Along $\overline{DE}$ the metals dissolve in their higher valence state but at low current efficiency, since evolution of oxygen, or other anodic reaction where possible, now occurs. The film which forms on these metals is apparently very thin and readily allows the transitions of electrons from the anion to the metal by conduction or the tunnel effect.

The metals such as Al, $\overline{Ta}$, Nb, etc., continue to react at 100 percent efficiency along $\overline{DE}$; the film generally increases in thickness and the oxidation of hydroxyl ion does not occur. Although it appears that the complete curves such as ABCDE have not been experienced for metals such as Al, it is believed

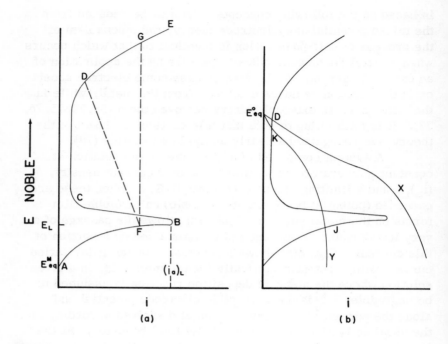

Fig. 8. (a) Schematic anodic polarization curve. (b) Polarization curves for self-passivation.

that these very active metals either go through the reaction
ABC very rapidly on immersion or else the stable air-formed
film already on the surface immediately situates them some-
where along CD.

    If the polarization curve is obtained under conditions of
constant current (galvanostatically) curves such as AFGE or
AFDE are usually obtained and it is found that the current-
voltage behavior is more time dependent. In many cases periodic fluctuations occur (34, 78). Since the potential is a multi-
valued function of the current, this behavior is readily understandable.

    Fig. 8(b) shows schematically the curves for the process
of self-passivation; X and Y represent two possible cathodic
polarization curves for an electron acceptor present in the

solution. In the case of curve X the limiting anodic current density, $(i_a)_L$, may be exceeded so that the film can form and the polyelectrode will assume the passive state exhibiting the mixed potential and corrosion current designated by point D.

On the other hand, the situation depicted by curve Y will not allow $(i_a)_L$ to be exceeded; the metal will not become passive but may assume the steady state condition at point J. However if the metal has been previously passivated by an air formed film or other means, it may be maintained in the passive condition shown by point K.

Stern (77) has recently discussed the mechanism of passivating-type inhibitors on the basis of the theory presented here. He points out that passivity may be accounted for operationally by anodic polarization phenomena irrespective of whether films are assumed to be responsible (79). This approach was also suggested by Mears (80). Tomashov (76) has proposed the use of the ratio of the extent of anodic polarization, E_{eq}^M - E_{MP} to the extent of the cathodic polarization, E_{eq}^o - E_{MP} at the mixed potential as a passivity factor. The greater the factor the higher degree of passivity. In this way he has classified the metals in a given solution according to their tendency to show passive behavior.

Recent work on the anodic protection of metals both by means of external current and local galvanic action is a direct application of the principles discussed here (81).

References

1. M. J. N. Pourbaix, Thermodynamics of Dilute Aqueous Solutions, p. 44, Edward Arnold and Co., 1949.
2. P. Van Rysselberghe, Electrochemical Affinity, Hermann & Cie, 1955; J. C. Warner, Trans. Electrochem. Soc., 83, 319 (1943).
3. J. A. V. Butler, Electrocapillarity, Chemical Publishing Co., Inc., 1940; Trans. Faraday Soc., 28, 379 (1932); N. K. Adam, The Physics and Chemistry of Surfaces, p. 300, Oxford University Press, 1941; R. W. Gurney and R. H. Fowler, Proc. Roy. Soc., A, 136, 378 (1932); Ions in Solution, Cambridge University Press, 1936.

4. F. H. MacDougall, Thermodynamics and Chemistry, p. 348, John Wiley and Sons, 1939.
5. R. Parsons, in J. O'M. Bockris, ed., Modern Aspects of Electrochemistry, p. 103, Butterworths Scientific Publications, 1954.
6. E. Lange, Z. Elektrochem., 55, 76 (1951).
7. W. J. Kieffer, J. Chem. Educ., 27, 659 (1950).
8. R. Piontelli, J. Inst. Metals, 80, 99 (1951-52).
9. W. M. Latimer, Oxidation Potentials, 2nd ed., Prentice-Hall, Inc., 1952.
10. G. E. Kimball, J. Chem. Phys., 8, 199 (1940); H. Eyring, S. Glasstone and K. J. Laidler, ibid., 7, 1053 (1939); H. Eyring, L. Marker and Ting-Chang Kwoh, J. Phys.& Colloid Chem., 53, 1453 (1949).
11. J. O'M. Bockris, in J. O'M. Bockris, ed., Modern Aspects of Electrochemistry, p. 180, Butterworths Scientific Publications, 1954.
12. R. Audubert, Discussions Faraday Soc., 1947, 72.
13. J. E. B. Randles, Trans. Faraday Soc., 48, 828, 937, 951 (1952).
14. R. Parsons and J. O'M. Bockris, Trans. Faraday Soc., 47, 914 (1951).
15. J. V. Petrocelli, J. Electrochem. Soc., 98, 187 (1951).
16. C. Wagner and W. Traud, Z. Elektrochem., 44, 391 (1938).
17. I. M. Kolthoff and C. S. Miller, J. Am. Chem. Soc., 62, 2171 (1940).
18. J. V. Petrocelli, J. Electrochem. Soc., 97, 10 (1950).
19. N. D. Tomashov, Doklady Akad. Nauk S. S. S. R., 30, 621 (1941).
20. A. N. Frumkin, Trudy Soveshchaniya Elektrokhim., Akad. Nauk S. S. S. R., Otdel. Khim. Nauk, 1950, 21 (1953).
21. M. A. Streicher, J. Electrochem. Soc., 106, 161 (1959).
22. W. R. Busing and W. Kauzmann, J. Chem. Phys., 20, 1129 (1952).
23. L. P. Hammett and A. E. Lorch, J. Am. Chem. Soc., 54, 2128 (1932).
24. A. N. Frumkin, Z. physik. Chem. (Leipzig), A, 160, 116 (1932).
25. A. N. Frumkin and Ya. Kolotyrkin, Acta Physicochim. U. R. S. S., 14, 469 (1941); Compt. rend. acad. sci.

U. R. S. S., 33, 445, 450 (1941); Zhur. Fiz. Khim., 15, 346 (1941); Ya. Kolotyrkin, ibid., 21, 581 (1947); 25, 1248 (1951).

26. J. V. Petrocelli, J. Electrochem. Soc., 98, 183 (1951); 99, 513 (1952).
27. J. V. Petrocelli, Trans. Electrochem. Soc., 85, 257 (1944).
28. M. Stern, J. Electrochem. Soc., 102, 663, 609 (1955); 104, 56, 559 (1957); M. Stern and R. M. Roth, ibid., 104, 390 (1957).
29. A. C. Makrides, N. M. Komodromos and N. Hackerman, J. Electrochem. Soc., 102, 363 (1955).
30. H. C. Gatos, J. Electrochem. Soc., 103, 286 (1956); Corrosion, 12, 322 (1956).
31. T. Heumann and B. Roschenbleck, Werkstoffe u. Korrosion 9, No. 6, 383 (1958).
32. H. Gerischer, Z. Elektrochem., 54, 362 (1950); F. P. Bowden and J. N. Agar, Ann. Repts. on Progr. Chem. Chem. Soc. London, 35, 90 (1938).
33. B. E. Conway and J. O'M. Bockris, Plating, 46, 371 (1958).
34. U. R. Evans, Metallic Corrosion Passivity and Protection, Longmans, Green and Co., 1948.
35. R. Piontelli, J. chim. phys., 45, 115 (1948); in International Committee of Electrochemical Thermodynamics and Kinetics, pp. 163, 185, Butterworths Scientific Publications, 1950; Z. Elektrochem., 55, 128 (1951); Chem. & Ind. London, 1957, 1304.
36. F. L. LaQue, Edgar Marburg Lecture, Am. Soc. Testing Materials, Proc., 1951, 1.
37. R. H. Brown, Trans. Electrochem. Soc., 74, 495 (1938); R. H. Brown, G. C. English and R. D. Williamson, Corrosion, 6, 186 (1950).
38. W. A. Wesley, Am. Soc. Testing Materials, Proc., 1940, 21.
39. W. J. Muller, Trans. Electrochem. Soc., 76, 167 (1939).
40. W. L. Pinner, Plating, 44, 763 (1957).
41. M. A. Streicher, J. Electrochem. Soc., 106, 161 (1959).
42. U. R. Evans, Trans. Faraday Soc., 40, 120 (1944).
43. T. P. Hoar, Trans. Electrochem. Soc., 76, 157 (1939).

44. N. D. Tomashov, Compt. rend. acad. sci. U.R.S.S., 52 601 (1946); Light Metals, 10, 637 (1947); 11, 8, 104, 155, 388, 503 (1948).
45. P. Delahay, J. Electrochem. Soc., 97, 198, 205 (1950).
46. C. V. King, J. Electrochem. Soc., 102, 693 (discussion) (1955).
47. W. Tragert and W. Robertson, J. Electrochem. Soc., 102, 86 (1955).
48. H. Leidheiser and A. T. Gwathmey, Trans. Electrochem. Soc., 91, 97 (1947).
49. R. Piontelli and G. Serravalle, Z. Elektrochem., 62, 759 (1958).
50. T. P. Hoar and R. D. Holliday, J. Appl. Chem., 3, 502 (1953).
51. R. B. Mears, J. Electrochem. Soc., 106, 467 (1959).
52. M. A. Streicher, J. Electrochem. Soc., 103, 375 (1956).
53. R. Piontelli, Z. Elektrochem., 55, 128 (1951).
54. W. A. Wesley, Hothersall Memorial Lecture, Trans. Inst. Metal Finishing, 33, 1 (1956).
55. N. J. Mott, Trans. Faraday Soc., 43, 429 (1947); N. Cabrera and N. J. Mott, Repts. Progr. in Phys., 12, 164 (1948-49).
56. J. J. Dewald, J. Electrochem. Soc., 102, 1 (1955); J. Phys. Chem. Solids, 2, 55 (1957); P. Van Rysselberghe and H. Johansen, J. Electrochem. Soc., 106, 355 (1959).
57. H. A. Johansen, G. B. Adams, Jr. and P. Van Rysselberghe, J. Electrochem. Soc., 104, 339 (1957).
58. J. V. Petrocelli, J. Electrochem. Soc., 106, 566 (1959).
59. U. R. Evans, Z. Elektrochem., 62, 619 (1958); H. H. Uhlig, ibid., 61, 700 (1958); N. Hackerman, ibid., 62, 632 (1958); Ya. Kolotyrkin, ibid., 62, 664 (1958); W. H. Wade and N. Hackerman, Trans. Faraday Soc., 53, (1957).
60. U. R. Evans, Nature, 168, 853 (1951).
61. T. P. Hoar and U. R. Evans, J. Electrochem. Soc., 99, 212 (1952).
62. D. M. Sowards and N. Hackerman, J. Electrochem. Soc., 102, 297 (1955).

63. K. F. Bonhoeffer and H. Gerischer, Z. Elektrochem., 52, 149 (1948); U. F. Franck and K. G. Weil, ibid., 56, 814 (1952); K. J. Vetter, ibid., 55, 274, 278, 675 (1951); 56, 16, 106 (1952); 58, 230 (1954); 59, 67 (1955); K. G. Weil and K. F. Bonhoeffer, Z. physik. Chem. (Frankfurt), 4, 175 (1955); M. Cohen, Can. J. Chem., 37, 286 (1959).
64. L. Young, Trans. Faraday Soc., 51, 1250 (1955).
65. D. A. Vermilyea, J. Electrochem. Soc., 101, 389 (1954).
66. M. Stern, J. Electrochem. Soc., 106, 376 (1959).
67. See also Ref. (61).
68. M. J. Pryor, J. Electrochem. Soc., 106, 557 (1959).
69. M. C. Cretella and H. C. Gatos, J. Electrochem. Soc., 105, 492 (1958).
70. A. Hickling and D. Taylor, Discussions Faraday Soc., 1947 277; A. Hickling, Trans. Faraday Soc., 41, 333 (1945); 42, 518 (1946).
71. E. J. Verwey, Physica, 2, 1059 (1935).
72. W. W. Harris, F. L. Ball and A. T. Gwathmey, Acta Met., 4, 153 (1956).
73. E. A. Gulbransen and K. J. Andrews, J. Electrochem. Soc., 106, 511 (1959).
74. N. D. Tomashov, Uspekhi Khim., 24, No. 4, 453 (1955).
75. T. H. Heumann and W. Rosener, Z. Elektrochem., 57, (1953); C. Edeleanu, Metallurgia, 50, 113 (1954); V. P. Batrakov, Doklady Akad. Nauk S.S.S.R., 5, 797 (1954).
76. N. D. Tomashov, Z. Elektrochem., 61, 717 (1958); Corrosion, 14, 229 (1958).
77. M. Stern, J. Electrochem. Soc., 105, 638 (1958).
78. E. S. Hedges, Protective Films on Metals, p. 165, D. Van Nostrand and Co. Inc., 1932.
79. See also M. A. Streicher, Corrosion, 14, 59 (1958).
80. R. B. Mears, Trans. Electrochem. Soc., 95, 1 (1949).
81. C. Edeleanu, J. Iron Steel Inst. London, 186, 122 (1958); W. R. Buck and H. Leidheiser, Nature, 181, 1681 (1958).

DISCUSSION

H. GERISCHER (Max Planck Institute): I would like to
comment on the method of presentation of corrosion data.
Dr. Petrocelli has used one extreme in plotting all the data on
logarithmic scales. This implies that all the reactions follow
Tafel's equation. Often, corrosion investigators follow the
other extreme by assuming that all reactions vary linearly with
voltage. Generally there are several reaction steps involved.
Thus, the usual situation would be intermediate between the
two extremes, the actual curve being governed by the rate
determining step. In brief, one cannot give a single method that
would be applicable for all corrosion systems.

J. V. PETROCELLI: I most certainly agree with your
comment. I pointed out that my presentation was oversimpli-
fied, and I am glad that you brought this up. One must know
the exact polarization curves for each system. There have
been several systems reported in the literature, however, that
fit Tafel plots very closely.

C. V. KING

New York University

Dissolution of Metals

ABSTRACT

IN REAGENTS WHICH form only soluble, non-adsorbed products, metals often dissolve at first-order rates controlled by convective-diffusion currents in electrode processes. Empirical and theoretical aspects of the "diffusion layer" are discussed, as well as practical methods of correlating rate constants with stirring speed, diffusion coefficients, solution viscosity and density.

Factors which cause deviations from standard transport-controlled kinetics are discussed. Some of these are: Surface roughness of the metal samples; adsorption of reaction products; a slow intermediate stage in the dissolution; and conditions which cause the metal to assume a passive potential.

1. INTRODUCTION

Dissolution from clean metal surfaces to form soluble products is discussed here, although in many cases films of known or of unknown nature may influence the dissolution

357

process. The rates vary from extremely small values to a limiting upper value fixed by the speed with which the reagent can reach the metal surface. The speed is determined by the characteristic rate of fluid flow, which depends on the type and speed of stirring and on the diffusion coefficient of the reagent in the particular solution. These factors have been discussed in detail by Bircumshaw and Riddiford (1) and will be reviewed briefly. Transport of reagents at electrodes is essentially the same problem and has been discussed by Tobias, Eisenberg, and Wilke (2).

2. DISSOLUTION RATES

Metal dissolution rates fall into one of three classes, as first pointed out by Van Name and Hill (3):

(1) The chemical process at the metal surface is slow, no appreciable concentration gradient exists, and the observed rate is that of the surface process, whatever its mechanism.

(2) The chemical process is so fast that convection and diffusion cannot maintain an appreciable concentration of reagent at the interface. The observed rate is that of transport to the surface.

(3) The two rates are of the same magnitude; a concentration gradient is formed, but the reagent concentration does not fall to a negligible value at the interface.

The simplest rate equation for case (1) is:

$$dn/dt = k_1 A c \qquad (1)$$

where dn/dt may be moles or equivalents dissolving per unit time, k_1 is the chemical rate constant, A the surface area and c the reagent concentration. This equation assumes the rate to be first order with respect to the reagent and ignores mechanism (e. g. an intermediate adsorption). It also ignores the problem of roughness, i. e. , the ratio of true to projected area, and the possible change in roughness as dissolution proceeds. The progress of rate with time depends on the solution volume, but k_1 is independent of the volume.

For case (2) it is customary to assume an "effective

thickness" δ of the Nernst layer and apply Fick's law for
linear diffusion:

$$dn/dt = D A c/\delta \tag{2}$$

where D is the diffusion coefficient. For a given set of conditions this may be written as:

$$dn/dt = k_2 A c \tag{2a}$$

The area A is now the projected area, at least if the roughness
is small.

In case (3) it is considered that the concentration falls
to c_s (s for surface) at the interface. The chemical rate may
be equated to the rate of diffusive transport through the gradient
$(c - c_s)$:

$$dn/dt = k_1 A c_s = k_2 A (c - c_s)$$

If the difference in effective areas is neglected or incorporated
into k_1, then

$$\frac{dn}{dt} = \frac{k_1 k_2 A c}{k_1 + k_2} = k_3 A c \tag{3}$$

Since equations (1), (2a), and (3) are formally the same,
it is necessary to find criteria to distinguish the three cases.
This is possible because δ varies so much with stirring speed,
and the diffusion coefficient D is affected by viscosity while the
parameters in chemical rates usually are not. Different metals
dissolve at the same rate in the same solution if the rate is
controlled by convection-diffusion. The activation energy of
diffusive transport, as measured from temperature coefficients,
is normally much lower than the activation energy of chemical
processes (3000-6000 cal/mole compared to 10,000-20,000
cal/mole, although some chemical reactions do have lower
values).

Usually the experimental apparatus can be calibrated in
terms of transport-controlled reactions and the rate constant

k_2 established. If a smaller value of k is found for another reaction, it indicates the presence of a slower process. The
table below gives data for the dissolution of various metals in
solutions containing excess acid and a small amount of p-
benzoquinone (4). The rate constant k corresponds to reduction
of the quinone. Evidently an average value of 0. 85 represents
the transport-controlled rate; some of the reactions were first-
order throughout, others fell off with time because products
blocked the surface.

Acid Solution	Metal	k, cm/min
0.1M HCl, 0.05M glycine	Cd	0.88
0.03M HCl, 0.07M KH phthalate	Cd	0.82
0.1M HAc, 0.1M NaAc (etate)	Cd	0.82*
0.1M HAc, 0.1M NaAc	Pb	0.86
0.1M HAc, 0.1M NaAc	Sn	0.0
0.1M HCl	Sn	0.86*
2.0M HCl	Sn	1.71
0.1M HAc, 0.1M NaAc	Cu	0.244

*from initial rate

Reduction of 0. 0035 M p-Benzoquinone at 25° C by
Metal Cylinders Rotating with Peripheral Speed of
20, 000 cm/min.

In a buffer with pH = 4. 7, Sn dissolved at a negligible rate. In
2M HCl the quinone was reduced at twice the normal rate, due
to oxidation of Sn^{++} to Sn^{+4} after leaving the metal surface.
Reaction with Cu was first order but much slower, and inser-
tion of k_2 = 0. 85, k_3 = 0. 244 in Equation (3) gives k_1 = 0. 34
cm/min, based on the apparent area.

2.1 Depolarizers

Metal dissolution requires an anodic and a cathodic process (Petrocelli, this volume). Most active metals, when pure,
are not good catalysts for the cathodic reaction

$$2H^+ + 2e^- \rightarrow H_{2(gas)}$$

and dissolution in acid is limited by the rate of H_2 evolution. The potential of the metal is usually more noble than its reversible value and is said to be "polarized." Many oxidants which require H^+ for reduction react freely at the otherwise polarized surface, and are called "depolarizers." An example is:

$$Zn - 2e^- \rightarrow Zn^{++} \qquad \text{anodic}$$

$$H_2O_2 + 2H^+ + 2e^- \rightarrow 2H_2O \qquad \text{cathodic}$$

Such reactions have been used in organic synthesis for many years, as in the reduction of nitro-compounds by metal and acid. It was formerly thought that the surface was polarized by H-atoms and that these were removed by the depolarizer:

$$H_2O_2 + 2H \rightarrow 2H_2O$$

This mechanism is kinetically indistinguishable from others. Often dissolution is controlled by the transport rate of either the acid or the depolarizer, whichever is not present in excess (5). The relative concentrations of the control changes depend on the diffusion coefficients as well as the effective reaction equivalents per mole of oxidant. Oxidizing agents which do not require H^+ for reduction, such as Fe^{+3}, Ce^{+4}, Cr^{+3} are sometimes called depolarizers, but the role of acid in the dissolution is secondary in these cases.

3. TRANSPORT-CONTROLLED RATES

The Nernst theory (6) originally assumed a linear concentration gradient in a stagnant layer of solution at the interface, the thickness δ of which depended on the rate of stirring. It is now considered that the concentration gradient is not linear; there is a region near the interface in which transport is essentially all due to diffusion, but outside of this is a region of "eddy diffusion" in which there is some mixing as well as some diffusion. If stirring is very weak, as with natural convection only, concentration gradients may extend through much of the solution. In most cases it is convenient to make use of equation (2), considering δ as the thickness of a linear gradient which would allow for the diffusion rate found in practice.

Since the diffusion coefficient can be measured, the prediction of transport-controlled dissolution rates depends on a calculation of δ, which is itself a function of D, as well as of stirring rate and viscosity. A complete solution of this problem has been obtained in only one case by Levich (7): that of an ideal rotating disk under non-turbulent conditions. The derivation was made for electrode processes, but is equally applicable to dissolution, heat transfer and other heterogeneous processes.

Consider one side of a disk whose diameter is large compared to δ, rotating in a large vessel of liquid. Since liquid rotates with the disk and acquires a radial as well as an angular motion, it must also flow toward the face of the disk. The velocity of the perpendicular flow can be considered independent of distance except very near the disk. The distance at which flow becomes essentially parallel to the disk can be called the hydrodynamic boundary layer thickness. The distance at which a concentration gradient begins was calculated by Levich (7) to be

$$\delta' = 1.805 \, D^{1/3} \, \nu^{1/6} \, \omega^{-1/2}$$

where ν is the kinematic viscosity (viscosity / density) and ω is the angular speed of rotation. Levich found, as an approximation, that $\delta = 0.8934 \, \delta'$. A better approximation is (8)

$$\delta = [0.8934 + 0.316 \, (D/\nu)^{0.36}] \, \delta'$$

Since in the usual aqueous solution D/ν is about 10^{-3}, the correction term is about 3%.

The Levich approximation gives the rate equation

$$k = 0.620 \, D^{2/3} \, \nu^{-1/6} \, \omega^{1/2} \tag{4}$$

The corresponding equation for transport-controlled electrolysis has been tested several times, but the results will not be discussed here. Riddiford and Bircumshaw (9) found equation

(4) to apply fairly well to the dissolution of Zn in I_2 - KI solutions in the speed range 5-21 radians/sec, using thin metal plates rotated on a glass holder. Gregory and Riddiford (8), using carefully prepared Zn disks 5.3 cm in diameter, in the speed range 73-292 rpm, at temperatures 20° - 45°, found excellent agreement with the corrected equation. It is of interest that the boundary layer thickness is independent of distance from the axis of rotation. Gregory and Riddiford found that a smooth mounting stud at the center of the disk had no appreciable effect on the dissolution rate.

Many investigators have measured dissolution rates using rotating cylinders. The method has the advantage that all parts of the surface move with equal velocity, but it has not yet been possible to calculate δ as a function of rotational speed. If the liquid were in true viscous flow about an infinitely long cylinder there would be no flow toward or away from the surface, hence no effect of rotation. In practice there is some turbulence at the lowest velocity, and it increases to the highest speeds which have been used. In general it can be assumed that the reagent concentration is uniform throughout, except within a thin film at the metal surface. Due to the irregular motion and pressure fluctuations there is certain to be some "eddy diffusion," but in the film next to the metal diffusion must account for all the transport. It is therefore possible to use an effective thickness δ for the boundary layer.

3.1 Dimensionless Group Analysis

The transport rate per unit area $\dot{n}$ may be expressed as a function of the variables which affect it (10):

$$\dot{n} = f \ (U, \ell, \ D, \ \nu, \ c)$$

where U is the characteristic velocity (as the peripheral speed of a cylinder) and ℓ is the characteristic length (cylinder diameter). The rate may be expected to be proportional to each variable to some power, the exponent of c being unity. For the present purpose the variables may be arranged in three dimensionless groups:

Nusselt (or Sherwood) number, $Nu = \dot{n}\ell/Dc$

Reynolds number, $Re = U\ell/\nu$

Prandtl (or Schmidt) number, $Pr = \nu/D$

The rate may be expressed by the relation:

$$\frac{\dot{n}\ell}{Dc} = B\left(\frac{u\ell}{\nu}\right)^a\left(\frac{\nu}{D}\right)^b \quad \text{or} \quad Nu = B\,(Re)^a\,(Pr)^b \tag{5}$$

where the constant B and the exponents a and b must be determined by experiment.

While equation (5) is empirical and incomplete, it has been found to apply within experimental error over a wide range of the variables in problems of dissolution and other mass transfer as well as heat transfer (with appropriate changes). In many dissolution experiments with rotating cylinders in baffled solutions, $\dot{n}$ has been found proportional to U, except at the lowest rotational speeds (5, 11). If the exponent a is unity, $\dot{n}$ is independent of ℓ, which agrees with experiment (5). Without baffling a may be smaller. The dissolution rate of Mg cylinders in HCl solutions, up to a peripheral speed of 27, 800 cm/min, was measured by Roald and Beck (12). Above 3500 cm/min $\dot{n}$ was proportional to $U^{0.71}$. The authors suggested that the power on U may increase to an upper limit of unity in well-baffled solutions. They found that hydrogen evolution increased the dissolution rate if sufficiently vigorous, i. e. above a definite acid concentration for each value of U. A certain alloy which became very rough dissolved at a faster rate.

Eisenberg, Tobias and Wilke (13) have studied the rate of a transport-controlled process at smooth cylindrical electrodes carefully centered in sealed cylindrical cells. Limiting current densities were proportional to $(U/\ell)^{0.70}$ up to peripheral speeds of about 26, 000 cm/min. The rate then depends on cylinder diameter as well as on peripheral speed, which may be due to the nature of the turbulence without baffles, or to the smoothness of the cylinders (see below). With many types of stirring, the exponent, a, varies from 0. 4 to 0. 8. In the dissolution of thin wires mounted near a rotating 2-cm grooved bakelite cylinder, the effect of changing the rotational speed from 2000-4000 rpm was rather small (14). Heat transfer from a thin Pt wire to water and sucrose solutions, in the same apparatus, has been expressed by the relation (15)

$$Nu = 9.1 \, (Re)^{0.41} \, (Pr)^{0.40}$$

although it is doubtful if the values of Re chosen are significant. In their work on dissolution of Zn in I_2 solutions, with coupons mounted on a rotating glass holder, Riddiford and Bircumshaw (16) found the relation

$$Nu = 0.558 (Re)^{0.56} \, (Pr)^{0.27}$$

The Levich theory gives 0.50 and 0.33 for the exponents.

When the dissolution rate is proportional to U, it is convenient to put equation (5) in the form

$$k_2 = B \, U \, (D/\nu)^{1-b} \tag{6}$$

For example, data for a variety of systems collected by King (17) are represented within the experimental error by

$$k_2 = 0.010 \, U \, (D/\nu)^{0.83} \, cm/min$$

These data were for cylinders with U = 18, 800 cm/min. For Mg cylinders in various acids (18) with U = 2000 cm/min, better agreement is found with 1-b = 0.70 and B = 0.011. The temperature was not varied and ν was considered constant.

In an ingenious ultramicroscopic study of the components of turbulent flow near a pipe wall, Fage and Townend (19) showed that a film of liquid at the wall possesses a small degree of jerky, laminar flow, while the v - component normal to the interface falls to very small values. To account for the exponential variation of k_2 with D, King (11b) assumed that v might be proportional to a small power, say the cube, of the distance d (Fig. 1):

$$v = a \, d^3$$

Since there is no net flow of liquid toward the interface, v must have the same (negative) value in the opposite direction.

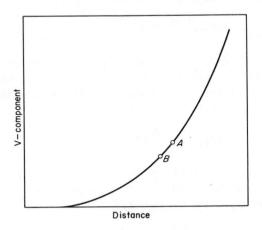

Fig. 1.   Possible relation of v - component of turbulence with distance at surface of rotating cylinder.

Assuming that outside the point A in Fig. 1 the reagent concentration is uniform, while inside the point B, v is too small to contribute appreciably to transport, reagent must reach the surface by diffusion. Between A and B there is eddy diffusion, and the effective thickness δ lies in this region. Consequently we can write

$$k_2 = D/\delta \ = a\delta^3$$

from which

$$k_2 = a' \, D^{3/4}$$

If experiment shows that the exponent must be 2/3, it must be assumed that $v = a \, d^2$, etc. In any case δ is not independent of D as the Nernst theory originally assumed.

3.2 Surface Roughness

Roughness can be ignored if the height of surface irregularities is small compared to δ . Enough roughness can decrease the critical Reynolds number for onset of turbulence; or with the rotating cylinder the increased friction factor leads to increased turbulence at a given U, with corresponding decrease in δ . Equation (5) can be modified by multiplying the right side by a dimensionless term $(h/\ell)^d$, where h is the average height of surface irregularities and d is a fractional constant, but this is not very satisfactory if ℓ is only involved in fixing U, as in the systems discussed above.

Makrides and Hackerman (20) have studied the dissolution of steel cylinders in 2M HCl with low concentrations of ferric chloride, benzoquinone and toluquinone as depolarizers. The specific rate at a given U increased as the surface became etched, reaching a steady value in a short time. The authors suggest an equation of the form

$$k_2 = (1.25 + 5.76 \log \ell/h)^{-2} U(Pr)^{-0.644}$$

which is based on the equation of Theodorsen and Regier (21) for the friction factor at rough surfaces, above the critical Reynolds number. However, the rates found were about three times as high as calculated at high rotational speeds, even with values of h which seem unreasonably large. The authors suggested that the linear relation between k_2 and U is due to surface roughness, and that the increased area due to roughness cannot be ignored.

Abramson and King (22) found that etched Fe cylinders dissolved somewhat faster than cylinders which were polished with fine abrasive paper between runs. The following experiment with a Ni cylinder illustrates the effect of progressive roughening (23). A cylinder 1.9 x 2.52 cm, cut from a rolled anode bar, was rotated at U = 18,000 cm/min in 400 ml of deaerated solution containing 1M HCl and 0.05M $FeCl_3$. Weight losses in consecutive three-minute periods were:

Time period: 1   2   3   4   5   6   7   8

Wt. loss, mg: 25.6 27.9 31.4 35.4 39.6 40.5 42.5 45.6

In the last three minutes the rate was 1.8 times the initial rate, although almost half of the ferric ion had been reduced. The roughness partly took the form of irregular grooves along the cylinder, which was in the direction of rolling of the anode bar. Annealed Ni cylinders became even rougher, with preferential dissolution around grain boundaries. While dissolution is obviously transport-controlled, it is evident that roughness increases the rate of transport, and also that the anodic and cathodic processes may be widely separated.

In the displacement of Cu from $CuSO_4$ by Zn and Cd, and of Ag from $AgNO_3$ by Zn and Cu (24), rates were found as high as eight times the values expected by comparison with dissolution from smooth cylinders. This was ascribed to enhanced transport by local cell electrolysis, but much of the effect was probably due to roughness caused by the metal deposit. With Zn in 2.5×10^{-6} M $AgNO_3$ (followed by radiotracer technique) the rate was not abnormal; of course very little Ag was deposited.

Johnson and McDonald (25) studied the rate of dissolution of sodium from cylinders in liquid ammonia at -40^0. This process is controlled by diffusion of Na from a saturated film at the surface, and was found to be kinetically first order. The rate was linear with U up to 9500 cm/min, except at low speeds. The authors found that the surface becomes rough very quickly.

3.3 Experimental Methods

Since the flow of liquid determines the interfacial transport rate, it is important to have exactly reproducible conditions of stirring if dissolution rates are to be compared. The rotating cylinder method is rather flexible; the vessel containing the solution can be of almost any size or shape, and the cylinders of any convenient diameter. Care should be taken to avoid end effects. If baffle plates are placed extremely close to the rotating cylinder the dissolution rates are increased at the same value of U; there is a pronounced effect if a thin scraper of light rubber is applied to the cylinder, especially at low speeds (26).

Most work on dissolution rates has been done with other experimental arrangements. The classical work of Van Name and his co-workers (3), showed that Zn, Cd, Fe, Ni, Co, Sn, Cu, Hg dissolve at essentially the same rate in identical I_2 - KI solutions; those metals which dissolve cleanly in dilute chromic acid with H_2SO_4, dissolve at the same rate. They used stationary metal disks mounted carefully near the ends of glass stirrer blades, and found the rate proportional to an average 4/5 power of rpm. Bircumshaw and Riddiford (27) used coupons mounted on glass rotors, finding that the leading edges dissolved somewhat faster than the trailing edges (Levich showed that δ increases with distance from the leading edge as corroding solution flows over a flat plate). Many variations of the arrangements mentioned have been used. Most of them have the disadvantage that far less turbulence is established at a given rpm than with rotating cylinders.

It would be helpful if various workers would adopt a few standard experimental arrangements, since the value of δ and its variation with D and ν could quickly be determined for each technique. An alternative would be to run a known reaction with each new method of stirring, thus establishing an "apparatus constant." Sometimes a knowledge of δ is useful in determining the mechanism of a reaction. For example, in the dissolution of Cu in O_2-saturated NH_3 solutions, studied by Halpern (28), the overall reaction is

$$Cu + 4NH_3 + 1/2\, O_2 + H_2O \rightarrow Cu\,(NH_3)_4^{++} + 2\,OH^-$$

With excess NH_3 the rate appears to be controlled by diffusive transport of O_2 to the Cu surface, and it is postulated that the first step in dissolution is the rapid chemisorption of oxygen (or possibly formation of oxide). The second step is the reaction with NH_3 and H_2O, and we may ask whether $Cu\,(NH_3)_2^+$ is formed and diffuses away to be oxidized mostly outside the diffusion layer, or whether $Cu\,(NH_3)_4^{++}$ is formed at the interface. In the first case each O_2 molecule reaching the surface accounts for 4 Cu atoms, in the second case, for only 2 Cu atoms.

We may choose from Halpern's data a numerical value of 27 mg Cu/cm^2-hr dissolved at 2 atm O_2 pressure (Fig. 4 of ref. 28), representing 2.1×10^{-4} moles O_2 reaching the surface if Cu^{++} is formed at once. The solubility of O_2 at 2 atm and 26^{0} is 2.5×10^{-6} moles $/cm^3$ (assuming that NH_3 does not affect it), and D for O_2 is 9.4×10^{-2} cm^2/hr (29). Inserting these values in equation (2), we find δ = 1.1×10^{-3} cm. However, if Cu^+ is formed initially, δ = 2.2×10^{-3} cm. It is impossible to tell which of these values is correct for the stirring speed used, but it would be quite easy to calibrate the apparatus with a known reaction.

Dietz and Halpern (30) have studied the dissolution of Ag in O_2-saturated NaCN solutions. With excess cyanide, O_2 is rate-controlling, and vice versa. The authors decided that the rate is determined by transport of oxygen or cyanide and not by chemical processes. The apparatus was similar to that used in the dissolution of Cu discussed above, but a different and less effective stirring blade was used. In the region of O_2 control, calculation as above gives δ = 0.013 cm if the correct mole ratio is $O_2/4$ Ag. However, the authors suggested that H_2O_2 is formed, and if this is quantitative the correct mole ratio is $O_2/2$ Ag, and δ = 0.0065 cm, which is a more reasonable value than 0.013 cm. Assuming that D for NaCN is half the value for O_2 (which is true for NaCl), calculation from rates in the region of cyanide control gives δ = 0.005 cm (using the ratio 2 CN^-/Ag). The two values of δ should be different, and the above results indicate that δ is about proportional to $D^{1/3}$. The stirring was evidently about as effective as that obtained by rapid gas bubbling (31). The activation energy found in these experiments was 2400 cal/mole.

4. DEVIATIONS FROM TRANSPORT CONTROL

That the rate-controlling process might change with conditions has been realized since the early days of the Nernst theory. For example at high stirring speeds the surface process might be slower than convective transport. In 1909 Wilderman (32) reported that benzoic acid reached a maximum dissolution rate; but examination of his data shows that the "stirring coefficient" a in equation (5) was very low and the rotational speed was not varied enough (see also ref. 24a).

An authentic change in rate control of this kind is found in the dissolution of Cd in acidified violet solutions of chromic chloride, which contain the ion $Cr(H_2O)_6^{+3}$. If a sample of Cd is allowed to stand at the bottom of a tube of the solution, the color around the metal changes to that of the chromous salt and a sharp boundary is formed with the violet solution (33). Under these conditions the rate is truly diffusion-controlled, but with stirring it is not, and the rate is independent of stirring speed. On the other hand, in acidified green solutions of chromic chloride containing the ion $Cr(H_2O)_4Cl_2^+$, the dissolution of cadmium is transport-controlled over a wide range of stirring speeds, although the standard free energy of reaction is small and the actual reaction does not go to completion.

Another type of deviation is found in the dissolution of Cu in O_2-saturated ammonia discussed above (28). For each concentration of NH_3 a maximum rate is reached with increasing oxygen pressure, as shown in Fig. 2. The maximum rates are not controlled by NH_3 transport since they are too small compared to the concentrations. Halpern considered that the Cu surface becomes saturated with oxygen and chemical reaction with NH_3 and NH_4^+ is rate-controlling. The activation energy is unusually small (5500 cal/mole), but perhaps this is not a normal chemical process. A similar mechanism is found for the dissolution of Cu in O_2-saturated solutions of ethylene diamine, glycine, α- and β-alanine and in methyl, ethyl and butyl amines (34) and for the corrosion of Cu-Au alloys in O_2-saturated ammonia, although in the last case the rates fall off with time because the Au is not attacked (35).

4.1 Adsorption of Products

Corrosion inhibition is often brought about by adsorption of some material in the solution, and this may be one of the reaction products. Van Name and Hill (3) found that Ag did not dissolve in ferric alum solutions as fast as other metals, and that the rate was decreased by the silver ion formed or by added silver sulfate.

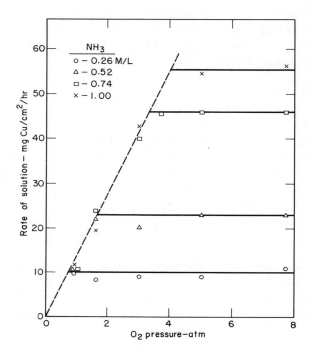

Fig. 2.   Dependence of dissolution rate of Cu on NH_3 concentration and O_2 pressure (28).

The Ag/Ag^+ and Fe^{++}/Fe^{+3} standard potentials are very close, so that the reaction

$$Ag + Fe^{+3} = Ag^+ + Fe^{++}; \quad E^o = -0.028 \text{ V}$$

does not have much driving force and does not go to completion. The kinetics have been studied in ferric sulfate and perchlorate solutions (36). At low concentrations of ferric ion the rate approaches that of transport control. Both Ag^+ and Fe^{++} decrease the dissolution rate and the effects could be explained in terms of non-equilibrium adsorption. The rate equation

$$R = \frac{k_1 c_3 - k_2 c_1 c_2}{1 + k_3 c_3 + k_4 c_1 + k_5 c_1^2 + k_6 c_2 + k_7 c_2^2 - k_8 c_1 c_2}$$

(where c_1, c_2, c_3 are concentrations of Ag^+, Fe^{++}, Fe^{+3} respectively) is complicated only because more than one substance is adsorbed, and slow desorption does not permit equilibrium while dissolution is proceeding; the potential of the Ag corresponds to a higher concentration of Ag^+ than is present in the solution. The rates are much smaller in perchlorate than in sulfate, and this was ascribed to the slower chemical attack on the positively charged Ag surface by hydrated Fe^{+3} ion than by $FeSO_4^+$ ion. The activation energy in perchlorate was higher (11, 500-19, 500 cal/mole) than in sulfate (3500-9000 cal/mole), and the effect of increased rotational speed was greater in the sulfate solutions.

It has been shown that Cu and Ag dissolve at essentially the same transport-controlled rate in acidified ceric sulfate solution (37). The authors postulate that the larger enthalpy of this reaction facilitates desorption of the product ions. The equilibrium adsorption of silver salts on silver is dependent on the anion and is much less than a monolayer at low concentrations (38).

T. P. Hoar (38a) has suggested that the different behavior of ferric and ceric ions in silver dissolution may be considered from a purely electrochemical viewpoint. The anodic and cathodic potentials are very close in the ferric system; their polarization curves meet at rather small values of the corrosion current, which does not require that all ferric ion near the metal surface be reduced to ferrous. On the other hand the potential of the ceric-cerous couple is about 0.8 V more noble, and complete reduction at the interface (or complete concentration polarization with respect to ceric ion) is necessary to lower this potential to the value of the Ag-Ag^+ couple.

Simpler examples of product adsorption are given elsewhere (4, 39).

4.2 Dissolution of Iron

As mentioned above, Fe was found to dissolve in ferric alum at the same rate as other metals (3). Abramson and
King (22) found the rate in dilute $FeCl_3$ to be first-order, linear with peripheral speed of the cylinders, and to have an activation energy of 5500-6100 cal/mole. Makrides and Hackerman
(20) found a similar activation energy. Gatos (40), studying
the dissolution of steel in 1N H_2SO_4 solutions of ferric sulfate
under conditions of natural convection, found a pronounced decrease in rate at higher concentrations of Fe^{+3}, the potential
of the metal becoming noble.

Abramson and King found that KNO_3 is a fairly efficient depolarizer for the dissolution of iron in dilute strong acids,
but not in weak acids; H_2O_2 behaves similarly. KNO_2 is not as
effective as KNO_3 and the rates decrease at higher concentrations of nitrite. Low concentrations of KCl, KBr and KNO_3
added to the dilute HNO_3 accelerate dissolution; larger amounts
of the first two salts, and any amount of K_2SO_4, retard it. Low
concentrations of salts increase the diffusion coefficients of
strong acids (18) by allowing hydrogen ion to move more rapidly. In this case they help to maintain an excess of NO_3^- ion at
the metal surface, which is necessary for efficient depolariza-
tion. Much of the reaction is

$$4\ Fe + NO_3^- + 10\ H^+ \rightarrow 4\ Fe^{++} + NH_4^+ + 3\ H_2O$$

The ionic equation implies that HNO_3 alone provides a large
excess of nitrate ions, but this is not true since electroneutral-
ity must be preserved. Makrides (41) has confirmed the rather
small effect of excess KNO_3 in increasing the rate in dilute
HNO_3 and has shown that excess H^+ (added $HClO_4$) has a much
larger accelerating effect. With a low concentration of NO_3^-
and sufficient excess H^+, the rate should be controlled by transport of NO_3^- unless unknown effects appear.

Generally the activation energy for iron dissolution in
dilute depolarized solutions at cylinder peripheral speeds of
10,000 cm/min is 5000-6000 cal/mole. In the same solutions
the rates reach a maximum at higher speeds and may even decrease. At 50,000-60,000 cm/min activation energies of

12, 000-14, 500 cal/mole were found (22). These results and the lower rates caused by excess salts, nitrite ion or even ferric ion (40) indicate a change in mechanism of the surface reaction. While the potential of the iron has not been determined in many of these solutions, it probably becomes more noble and enters the passive region. As long as the metal dissolves freely, for example in dilute H_2SO_4-KNO_3, the potential is in the active region; if the surface process is not extremely rapid, high stirring speeds can bring H^+ and NO_3^- to the interface in sufficient concentrations to provide an oxidation potential which passivates the metal. The nature of polarization curves which lead to passivity, and the action of passivating oxidizers, have been presented and clearly discussed by Stern (42).

4. 3 Mixed Solvents

Sclar and Kilpatrick (43) studied the dissolution of Mg cylinders in several acids in absolute ethanol. They found the process to be autocatalytic; the rate goes through a maximum and dissolution continues after the acid is neutralized, the solution becoming alkaline. Small amounts of water retard the reaction. The authors ascribe the behavior to the film of oxide which is always present on magnesium when in contact with air. In aqueous acid this film dissolves immediately, but in ethanol it dissolves slowly and the clean metal can then react with the solvent until and after the acid is neutralized. Eventually the water present or formed by reaction forms an inhibiting film again.

Roehl, King and Kipness (44) studied the dissolution of Mg in hydrochloric and acetic acids in H_2O-ethanol mixtures, and of Zn in HCl solutions in the same solvents, with KNO_3 and H_2O_2 as depolarizers. The diffusion coefficients of the acids were also determined. The relative rate constants, diffusion coefficients and fluidities are shown in Figs. 3 and 4. The departure of D/D_0 from the relative fluidity curve in the case of HCl is ascribed to the change in solvation from H_3O^+ to $C_2H_5OH_2^+$. The agreement of k for Mg and Zn, and the comparison of k with D up to 78% ethanol are striking (the pairs of points for k/k_0 in Fig. 3 refer to Mg and Zn).

Since acetic acid is not much ionized or solvated, D

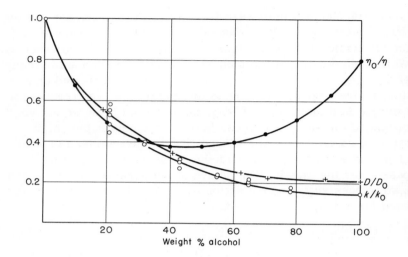

Fig. 3. Relative dissolution rates of Mg and Zn in HCl in
ethanol-water mixtures, compared to relative diffusion coefficients and relative viscosities (44).

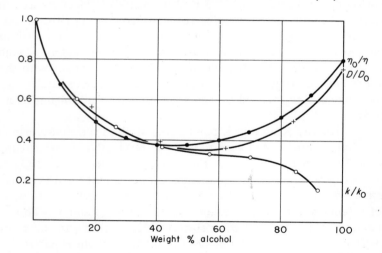

Fig. 4. Relative dissolution rates, diffusion coefficients and
viscosities with acetic acid in ethanol-water mixtures
(44).

follows the fluidity throughout; closer agreement is obtained by plotting the relative "kinematic fluidity." The departure of k/k_o from the D/D_0 curve seems to indicate some change in mechanism, although the temperature coefficient in 92% alcohol was found typical of a diffusion process.

Garrett and his coworkers (45) measured the dissolution rates of Mg, Cd and Zn in 90% methanol solutions of HCl, with nitroethane in excess as depolarizer, at temperatures from -60° to +25°. Flat metal plates were mounted on a glass rotor, and k was linear between 700 and 2700 rpm but not linear at low speeds. The activation energy is about 4000 cal/mole, and the dissolution is apparently transport-controlled; curiously, while values of k for Mg and Zn are about the same, Cd dissolved about 40% as fast, but this was probably due to some difference in stirring. Enough measurements were made with Zn in H_2O-methanol mixtures, with HCl and acetic acids, to prepare a plot of k/k_o and relative fluidities, which resembles the results in Figs. 3 and 4. It was noted that polished Zn plates dissolved at increasing rates until they became somewhat etched, and that pre-etched plates, although still mirror-bright, dissolved at the same higher rate.

References

1. L. L. Bircumshaw and A. C. Riddiford, Quart. Revs. (London) 6, 157 (1952).
2. C. W. Tobias, M. Eisenberg and C. R. Wilke, J. Electrochem. Soc., 99, 359C (1952).
3. R. G. Van Name and D. U. Hill, Am. J. Sci., (4) 42, 301 (1916).
4. M. Hochberg and C. V. King, J. Electrochem. Soc., 97, 191 (1950).
5. C. V. King and M. Schack, J. Am. Chem. Soc., 57, 1212 (1935).
6. W. Nernst, Z. physik. Chem., 47, 52 (1904).
7. B. Levich, Acta Physicochim U.R.S.S., 17, 257 (1942); Discussions Faraday Soc., 1, 37 (1947).
8. D. P. Gregory and A. C. Riddiford, J. Chem. Soc., 1956, 3756.

9. A. C. Riddiford and L. L. Bircumshaw, J. Chem. Soc., 1952, 697.
10. J. N. Agar, Discussions Faraday Soc., 1, 26 (1947).
11. a) C. V. King and M. M. Braverman, J. Am. Chem. Soc., 54, 1744 (1932);
    b) C. V. King, Trans. N. Y. Acad. Sci., (II) 10, 262 (1948).
12. B. Roald and W. Beck, J. Electrochem. Soc., 98, 277 (1951).
13. M. Eisenberg, C. W. Tobias and C. R. Wilke, J. Electrochem. Soc., 101, 306 (1954).
14. C. V. King and P. L. Howard, Ind. Eng. Chem., 29, 75 (1937).
15. A. W. Hixon and S. J. Baum, Ind. Eng. Chem., 33, 1433 (1941).
16. A. C. Riddiford and L. L. Bircumshaw, J. Chem. Soc., 1952, 701.
17. C. V. King, J. Am. Chem. Soc., 57, 828 (1935).
18. C. V. King and W. H. Cathcart, J. Am. Chem. Soc., 59, 63 (1937).
19. A. Fage and H. C. H. Townend, Proc. Roy. Soc. (London), A135, 656 (1932).
20. A. C. Makrides and N. Hackerman, J. Electrochem. Soc., 105, 156 (1958).
21. T. Theodorsen and A. Regier, Nat. Advisory Comm. Aeronaut. Report, 793 (1944).
22. M. B. Abramson and C. V. King, J. Am. Chem. Soc., 61, 2290 (1939).
23. Unpublished experiments by P. M. Christopher, this laboratory.
24. a) C. V. King and M. M. Burger, Trans. Electrochem. Soc., 45, 403 (1934);
    b) R. Glicksman, H. Mouquin and C. V. King, J. Electrochem. Soc., 100, 580 (1953).
25. R. S. Johnson and H. J. McDonald, J. Am. Chem. Soc., 72, 666 (1950).
26. Unpublished experiments in this laboratory.
27. L. L. Bircumshaw and A. C. Riddiford, J. Chem. Soc., 1951, 598, 1490; also refs. 8 and 16.
28. J. Halpern, J. Electrochem. Soc., 100, 421 (1953).

29. C. S. Miller and I. M. Kolthoff, J. Am. Chem. Soc., 63, 1013 (1941).
30. G. A. Deitz and J. Halpern, J. Metals, 1109 (1953).
31. C. V. King, J. Electrochem. Soc., 102, 193 (1955).
32. M. Wilderman, Z. physik. Chem., 66, 445 (1909).
33. C. V. King and E. Hillner, J. Electrochem. Soc., 103, 261 (1956).
34. J. Halpern, H. Milants and D. R. Wiles, J. Electrochem. Soc., 106, 647 (1959); S. C. Sircar and D. R. Wiles, ibid. (submitted for publication).
35. J. I. Fisher and J. Halpern, J. Electrochem. Soc., 103, 282 (1956).
36. H. W. Salzberg and C. V. King, J. Electrochem. Soc., 97, 290 (1950); C. V. King and F. S. Lang, ibid., 99, 295 (1952).
37. H. W. Salzberg, H. Knoetgen and A. M. Molless, J. Electrochem. Soc., 98, 31 (1951).
38. C. V. King and R. K. Schochet, J. Phys. Chem., 57, 895 (1953);
a) T. P. Hoar, in J. O'M. Bockris, ed., Modern Aspects of Electrochemistry, No. 2, Academic Press, 1959.
39. C. F. Prutton and J. H. Day, J. Phys. & Colloid Chem., 53, 1101 (1949).
40. H. C. Gatos, J. Electrochem. Soc., 103, 286 (1956).
41. A. C. Makrides, J. Electrochem. Soc., 106, 7 (1959).
42. M. Stern, J. Electrochem. Soc., 105, 638 (1958).
43. M. Sclar and M. Kilpatrick, J. Am. Chem. Soc., 59, 584 (1937).
44. E. J. Roehl, C. V. King and S. Kipness, J. Am. Chem. Soc., 63, 284 (1941).
45. A. B. Garrett and R. R. Cooper, J. Phys. & Colloid Chem., 54, 437 (1950); A. B. Garrett and J. R. Heiks, J. Phys. Chem., 56, 449 (1952); J. Y. Welsh and A. B. Garrett, ibid., 56, 727 (1952).

DISCUSSION

M. EISENBERG (Lockheed): I think that this was an important paper; I have felt that many electrochemists did not appreciate the necessity of incorporating the dynamics of the diffusion layer and convection hydrodynamics in their studies. As you mentioned, two methods that can be used experimentally have been solved mathematically; namely, the flat rotating disc by Levich [Acta Physicochim. URSS, 17, 257 (1942); Discussions Faraday Soc., 1, 37 (1947)] and the rotating cylinder by Eisenberg, Tobias and Wilke [J. Electrochem. Soc., 101, 306 (1954)]. These methods allow one to accurately predict the thickness of the boundary layer. For the case of the rotating cylinders, you have taken the exponent a of the Reynolds number to be unity. I do not understand why you prefer unity rather than, say, 0.7 which has been found experimentally by others for both smooth and rough surfaces [Roald and Beck, J. Electrochem. Soc., 98, 277 (1951)]. There is a good theoretical reason why this value should be approximately 0.7. The reasoning is thus. If you have two concentric cylinders, the outer one stationary and the inner one rotating, it is found that turbulence sets in at very low velocities. For example, a velocity corresponding to a Reynolds number of just 2 causes turbulence for a cylinder 2 cm in diameter. Under these conditions a must be approximately 2/3 according to the Chilton Colburn analogy. It is furthermore important to note that in careful experiments in which account is taken of changes in the Schmidt number the dependence on the 2/3 power of the Reynolds number is usually found if well defined geometries are employed.

C. V. KING: You are correct, one cannot use a as unity for all systems. The value of a depends, not on roughness, but on baffling. In your system and in Roald and Beck's, baffling was not used; as you point out a is a fractional power. Roald and Beck, however, suggest that for well baffled solutions a may increase to an upper limit of unity. As baffles are placed closer to the rotating cylinder, the dissolution rate increases. If light rubber baffles actually scrape the cylinder, there is a great increase in the dissolution rate.

HARRY C. GATOS
Lincoln Laboratory
Massachusetts Institute
of Technology

The Reaction
of Semiconductors
with Aqueous Solutions

ABSTRACT

THE COVALENT BONDING of semiconductors
plays an important role in their reaction with
aqueous solutions. This role is demonstrated
for the dissolution processes of germanium and
III-V compounds in oxidizing media. Results are
presented which point out the significance of the
low and readily variable concentration of mobile
carriers in semiconductors. The majority of
the semiconductors considered are chemically
inert in the absence of oxidizing agents. In concentrated nitric acid solutions, germanium and silicon as well as some of the III-V compounds become passive. The passivity of the compounds is
phenomenologically related to their lattice spacings.

1. INTRODUCTION

Certain well-known differences between metal and
semiconductor surfaces, particularly with respect to electri-

cal and electrochemical properties, result from the fact that
the concentration of mobile carriers in semiconductors is orders of magnitude smaller than in metals. In reactions with
aqueous solutions and possibly with gases and solids, the
predominently covalent bonding of the semiconductors is the
most important characteristic which distinguishes them from
metals. This type of bonding is principally responsible for the
relatively low chemical reactivity of semiconductors.

One consequence of their covalent bonding is that semiconductor surfaces can be treated from an atomistic point of
view as contrasted to the physical continuum treatment usually
employed for surfaces in general. Assuming that the covalent
bonding of the interior of a crystal extends to its outermost
surface layer, a formal configuration can be assigned to the
individual surface atoms. Although this assumption involves
certain simplifications, it does nevertheless lead to significant
conclusions and accounts for many experimental facts.

In the present paper the reaction of some elemental and
compound semiconductors with aqueous solutions will be considered in relation to their surface structure. The influence of
their semiconducting nature will be discussed where it is of
significance. This paper is based primarily on work on germanium and III-V compounds performed at the Lincoln Laboratory
of M. I. T. over the last few years.

2. SURFACE STRUCTURE

In metals it does not appear advantageous to consider
the surface atoms as individual structural units because of the
predominantly non-directional nature of the metallic bond and
the relatively large number of nearest neighbors (typically 8 or
12). In the case of semiconductors, however, directional covalent bonding prevails and the number of the nearest neighbors
is relatively small (4 in the case of the diamond or zinc blende
structure). It is reasonable to assume that the covalent bonding
in diamond-type crystals extends to the atoms of the outermost
surface layer. The character of the surface atoms is modified
to some extent by possible structural surface re-arrangements
such as those observed in germanium (1). In addition, it is

expected that the unshared electrons (dangling bonds) of the surface atoms interact with one another to a certain extent. As in all surfaces, the presence of surface films or adsorbed layers contributes to the complexity of surface behavior.

2.1 Group IV Elements

Silicon and germanium are the most important elemental semiconductors. They have the diamond cubic structure with sp^3 hybrid bonds. The structure of the low index crystallographic planes, the only ones to be considered here, is shown in Fig. 1. It is seen that in the $\{111\}$ surfaces the atoms are triply bonded to the layer below and thus have one unpaired electron (dangling bond). Each atom of the $\{110\}$ surfaces also

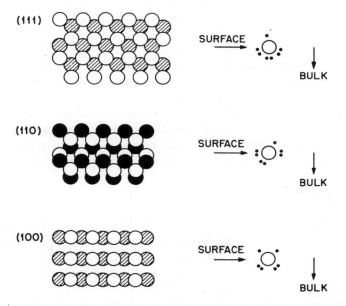

Fig. 1. Structure of the $\{111\}$, $\{110\}$ and $\{100\}$ surfaces of the diamond-type crystals (Ge or Si for example) or zinc blende crystals. In the zinc blende crystals such as the III-V compounds (InSb) the plain and shaded atoms correspond to the group V and group III atoms respectively. Electron configuration shown is for group IV elements.

has one unpaired electron, but it is bonded to two surface atoms and to one atom of the layer below. In the $\{100\}$ surfaces, the atoms form only two bonds to the crystal and have two unshared electrons. Distortion of the sp^3 hybridization of the surface atoms is expected to be rather limited because the atoms immediately below them must retain their tetrahedral configuration.

The unfilled orbitals, which are believed to be associated with the surface states, can trap conduction electrons, thus leading to a p-type layer. Trapping of conduction electrons or holes by the surface atoms is represented as follows (2):

$$\searrow\!\!\!\nearrow Ge^+ \qquad \overset{e^+}{\underset{e^-}{\rightleftarrows}} \qquad \searrow\!\!\!\nearrow Ge\cdot \qquad \overset{e^-}{\underset{e^+}{\rightleftarrows}} \qquad \searrow\!\!\!\nearrow Ge\colon^-$$

electron   recombina-   hole
trap   tion center   trap

An atom capturing both an electron and a hole functions as a recombination center. In the case of the $\{100\}$ surface, however, it is conceivable that the surface atoms acquire the sp^2 configuration (2). Such interactions do not necessarily lead to surface stabilization. For simplicity, interactions of the dangling bonds and the structural rearrangements of the surface atoms will not be given further consideration.

2.2 III-V Compounds

The III-V compounds have the zinc blende structure, which is the same as the diamond structure except that two types of atoms are present; each group III* atom has four group V atoms as its nearest neighbors and vice versa. Although the crystalline structure of the surfaces of the compounds is as that of the group IV elements (Fig. 1), the electronic configuration of the surface atoms of the III-V compounds is different from that of the group IV elements.

---

*For convenience, the group III and group V atoms will be designated as A and B atoms, respectively, throughout this paper.

In the case of the $\{111\}$ surfaces, the electronic configuration of A and B atoms can be represented as in Fig. 2. It is believed that the B surface atoms retain their sp^3 tetrahedral configuration and can be considered analogous to the nitrogen atom in the $H:\overset{..}{\underset{H}{N}}:H$ molecule. On the other hand, the A surface atoms cannot maintain the sp^3 configuration, since one of the s-p orbitals is now unfilled. It is not likely, however, that they acquire a planar bond configuration since the atoms of the layer below presumably have the tetrahedral symmetry. Thus it is reasonable to assign to the A surface a somewhat distorted tetrahedral symmetry.

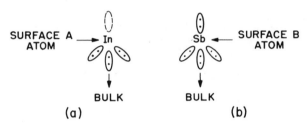

SURFACE A ATOM → In

Sb ← SURFACE B ATOM

BULK   BULK

(a)   (b)

Fig. 2.   Atomic model of the A and B $\{111\}$ surfaces (20).

The atoms of the $\{111\}$ surface layer (let us say B atoms) are triply bonded to the lattice (Fig. 1). The atoms of the layer immediately below (in this case A atoms) are singly bonded to the lattice and triply bonded to the surface layer. If the B layer is removed, the A layer immediately below is highly unstable. Thus the $\{111\}$ surfaces with this particular orientation, ($\overline{111}$), must terminate with B atoms. For the same reasons, the $\{111\}$ surfaces with the opposite orientation, (111), must terminate with A atoms. Consequently " steps" on $\{111\}$ surfaces must consist of at least two atomic layers (Fig. 3). This must be also true in the case of the group IV elements, but in the case of the III-V compounds two types of $\{111\}$ surfaces result; viz. , those terminating with A atoms and those terminating with B atoms. The two types have distinctly different properties as will be pointed out below. One speaks of crystallographic polarity along the < 111 > directions.

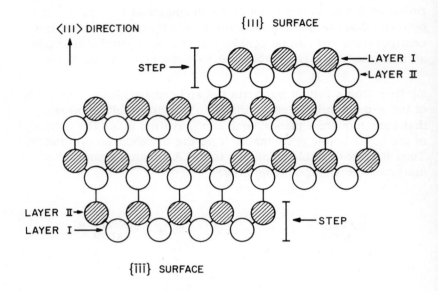

Fig. 3. Two-dimensional representation of the zinc blende
         structure with surface steps (20).

The {110} surfaces contain both A and B atoms with
one dangling bond. The configuration of these atoms is shown
in Fig. 1. There is only one type of {110} surface.
        Regarding the {100} surfaces (Fig. 1), their outer-
most layer consists of doubly bonded atoms. On an atomically
flat surface, all atoms can be either A or B. Since, however,
the atoms of the layer immediately below are also doubly bonded to the lattice, atomic "steps" can exist; thus the "real"
{100} surfaces contain both A and B atoms. Consequently there
is only one type of {100} surface also. The electronic configuration of the {100} surface atoms is expected to be unstable.

3. THE REACTION OF GERMANIUM

3. 1 Solutions Containing Dissolved Oxygen

It has been demonstrated that germanium does not react with water or solutions of non-oxidizing electrolytes over a wide range of pH and temperature (2), although the reaction of germanium with water is thermodynamically feasible. Actually, by taking tedious precautions to eliminate dissolved oxygen, it has been possible to obtain, to within one millivolt, the reversible hydrogen potential on germanium electrodes (3).

The kinetics of the reaction of germanium with dissolved oxygen can be related to the surface structure. Thus it was found (2) that the dissolution rates for the three principal low-index planes vary in the order of the densities of dangling bonds as shown in Fig. 4 and Table I. It was speculated that the intermediates Ge-OH and Ge-O_2H are formed on the surface during dissolution. Orientation effects have also been observed in fast etching media (4), although high rates usually mask relatively small differences due to orientation.

In water or inert electrolytes containing oxygen, the semiconducting nature of germanium, as characterized by the type of conduction and resistivity, does not play a role in the dissolution reaction of germanium (2). Furthermore in oxygen-free inert electrolytes, the hydrogen overvoltage on germanium is also independent of the type and resistivity of germanium (3, 5, 6).

3. 2 Specific Adsorption of Ions

The electronic configuration of the germanium surface atoms pointed out above accounts for the pronounced effects of chemisorbed ions on germanium surfaces (2). Fig. 5 illustrates the effect of the halogen ions on the dissolution rate of germanium. These effects are attributed to the tendency of the surface atoms to attain a stable electronic configuration (Eq. 1). The specific adsorption of anions into germanium may be represented as follows (2):

$$Ge. + X^- \rightarrow Ge\text{-}X + e^- \tag{2}$$

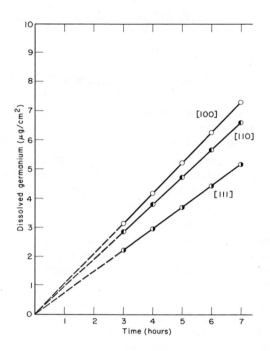

Fig. 4. Typical data showing amount of Ge dissolved as a
function of orientation in oxygen-saturated water at
35°C (2).

TABLE I

Density of Free Bonds on Germanium Surfaces and Dissolution

Rates in O_2-Saturated Water (2)

Orientation	Free bonds/cm^2	Relative free bond density	Relative dis- solution rate
{100}	1.25 x 10^{15}	1.00	1.00
{110}	8.83 x 10^{14}	0.71	0.89
{111}	7.22 x 10^{14}	0.58	0.62

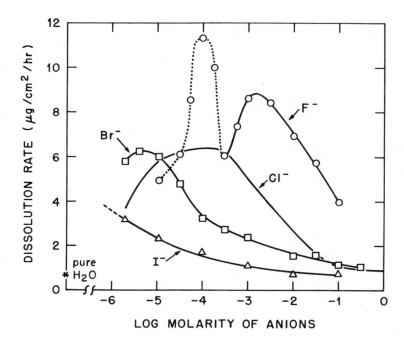

Fig. 5. Specific effects of halogen ions on the dissolution rate of Ge in oxygen-saturated solutions of potassium salts at 30°C and pH 6. The anion molarities have been corrected for additions of the corresponding acids in pH adjustments. The experimental points for KCl are omitted for clarity (2).

where Ge· is a surface atom having an unpaired electron. The electron liberated in Eq. (2) participates in the reduction of oxygen. Adsorbed anions regain their charge on detachment of underlying germanium atoms and thus function as catalysts for the reduction of oxygen. It is for this reason that the dissolution rate of germanium increases in the presence of anions (ascending branches of curves in Fig. 5). With increasing concentration of adsorbable ions, however, competition for active surface sites between anions and oxygen molecules results eventually in a decrease in the number of sites available for

the adsorption and reduction of oxygen, and hence, in a decrease
in the dissolution rate. The two maxima observed in the case
of KF solutions were attributed to the presence of two compet-
ing adsorbable species, viz., HF and F .

Specific adsorption of anions leads to a shift of the electrode potential of germanium towards more anodic values apparently because the surface becomes less p-type. Accordingly,
the effect of illumination on the potential of electrodes other
than strongly p-type is decreased in the presence of anions (7).
As shown in Fig. 6, a given photoeffect in the presence of 0.1 N
KCl corresponds to the photoeffect exhibited by a more p-type

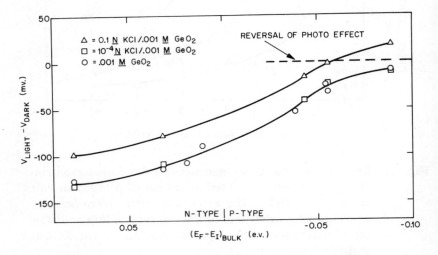

Fig. 6. Dependence of the photoeffect at a given light intensity
        upon the bulk resistivity of n- and p-type germanium
        electrodes in oxygen-saturated solutions (7).

electrode in 10^{-4} N KCl. For strongly p-type electrodes the
adsorption of anions apparently predominates over that of
chemisorbed oxygen, causing the surface to become less p-
type than bulk, and leads to a reversal of the photoeffect. The
observed photoeffects are consistent with the specific adsorption of anions represented by Eq. (2).

3.3 Reaction in Nitric Acid Solutions

The reaction of germanium with nitric acid (8) as shown in Fig. 7 closely resembles that of metals such as copper, iron, and aluminum (9). At concentrations of nitric acid below approximately 7N, the dissolution process is controlled by the reduction of nitric acid. In fact, it was shown (8) that the rate determining step is:

$$HNO_3 + HNO_2 \rightarrow 2NO_2 + H_2O \tag{3}$$

which is also rate determining in the reduction of HNO_3 on platinum electrodes (10).

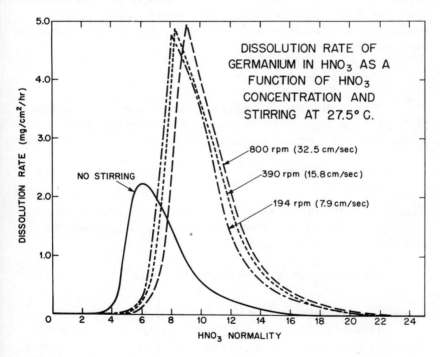

DISSOLUTION RATE OF GERMANIUM IN HNO_3 AS A FUNCTION OF HNO_3 CONCENTRATION AND STIRRING AT 27.5° C.

800 rpm (32.5 cm/sec)

390 rpm (15.8 cm/sec)

194 rpm (7.9 cm/sec)

NO STIRRING

Fig. 7.   Dissolution rate of Ge in HNO_3 as a function of HNO_3 concentration and stirring at 27.5°C (8).

In nitric acid solutions more concentrated than 7N, germanium becomes passive due to the formation of an insoluble oxide layer (probably GeO_2). The thickness of this layer varies from 150 Å or less in the concentrated solutions to 1000 Å or more in the less concentrated solutions. The conductivity and type of germanium play no role in the passivity process.

The charge transfer reaction of the reduction of nitric acid is believed to be:

$$NO_2 + e^- \rightarrow NO_2^- \tag{4}$$

In the corresponding anodic reaction two holes (e^+) are supplied from the germanium electrode (for a discussion of the current multiplication associated with germanium electrode reactions, see ref. 11).

$$Ge + 2e^+ \rightarrow Ge^{+4} + 2e^- \tag{5}$$

The partial reactions (4) and (5) are fast since reaction (3) is rate determining in the overall dissolution process. These reactions can be combined as follows:

$$Ge + 4NO_2 + 2e^- + 2e^+ \rightarrow Ge^{+4} + 4NO_2^- \tag{6}$$

Carriers for the dissolution reaction as represented by Eq. (6) are supplied from germanium. Alternatively the dissolution reaction can be represented as

$$Ge + 4NO_2 \rightarrow Ge^{+4} + 4NO_2^- + 2e^- + 2e^+ \tag{7}$$

where carriers are injected into the semiconductor.

Dewald (11) has argued that the charge transfer of the reduction of nitric acid (Eq. 4) goes primarily into the valence band (injection of holes) and that the dissolution of germanium in nitric acid (or HNO_3/HF mixtures) should be independent of semiconductor doping. He also reported that isolated p-type samples etch at the same rate as n-type samples. In addition, Dewald stated that the potential and the dissolution rate are not significantly photosensitive.

Dewald's results are in variance with those of Cretella and Gatos (8), who reported that in nitric acid concentrations up to 4N, p-type germanium reacts twice as rapidly as n-type germanium. In view of this discrepancy, the earlier experiments were repeated and extended. The new results (hitherto unpublished) are shown in Fig. 8. It is seen, for resistivities

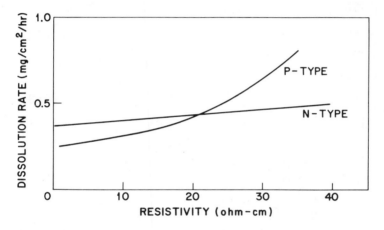

Fig. 8. Dissolution rate of n- and p-type Ge in 4.3 N HNO_3 as a function of bulk resistivity at 27.5°C.

above approximately 20 ohm-cm, p-type germanium reacts more rapidly than n-type. The cross-over of the rate curves at about 20 ohm-cm germanium is not clear at this time. Similar results were obtained in a HNO_3/HF mixture as shown in Table II. In addition, a significant increase in dissolution rate was observed upon intense illumination (Table II); the temperature of the solutions was maintained constant during illumination. In accord with these results, it was found that the mixed potential of both n- and p-type germanium in nitric acid is indeed photosensitive as shown in Fig. 9 for an n-type sample.

The variation of the germanium dissolution rate with the

TABLE II

Effect of Resistivity and Illumination on the Dissolution Rate of Ge in 4N HNO$_3$ + 6N HF

Resistivity of Ge ohm-cm	Dissolution rate in mg/cm^2/hr	
	Dark	Light
p-type		
1	0.40	0.86
30	0.47	0.91
n-type		
1	0.52	0.83
10	0.45	0.72
40	0.36	0.78

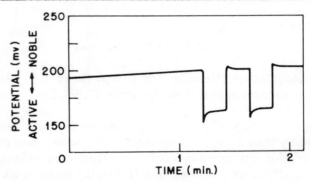

Fig. 9. Effect of illumination upon the mixed potential of n-type Ge in 4 N HNO$_3$ at room temperature.

resistivity and illumination indicates that the mechanism involving the supply of carriers from germanium (Eq. 6) enters into the dissolution process. The dissolution rates reported here are higher than those corresponding to the typical minority-carrier saturation currents on germanium electrodes

(~ 0.5 ma/cm^2 or 0.25 mg/cm^2/hr). On the basis of these
high rates, the mechanism involving the injection of carriers
as represented by Eq. (7) is also operative (cf. ref. 11). It is
important to emphasize that in oxygen-saturated inert-electrolyte
solutions, the dissolution rates of germanium are insensitive
to the resistivity of germanium or to illumination, since they
are appreciably smaller than the corresponding minority-carrier
saturation currents.

4. THE REACTION OF III-V COMPOUNDS

4.1 Hydrolysis

One aspect frequently overlooked with regard to etching
and dissolution   of III-V ($A^{III}B^V$) intermetallic compounds is
their tendency to hydrolize according to the equation:

$$A^{III}B^V + 3 H_2O \rightarrow A^{III}(OH)_3 + B^V H_3 \qquad (8)$$

The hydrolysis of the III-V compound AlP has been employed (12) for some time in the preparation of PH_3. A study
(13) was recently performed on the hydrolysis of the III-V
compounds InP, GaAs and GaSb, typical among those of current
interest in the semiconductor field. The compounds studied
were prepared with trace quantities of a radioactive isotope of
the group V element. The hydrides, formed in the hydrolysis
vessel (PH_3, AsH_3 or SbH_3), were collected in traps containing
an oxidizing solution ($I_2 + KI + NaHCO_3$). Upon determination
of the radioactivity in the traps, it was found that all of the
above compounds hydrolize in acid solutions. Table III shows
that the extent of hydrolysis is greatest for the phosphides and
smallest for the antimonides. Since the hydrides are rather
unstable, the amounts of hydrides recovered in the traps do not
represent quantitively the extent of hydrolysis of the corresponding III-V compounds. In neutral or alkaline solutions, no
hydrolysis was detected by this method.

TABLE III

Formation of Volatile Hydrides by Hydrolysis of III-V
Compounds in Contact with HCl Solutions for 16 Hours (12)

Compound	Normality of HCl Solution	Amount of Hydride Recovered in γ per cm^2 of Compound	Hydride
InP	0.1	0.35	PH_3
	1.0	45.00	
GaAs	0.1	0.35	AsH_3
	1.2	0.35	
GaSb	0.06	0.01	SbH_3
	1.8	0.01	

4.2 Reaction in Oxidizing Media

As in the case of Ge, it was found that InSb is also inert to water or nonoxidizing electrolytes. In fact, by applying extreme care to remove oxygen and other oxidizing impurities, it was possible to obtain a reversible hydrogen electrode on InSb (3). Like Ge, however, InSb is attacked by aqueous electrolytes containing oxygen or other oxidizing agents.

In oxygen-saturated H_2SO_4 solutions the dissolution rate of InSb (14) varies with the normality of the acid (0.06 $mg/cm^2/$ hr in 0.1 N H_2SO_4; 0.04 $mg/cm^2/$hr in 1N; 0.03 $mg/cm^2/$hr in 4N, at room temperature). That the solubility of oxygen is decreased by 40% in going from 0.1N to 4N H_2SO_4 accounts in part for the variation in dissolution rate. Adsorption of $SO_4^=$ ions must also contribute to the decrease in rate with increasing H_2SO_4 normality.

In solutions of strongly oxidizing ions, the dissolution rate of InSb (and other III-V compounds) is controlled by the transport of the oxidizing species to the solid-liquid interface (14). As shown in Fig. 10, the dissolution rate of InSb is a linear function of the concentration of Fe^{+3}, Ce^{+4} and $V(OH)_4^+$

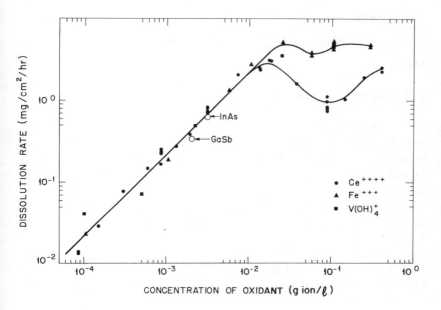

Fig. 10. Dissolution rate of InSb as a function of the concentration
of oxidizing ions at 25°C. The dissolution rate of GaSb and
InAs in one concentration is also shown (14).

ions over the range 10^{-4} to 10^{-2} g ion/l. It is of interest to note that
the dissolution rates of GaSb and InAs fall on the same rate curve with
InSb. This result and the fact that the activation energy for dissolution in the concentration range indicated is approximately 5 kcal/
mole are consistent with a diffusion controlled mechanism. It is
also of interest to note that, within experimental error Fe^{+3}, Ce^{+4}
and $V(OH)_4^+$ diffuse to the semiconductor surface at approximately
the same rates.

It can be seen from Fig. 10 that above 10^{-2} g ion/l the dissolution rate is no longer proportional to the concentration of the oxidizing species. Surface films formed at this range apparently interfere with the diffusion mechanism. It is believed that here dissolution
proceeds through the pores of the films, as diffusion through the films
is unlikely under the present experimental conditions. Since the
porosity and other physical characteristics of the film depend in a
complex manner on the rate of the film formation, it is likely that at

this high concentration range the variation of the dissolution rate (including the observed minima) reflects the ease with which the reaction can proceed through the pores of these semi-protective films.

4. 3 The Role of Crystallographic Polarity

As pointed out earlier, crystallographic polarity in the zinc blende structure along the <111> directions results in two types of {111} surfaces: those terminating with group III atoms (A surfaces), and those terminating with group V atoms (B surfaces). The two types of {111} surfaces exhibit striking differences. Thus in commonly employed oxidizing etchants, dislocation etch pits are observed on the A surfaces but not on the B surfaces of all compounds studied (15, 16) (see for example Fig. 11). Whenever etch figures developed, they were distinctly different on the two surfaces (16) (see for example Fig. 12). Marked differences have been reported on the anodic (17) and

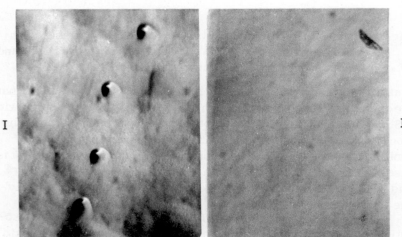

I   II

Fig. 11. {111} surfaces of InSb etched for 4 seconds at room temperature in 2 parts by volume conc. HNO_3 + 1 part conc. HF + 1 part glacial CH_3COOH; X315 before reduction for publication; I surface A; II surface B.

air oxidation (18) of the In and Sb {111} surfaces of InSb. The mixed potential of the A surfaces of InSb is usually more noble than that of B surfaces in the same electrolyte (16). In addition, it has been shown that under given experimental conditions, crystals of InSb grown in the A <111> direction are less perfect than those grown in the B <111> direction (19).

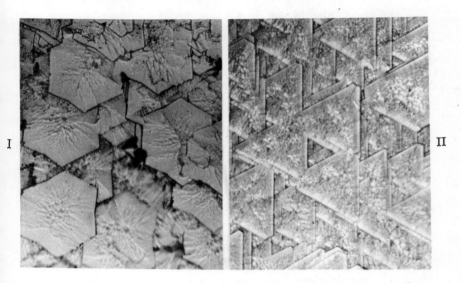

Fig. 12. {111} surfaces of InSb etched for 30 minutes at 80°C (0. 2 N Fe^{+3} in 6 N HCl); X315 before reduction for publication; I surface A; II surface B.

Regarding the differences in chemical reactivity between the A and B surfaces, it is believed that in reactions where oxidizing agents are involved, B atoms are more reactive than A atoms owing to their unshared pair of electrons which are readily available for oxidation (16). Consistent with these views, it appears that specific adsorption of amines from acid solutions (substituted ammonium ions) takes place primarily on the B atoms, thus altering the differences in reactivity between the A and B atoms (20). One of the consequences has been the development of dislocation etch pits on the B surfaces. A detailed account of these findings is given elsewhere (20). At high or low temperatures (above 80°C or below 10°C) the relative reactivities are also affected to the extent that dislocation etch pits appear on the B surfaces (20) (Fig. 13).

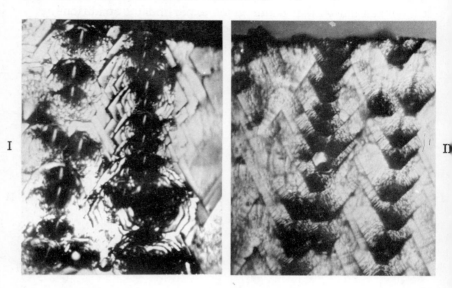

I   II

Fig. 13. {111} surfaces of InSb etched for 30 minutes at 92°C (0.2 N Fe^{+3} in 6 N HCl); X315 before reduction for publication; I surface A; II surface B; the one to one correspondence of the dislocation etch pits on the two surfaces is apparent.

Differences in crystal growth between the A and B < 111> directions, pointed out above, were attributed (19) to the distortion from tetrahedral symmetry associated with the A surface atoms as contrasted to the normal sp^3 tetrahedral configuration of the B surface atoms (see also Fig. 2).

4.4 Effect of Temperature on the Dissolution Rate

Since the dissolution of the III-V compounds at room temperature in commonly employed oxidizing agents is diffusion controlled, no differences in dissolution rate are observed

among the various crystallographic surfaces, although the
nature of their chemical attack (etch figures) can be quite different (16). At lower temperatures, however, the rate of the
dissolution reaction can decrease to such an extent that diffusion is no longer the rate determining step. Thus it was found
that at 4^0C in 2 parts by volume conc. HNO_3 + 1 part conc. HF
+ 1 part glacial CH_3C OOH, the relative rates of the low index
crystallographic surfaces of InSb are as follows (16):

$$B\{111\} > \{100\} > \{110\} > A\{111\}$$

Neglecting the $B\{111\}$ surfaces, the order of reactivity of the
various surfaces of InSb is the same as that found for Ge (Fig.
4).

The temperature dependence of the dissolution rate of
the A and B surfaces of InSb in a mixture of HNO_3 + HF +
CH_3COOH is shown in Fig. 14. The dissolution rate of B sur-

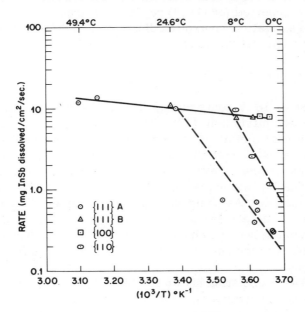

Fig. 14.   Dissolution rate of InSb as a function of temperature
           in 2 parts by volume conc. HNO_3 + 1 part conc. HF +
           1 part glacial CH_3COOH (20).

faces remains under diffusion control even down to $4^{\circ}C$. The activation energy of the two segments of the rate vs. temperature curve for the A surfaces is 5 and 25 kcal/mole. The 5 kcal/mole value is believed to be associated with a diffusion control mechanism, the 25 kcal/mole with an activation control mechanism.

Rate vs. temperature curves similar to that shown in Fig. 14 for the A surfaces have been obtained for the dissolution of germanium in $HF + H_2O_2 + H_2O$ etchants (4). These curves were attributed to two consecutive reactions taking place on the surface. Each reaction was assumed to take place on a distinct fraction of the surface. Such a mechanism is unlikely for an etching process. In addition, one of the activation energy values associated with two segments of the Ge rate curves is well below 10 kcal/mole, indicative of diffusion control, and the other is well above 10 kcal/mole, indicative of activation control. It appears thus more likely that the curve of Fig. 14 and those reported for Ge (4) represent a transition from diffusion to activation-controlled dissolution rather than two consecutive chemical reactions.

4.5 Passivity

Some III-V compounds, like Ge, become passive in concentrated nitric acid (13). This property, however, is not a characteristic of all III-V compounds as shown in Table IV. It is of interest to note that the individual constituents of the compounds susceptible to passivity do not become passive in HNO_3, whereas elemental Al and Sb become passive. It is further seen that As compounds as well as In and Ga compounds are found in the passive and in the nonpassive region of Table IV. Here again the bonding characteristics of the compounds appear to prevail over the chemical characteristics of the individual constituents.

The correlation shown in Table IV between passivity and the lattice parameters of the group IV elements and III-V compounds is striking. Although the composition and structure of the protective passive oxide films on the III-V compounds are not known, it appears likely that epitaxy plays an important role.

TABLE IV

Lattice Spacing and Passivity of Group IV Elemental Semiconductors and III-V Compounds in Concentrated HNO_3

Material	Distance of closest approach (A-B) in Å	Distance of closest approach (A-A or B-B) in Å	Passive
Si	2.35	3.84	Yes
Ge	2.45	4.00	"
GaP	2.35	3.85	"
GaAs	2.44	3.98	"
InP	2.53	4.14	"
InAs	2.62	4.28	No
GaSb	2.64	4.31	"
AlSb	2.65	4.33	"
InSb	2.85	4.58	"

Matching of the lattice spacings between the substrate and the
protective film must be the passivity-determining factor in the
present case. Since the chemistry of the As and P oxides is
rather complex, the problem cannot be pursued further until
more is known about the nature of the protective oxides.

5. SUMMARY

An attempt was made in this paper to sketch the behavior of elemental semiconductors (with the diamond-type structure) and of the III-V compounds (with the zinc blende structure)
in aqueous solutions. These covalent materials, in contrast to
metals, exhibit properties which sharply reflect their crystalline structure. Although they have already contributed heavily
to the understanding of surfaces in general, semiconductors
with their extremely high purity, crystalline perfection, and
well-defined surfaces are the most promising of materials for
surface studies in liquid and in gaseous ambients.

Acknowledgements

The work reported in this paper was performed at the Lincoln Laboratory under the support of the U. S. Army, Navy and Air Force. The author wishes to express his appreciation to Mrs. M. Cretella Lavine for performing the experiments presented in Fig. 8 and Table II and to Mr. S. Sheff for the experiment of Fig. 9. The author is also indebted to Dr. W. W. Harvey for his constructive comments on the manuscript.

References

1. H. E. Farnsworth, R. E. Schlier, T. H. George and R. M. Burger, J. Appl. Phys., 26, 252 (1955); ibid., 29, 1150 (1958).
2. W. W. Harvey and H. C. Gatos, J. Electrochem. Soc., 105, 654 (1958); ibid., 107, 65 (1960).
3. S. Sheff and H. C. Gatos, unpublished results.
4. P. R. Camp, J. Electrochem. Soc., 102, 586 (1955).
5. V. R. Erdelyi and M. Green, Nature, 182, 1592 (1958).
6. S. Sheff, H. C. Gatos and S. Zwerdling, Rev. Sci. Instr., 29, 531 (1958).
7. W. W. Harvey and H. C. Gatos, J. Appl. Phys., 29, 1267 (1958).
8. M. C. Cretella and H. C. Gatos, J. Electrochem. Soc., 105, 487 (1958).
9. U. R. Evans, Metallic Corrosion Passivity and Protection, p. 247, Edward Arnold and Co., 1948.
10. K. J. Vetter, Z. anorg. Chem., 260, 244 (1949).
11. J. F. Dewald, in N. B. Hannay, ed., Semiconductors, p. 727, Reinhold Publishing Co., 1959.
12. L. Moser and A. Brukl, Z. anorg. Chem., 121, 73 (1922).
13. J. A. Kafalas, H. C. Gatos and M. J. Button, J. Am. Chem. Soc., 79, 4260 (1957).
14. M. C. Lavine, A. J. Rosenberg and H. C. Gatos, unpublished results.
15. J. W. Allen, Phil. Mag., 2, 1475 (1957).
16. H. C. Gatos and M. C. Lavine, J. Electrochem. Soc., 107, 427, 433 (1960).

17. J. F. Dewald, J. Electrochem. Soc., 104, 244 (1957).
18. M. C. Lavine, A. J. Rosenberg and H. C. Gatos, J. Appl. Phys., 29, 1131 (1958)
19. H. C. Gatos, P. L. Moody and M. C. Lavine, J. Appl. Phys., 31, 212 (1960).
20. H. C. Gatos and M. C. Lavine, J. Phys. Chem. Solids, in press.
21. H. C. Gatos and M. C. Lavine, J. Appl. Phys., 31, 743 (1960).

DISCUSSION

P. GOLDBERG (Sylvania): In the etching of cubic ZnS, we find one side shows different etching characteristics than the opposite side. The etch was HCl, and the reaction products were probably H_2S and $ZnCl_2$. This is not ordinarily thought of as an oxidizing reaction. Do you have any ideas on how these observations fit into your interesting mechanism that involves oxidizing agents in the dissolution of III-V intermetallic compounds?

H. C. GATOS: Our surface model suggests reactivity differences in all types of environments. Actually, if no oxidizing agents are involved, I would expect that the A surfaces are more reactive than the B surfaces.

J. F. DEWALD (Bell Telephone Laboratories): I believe that the answer lies in a statement made by Dr. Engell in the discussion of Professor Hackerman's paper. He pointed out that even for the simple ionic dissolution reaction the rate can be a function of the potential.

H. C. GATOS: This relationship is indicative of an electrochemical reaction but I do not believe it necessarily elucidates the mechanism of the reactions involved.

F. B. HUGLE (Westinghouse): Would you please elaborate on the x-ray technique for distinguishing A from B surfaces?

H. C. GATOS: The x-ray diffraction technique has been discussed by Warekois and Metzger [J. Appl. Phys., 30, 960 (1959)]; however, it is not simple enough for general use. One can now distinguish the A and B surfaces quite conveniently by etching. Warekois and Metzger have shown that the surface upon which pitting occurs at dislocations is the A surface.

  G. A. WOLFF (U. S. Army Signal Research and Development Laboratory): I have two comments that I would like to make. The first one concerns your explanation of the formation of a passive layer on the III-V intermetallic compounds. These layers could be mixed oxides rather than simple ones. For example, gallium phosphate has a quartz lattice and could form on gallium phosphide. Gallium arsenate and indium phosphate are also quite stable while the corresponding antimonates are less stable. The second concerns the etch rate of $\{111\}$ and $\{\bar{1}\bar{1}\bar{1}\}$ planes. You will only be able to measure the true etch rate of the most slowly etching plane. The reason for this is that the slowest etching planes remain in an etch pit, so on the group V side the pits will be faceted only by group III planes. Finally, I would like to mention that the A and B sides of several III-V and all of the II-VI intermetallic compounds can be differentiated by piezoelectric measurements as well as x-ray techniques.

  H. C. GATOS: In regard to your comment on the passivity of the III-V intermetallic compounds, I suggest that on the basis of the available information we cannot reliably conclude whether it is only the group V oxides or mixed oxides that are involved. Regarding your second comment I would like to point out that the detectable pits represent only a small fraction of the total surface.

SURFACE REACTIONS
IN
GASEOUS MEDIA

M. BOUDART

Princeton University

Adsorption and Chemisorption

ABSTRACT

IN THIS SURVEY of current concepts in adsorption and chemisorption, it is pointed out that entropy relations, both thermodynamic and kinetic, have made a relatively late appearance on the scene of adsorption research. Exaggerated preoccupation with heats of adsorption and energies of activation has led to a frozen formalism which appears to have outlived much of its usefulness. This situation is now being corrected by more attention to molecular structure of adsorbed layers and its relation to entropies of adsorption.

1. INTRODUCTION

In the study of physico-chemical systems, the intuitive concept of energy always precedes the more refined treatment based on the more subtle idea of entropy. This evolution from energy to entropy is such a characteristic feature of refinement in theory and experiment that the appearance of entropy considerations in a given field signals its coming of age.

409

Thus in 1867, Berthelot first stated his principle that
the direction of chemical change is determined by the exother-
micity of the reaction. The problem of chemical equilibria
remained obscure for a long time, in spite of the early work of
Carnot (1824), Lord Kelvin (1852) and Clausius (1854). The
theorems of Gibbs (1875) and von Helmholtz (1882) did not succeed in giving to entropy its proper place in the prediction of
chemical equilibrium; this happened only after Nernst (1906)
established his Heat Theorem. Even so, the prestige of the
simple energectic considerations is so powerful that Nernst
himself, as late as 1912, included in the 6th German edition
of his famous textbook the following well-guarded statement on
the principle of Berthelot: "This rule cannot be regarded as a
natural law. Yet, it is verified so often that it cannot be overlooked. Consequently, it is not more absurd to consider it as
absolute than to ignore it completely. In the study of natural
phenomena, it is often forgotten that a rule which is verified
in many cases but fails in a few instances, may contain a ker-
nel of truth which must be brought to light. In the situation
considered here, as I have stated it in the previous editions of
this book, it appears quite possible that some day the principle
of Berthelot will again assert itself in a rejuvenated and clearer
form. "

A similar slow evolution from energy to entropy with a
final synthesis of both concepts can also be observed in the
historical development of chemical kinetics. The energy factor
was first pointed out by Arrhenius (1889) when he explained the
temperature effect on reaction rates. But in spite of the early
work of Kohnstamm and Scheffer (1911) who introduced the idea
of activation entropy, the importance of entropy was generally
recognized only after Eyring (1935) formulated clearly the
thermodynamic treatment of the transition state method.

With these classical examples in mind, it would come
as a surprise if our theoretical and experimental knowledge of
adsorption phenomena had followed a different path of evolution.
In fact what is surprising is that entropy considerations have
appeared only very recently in this field and the traditional
overemphasis on energy factors remains so well entrenched
that it appears worth while to review briefly what has been done

in the last few years to establish a proper perspective in theoretical and experimental investigations of adsorption of gases on solid surfaces.

2. THERMODYNAMICS OF ADSORPTION

The most comprehensive survey of physical adsorption remains the work of Brunauer (1). It is quite significant that the only reference to entropy in this masterful monograph published in 1943 is in a broad qualitative statement. It is pointed out that since gas molecules move freely in three dimensions and since adsorbed molecules are, at best, restricted to two-dimensional motion, the adsorption process is accompanied by a decrease in entropy. Further, since the change in free energy ΔF must be negative for adsorption to take place, ΔH the heat of adsorption, must be negative. It is therefore concluded that all adsorption processes are exothermic.

This conclusion, like the rule of Berthelot, applies to most cases, though not to all. Indeed, a more refined reasoning shows that endothermic adsorption is always possible on a bare surface because a molecule will gain more in configurational entropy than it loses in entropy of translational and/or rotational motion. Of course, adsorption will cease to be possible after a very small surface coverage is reached. In spite of the small value of surface coverage that can be reached in endothermic adsorption, the feasibility of the phenomenon is of more than academic interest. Thus de Boer (2) has attracted attention to the possible role of endothermic adsorption in catalytic reactions where only a minute concentration of surface intermediates can be quite significant from a kinetic point of view. A simple refinement in thermodynamic reasoning which properly defines the entropy of adsorption therefore appears to be quite valuable, if not to the surface chemist, at least to the catalytic kineticist.

The lack of attention to entropy relations in Brunauer's book is easy to understand. Indeed, it was only in 1943 that the first paper appeared in which an attempt was made to calculate and define entropies of adsorption: It was only a rough attempt by Damköhler and Edse (3). The concepts, including a defini-

tion of the standard state in the adsorbed layer for both mobile
and localized adsorption were examined thoroughly and in rapid
succession by Kemball (4), Hill (5), Everett (6) and Morrison
(7). A complete clarification of the subject was achieved by
Kruijer and de Boer (8) who calculated entropies of adsorption
from published data in a representative number of situations
involving physical adsorption. It is perhaps interesting to note
that among the sources of data analyzed by Kruijer and de Boer,
some of the more interesting are the classical adsorption experiments of Titoff (9) and Miss Homfray (10), published some
forty years earlier. This is indeed a striking illustration of
the slow permeation of entropy concepts in physical chemistry.

Yet, the information that can be obtained from an entropy calculation is at least as interesting as a knowledge of the
heat of adsorption. It is possible in principle to decide whether
the adsorbed layer is mobile or localized. In favorable cases
the adsorption entropy will also reveal whether a molecule is
rotating freely or not in the adsorbed state.

While a knowledge of surface mobility is of great interest in physical adsorption, it becomes essential in chemisorption phenomena. For instance in calorimetric work a curve of
differential heats of adsorption versus surface coverage will be
horizontal if adsorption is localized but shows the customary
slope from high to low values of the heat of adsorption if the
adsorbed layer is mobile. Furthermore if a chemisorbed intermediate takes part in a surface reaction (crystal growth,
corrosion, catalysis), it is essential to know whether, after
adsorption anywhere on the surface, it can migrate to a locus
of reaction (dislocation, etch pit, active center). Yet here
again, while innumerable adsorption data have been scrutini-
zed for their heat values, very few calculations have been made
of the entropies of chemisorbed layers. A few can be found in
the review of Kemball (4) and in the book of Trapnell (11).
While in general a strongly chemisorbed species is expected to
be strictly localized, a more weakly bound intermediate of
much more vital interest in surface reactions can exhibit all
degrees of surface mobility (although complete two-dimensional
translational freedom is not expected).

An exaggerated emphasis on heats of chemisorption has probably been harmful in the proper understanding of the role of chemisorption in surface phenomena. Thus the marked non-uniformity of all surfaces with respect to heats of chemisorption has led to rather elaborate treatments where models of surface heterogeneity (statistical distribution of energy sites) or, less successfully, specific forces of interaction between adsorbed species have been invoked to explain the non-Langmuirian adsorption isotherms. For instance the Frumkin isotherm can be obtained with a linear variation of heats of adsorption with coverage, and the Freundlich isotherm is attributed to an exponential variation of heats of adsorption.

Such formal successes are not satisfying. Indeed, if the heat of adsorption varies with coverage, is it not expected that the entropy of adsorption will also change? The answer is yes, since the tighter the binding, the less mobile will be an adsorbed layer. A linear relation has been found by Everett (6) between heats and entropies on physical adsorption. Similarly Halsey (12), revising a previous analysis (13) of the Freundlich isotherms obtained by Frankenburg (14) in an unusual study of hydrogen chemisorption on tungsten, shows that it is necessary to include a variation of entropies of adsorption in a more rigorous analysis. This correction is by no means trivial since it indicates that hydrogen atoms on tungsten have no surface mobility at low coverage but that their mobility is very substantial in the region of high coverage, demonstrated by Trapnell (15) to be the region of interest in hydrogen-deuterium exchange on a tungsten catalyst.

Finally it is important to note that the variation of heats of adsorption tends to be compensated for by a simultaneous variation in entropies of adsorption, as already noted above in connection with the relation discovered by Everett. Consequently the adsorption equilibrium constant will not drift with coverage as much as expected from a consideration of heats of adsorption alone. This remark again supports the view that emphasis on heats of adsorption has distorted the complete thermodynamic picture of surface phenomena.

3. KINETICS OF ADSORPTION

While the theoretical development in thermodynamics of adsorption has reached full maturity during the past decade, the situation is not so favorable in adsorption kinetics where only partial clarification has been reached.

The existence of an activation energy for chemical adsorption, first proposed by Taylor in 1932, is now a solid experimental fact. For a long time it had been argued that the failure of a molecule to be chemisorbed on virtually every collision with the surface could be attributed to surface contamination. The slow processes of gas uptake by a solid adsorbent were often ascribed to secondary processes of surface or bulk diffusion so that the very concept of "activated adsorption" remained controversial. This lingering doubt has been finally dispelled during the past few years, due largely to the systematic researches of Beeck, Trapnell and Kemball who initiated and generalized the use of clean metallic evaporated films in chemisorption studies. The existence of an intrinsic activation step in chemisorption is now universally recognized. But chemisorption, like any chemical reaction, is a very specific phenomenon: The height of the activation barrier can be so low that it cannot be measured or it can be high enough so that chemisorption even on a clean metal film will not take place at all until elevated temperatures are reached.

The question still in doubt concerns the nature of the activation barrier. In the classical treatment, the only one described in Trapnell's monograph (11), a gas molecule diving to an adsorption site must surmount an activation barrier. As pointed out previously by Taylor in his 1932 paper introducing the concept of activated adsorption, this simple picture immediately raises the question of a very small probability factor for adsorption, of the order of 10^{-6}. Of course this small probability factor may be explained away if it is identified with the small fraction of active sites available at the surface. Another possibility is the relatively large negative value of the activation entropy that can be obtained for certain models of the activated complex. A treatment of chemisorption by absolute rate theory was first given in 1940 (16), but the use of the concept of activation entropy in adsorption kinetics has been severely hampered by the lack of adequate experimental data.

There is yet another possible way to explain the small probability factor often noted in chemisorption kinetics. It relies on a completely different picture of the activated step. Instead of assuming an activation barrier between the diving molecule and the surface, one can postulate that the activation energy must be supplied entirely by the solid absorbent. This was the other alternative advanced by Taylor in his 1932 paper and it received strong support in the results of a critical negative experiment performed two years later (17). Because of its importance, this critical experiment was repeated recently (18) and the negative results fully confirmed and extended the older data. The experiment consists of measuring the relative rates of slow chemisorption of hydrogen and deuterium on an adsorbent such as zinc oxide. The striking identity of the measured rates over a wide temperature range completely rules out the picture of a diving molecule surmounting an activation barrier. With this classical picture, a measurable isotope kinetic effect should be observed. A more detailed discussion (18) reveals that the only alternative left open is a slow step which does not involve hydrogen as a molecule or as adsorbed fragments. Then the slow step involves the generation of an active site. Adsorption can proceed only on activated sites.

This alternative is quite attractive from another standpoint. If the generation of an active site is the slow step in certain chemisorption processes, what is the nature of this site generation? An answer must be found in the chemistry of the solid state so that an inquiry into the detailed kinetics of adsorption rejoins a current active trend in catalytic research. While interesting models involving the electronic behavior of adsorbents and catalysts have been proposed during the last ten years, none can be considered as definitely proved and progress has been slow because of the usual experimental difficulties in surface definition and reproducibility.

Closely related to the problem of identification of the slow step is the question of non-uniformity of the surface in chemisorption. Here, as in thermodynamic relations, the activation energy has been stressed almost exclusively at the

expense of the activation entropy. The weakness is logical. If
it is assumed that the only thermodynamic quantity varying
with surface coverage is the heat of adsorption, a plausible
corollary is that, in Brönsted fashion, the only kinetic entity
that changes with surface coverage is the activation energy.
With this assumption, a number of formal relations have been
derived which describe the amount of gas taken up as a function
of time. A particularly popular relation of this kind, going
back to Langmuir, Zeldovich, Emmett and Brunauer, but known
in the recent Western literature as the Elovich equation, can be
easily derived on the assumption that the activation energy for
adsorption increases linearly with coverage. It is only quite recently that Scholten and Zwietering (19), in a more searching
kinetic study of chemisorption of nitrogen on iron catalysts,
have shown that the activation entropy for adsorption also
changes markedly with coverage. Yet an important compensa-
tion is introduced here also. The variations of both energy and
entropy of activation are in opposite directions so that from a
kinetic standpoint as well, the surface does not appear as non-
uniform as would be expected from a consideration of activation
energies alone.

4. CONCLUSION

If the introduction of entropy concepts is a sign of the
maturity of a field of research, it can be concluded from this
survey that our present concepts on adsorption and chemisorption have now reached their ultimate stage of refinement. But
the evolution from energy to entropy is very recent history.
The lateness of this development is perhaps surprising, yet a
mere catalogue of entropies would have been useless before
data became available to interpret the entropies in terms of
molecular structure and reaction mechanisms. Data of this
sort are now being obtained by means of new tools which probe
into the molecular structure of adsorbed species.

It is hoped that the new information backed by the theoretical framework reviewed here will somehow bring adsorption
and chemisorption back into the fold of catalytic research. In
the past both subjects have frequently cross-fertilized each

other but lately they have been almost divorced. One significant example of this separation is to be found in the kinetics of catalytic reactions which are almost always interpreted following the classical Langmuir model of a uniform surface. This approach has been consistently fruitful and coherent although the surfaces of the catalysts used are known from adsorption data to be widely non-uniform. The paradox must be resolved and its solution sought in a coordinated approach of chemical kinetics and chemisorption studies. New information on surface mobilities (entropies of adsorption) and reactivity of active surface species (completely described by heats and entropies of activation) will clarify the remaining problems.

Acknowledgment

This work was supported in part by the United States Air Force under Contract No. AF 49 (638)-32, monitored by the Air Force Office of Scientific Research.

References

1. S. Brunauer, Physical Adsorption, Princeton University Press, 1943.
2. J. H. de Boer, in W. G. Frankenburg, V. I. Komarewsky, and E. K. Rideal, eds. , Advances in Catalysis, Vol. IX, p. 472, Academic Press, 1957.
3. G. Damkohler and R. Edse, Z. physik. Chem., B53, 117 (1943).
4. C. Kemball and E. K. Rideal, Proc. Roy. Soc., A187, 53(1946); C. Kemball, in W. G. Frankenburg, V. I. Komarewsky, and E. K. Rideal, eds. , Advances in Catalysis, Vol. II, p. 283, Academic Press, 1950.
5. T. L. Hill, J. Chem. Phys. , 14, 441 (1946).
6. D. H. Everett, Trans. Faraday Soc. , 46, 942, 957 (1950).
7. L. E. Drain and J. A. Morrison, Trans. Faraday Soc. , 48, 316 (1952); 49, 654 (1953).
8. S. Kruijer and J. H. de Boer, Koninkl. Ned. Akad. Wetenschap. Proc. , Ser. B, 55, 451 (1952); 56, 67, 236 (1953); 57, 92 (1954); 58, 61 (1955).
9. A. Titoff, Z. physik. Chem. , 74, 641 (1910).
10. I. F. Homfray, Z. physik. Chem. , 74, 129 (1910).

418   M. BOUDART

11. B. M. W. Trapnell, Chemisorption, Butterworths, 1955.
12. G. Halsey, in W. G. Frankenburg, V. I. Komarewsky, and E. K. Rideal, eds., Advances in Catalysis, Vol. IV, p. 259, Academic Press, 1952.
13. G. Halsey and H. S. Taylor, J. Chem. Phys., 15, 624 (1947).
14. W. G. Frankenburg, J. Am. Chem. Soc., 66, 1827 (1944).
15. B. M. W. Trapnell and E. K. Rideal, Discussions Faraday Soc., 8, 114 (1950).
16. K. J. Laidler, S. Glasstone and H. Eyring, J. Chem. Phys., 8, 659 (1940).
17. J. Pace and H. S. Taylor, J. Chem. Phys., 2, 578 (1934).
18. G. Parravano, H. G. Friedrick and M. Boudart, J. Am. Chem. Soc., 63, 1144 (1959).
19. J. J. F. Scholten and P. Zwietering, Trans. Faraday Soc., 53, 1363 (1957).

DISCUSSION

K. HAUFFE (Kalle & Co. AG): I would like to comment on the difference between physical and chemical adsorption. Our present opinion is that physical adsorption can be studied at low temperatures without difficulty and follows the Langmuir equation. If, however, the adsorbing gas is electronegative and the temperature not too low the situation becomes more complex because of electronic interaction with the surface. That this is so can be deduced by electrical conductivity measurements. In chemisorption, we have a neutral gas molecule or atom going to an ionized molecule or atom plus an electron or hole. When dealing with charged particles we can no longer use the chemical potential μ but must use the electrochemical potential η which, of course, is equal to μ plus the electrostatic potential. One can then set up a general adsorption equation for the fraction of the surface covered as a function of the partial pressure of the gas, the Fermi potential, etc. For a system involving no charged particles, the equation reduces to the well known Langmuir equation. This, then, is on what I would base a differentiation criterion.

M. BOUDART: Dr. Hauffe has given one way of approaching the electronic details of the adsorption mechanism. I would

like to mention a few difficulties that one encounters in trying
to differentiate between physical and chemical adsorption. One
can find numerous criteria and just as numerous exceptions.
For example, one criterion is based on heats of adsorption:
chemisorption has high heats while physical adsorption has low
heats. We know of chemisorption phenomena in which the heats
of adsorption are probably zero and some that are endothermic.
Another criterion is based on rates of adsorption, fast for physical, slow for chemical. There are chemisorption phenomena
that are too fast to be measured, and also some physical adsorption phenomena are too slow to be measured. If I understand Dr. Hauffe, his criterion would be that physical adsorption does not perturb the electronic economy of the solid while
chemisorption does.. Mignolet [Rec. trav. chim., 74, 685
(1955)] found that noble gases adsorbed on evaporated metal
films changed the work function by approximately one volt.
Thus Dr. Hauffe's criterion would call this chemisorption, yet
by all standard criteria this is physical adsorption. I believe
that the distinction between chemical and physical adsorption
is not a fundamental one.

   H. GERISCHER (Max Planck Institute): Could you elaborate on your statement concerning the mechanism of activated
adsorption or chemisorption? Chemisorption usually involves
a molecular rearrangement. How can one say for certain that
the activation energy for this rearrangement comes through a
change in the surface structure and not through the activation
energy of the reaction path itself?

   M. BOUDART: In my talk I mentioned one experiment
in which we know that the activation barrier is not of the usual
type that is between the impinging molecule and the surface.
The activation energies for various processes can have a wide
variety of values. The chemisorption of hydrogen on nickel,
for example, has an activation energy of essentially zero at
20° Kelvin. This is a fast adsorption with dissociation of the
hydrogen, and thus is a chemical process with no activation barrier. This would be comparable to some reactions between free
radicals in the gas phase; there are chemical reactions with no
activation barrier. I do not see the conceptual difficulty. I am
glad that you raised this question since for many years people

have defended the viewpoint that the surface was so active that
no activation barrier was ever needed. In reality, an activation
energy is sometimes necessary and other times unnecessary.

K. HAUFFE: I do not believe that the rate of physical
and chemical adsorption is of primary significance as a criterion. As for heats of adsorption, you mentioned that many cases
of physical adsorption involve high heats. I find this hard to
reconcile with the fact that Van der Waals forces are relatively
weak. You mentioned the adsorption of hydrogen on certain
metals as an example; I would call this chemisorption rather
than physical adsorption.

E. A. GULBRANSEN (Westinghouse): How do you estimate the entropy of the activated state? What model do you
use?

M. BOUDART: Let us take a simple case that of a
gas on a liquid surface; the principle is the same for a solid
surface. Consider now a molecule impinging on the liquid surface, will it stick or rebound? Knudsen would say that it would
stick. For a simple molecule condensing on a simple liquid,
we postulate that in the transition state between the gas and the
surface layer the molecule has two-dimensional translational
freedom and is still free to rotate. Then the sticking probability would be unity. If, however, the activated complex has no
rotational freedom, the sticking coefficient is much less than
unity in accordance with measurements. Various values of the
activation entropy will be obtained for other systems depending
on the number of translational, rotational, and vibrational degrees of freedom involved.

M. EISENBERG (lockheed): I would like to ask a question on the differentiation between physical and chemical adsorption. Since a number of criteria for differentiating between
the two have been mentioned and found to be lacking, let us assume that bond rearrangement will settle the question. What
experimental techniques, then, can we use for this?

M. BOUDART: Your question and the comments of
others convinces me even more that it is futile to try to set up
a rigid criterion to differentiate between the two. Indeed, on
the basis of some of the conventional criteria, the adsorption
of caesium on tungsten should be regarded as a typical case of
chemisorption, yet, there is no bond rearrangement involved.

R. P. EISCHENS

Texaco Research Center

Chemisorption and Catalysis

ABSTRACT

THE RELATIONSHIP BETWEEN infrared spectra of chemisorbed carbon monoxide and the catalytic activity of metals for the methanization reaction is discussed in conjunction with experiments dealing with the effect of dissolved hydrogen on the catalytic activity of nickel. The purpose of this discussion is to illustrate the type of reasoning involved in seeking a relationship between spectra of chemisorbed molecules and catalytic activity. The underlying concepts of this relationship are extended to include recent advances made in studies of the effect of the semiconductor properties of the carrier on the activity of supported metal catalysts.

1. INTRODUCTION

The chemical properties of adsorbate molecules are altered by formation of a chemical bond with surfaces of a catalyst. This alteration of chemical properties is the paramount factor in the phenomenon of catalysis. Many excellent comprehensive review articles concerning theories of chemi-

421

sorption and the relationship between chemisorption and catalysis have been written (1). Therefore this discussion will be
confined to the consideration of a possible relationship between
infrared spectra of chemisorbed molecules and catalytic activity and of the possible influence of metal-semiconductor interfaces on the catalytic activity of metal particles dispersed on
carriers.

2. INFRARED SPECTRA AND CATALYTIC ACTIVITY

2.1 Spectra of Chemisorbed Carbon Monoxide

The infrared spectra of chemisorbed molecules provide
relatively clear and direct evidence concerning the structure of
these molecules. Most of the problems to which the infrared
techniques have been applied have been stimulated by an interest in heterogeneous catalysis. Since chemisorption is vital to
catalysis and since the structure of chemisorbed molecules can
be determined by infrared, it is reasonable to ask what has been
learned about catalytic activity from these spectra. The number
of cases where even a tenuous relationship between the spectra
and activity is seen is not large. However, the infrared experiments were not designed specifically to seek such relationships.
Despite this, interesting observations concerning catalytic activity have been made and will be described here to illustrate
the type of reasoning involved rather than to claim well-defined
relationships.

Reproducible infrared techniques for recording spectra
of gases chemisorbed on metals were first developed for samples consisting of small ($<100Å$) particles of metal dispersed on
silica (2). This method was applied to a study of carbon monoxide chemisorbed on copper, platinum, nickel and palladium.
The resulting spectra of chemisorbed carbon monoxide are
shown in Fig. 1. Carbon monoxide produces a strong band in
the 2100 cm^{-1} region when chemisorbed on copper and platinum,
while on nickel and palladium it produces strong bands in the
1900 cm^{-1} region. The bands are due to the carbon-oxygen
stretching vibration of chemisorbed carbon monoxide. On the
basis of analogy with spectra of metal carbonyls the spectra of
Fig. 1 show that carbon monoxide chemisorbs mainly in the

linear structure, M-C≡O, on copper and platinum. On nickel and palladium carbon monoxide is mainly in the bridged structure,

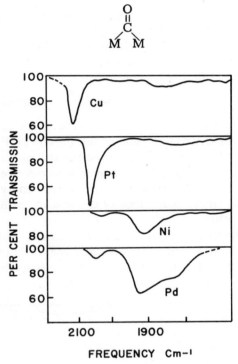

Fig. 1. Spectra of carbon monoxide chemisorbed on silica-supported metals.

The pairing of copper with platinum and nickel with palladium was reminiscent of the work of Taylor and McKinney (3) who pointed out that copper and platinum were relatively poor catalysts for the hydrogenation of carbon monoxide to methane, while nickel and palladium were active catalysts for this reaction. Although this pattern could be coincidental, it is more reasonable and productive to assume a relationship between the spectroscopic results and the catalytic activities and to conclude that metals which chemisorb carbon monoxide in the bridged form are better catalysts for the hydrogenation to methane than are metals which chemisorb carbon monoxide in the linear structure.

If the relationship is accepted, the question remains whether it shows that the bridged form of chemisorbed carbon monoxide is more easily hydrogenated or whether the structure of the adsorbed carbon monoxide and the catalytic activity both reflect some third factor.

2.2 Effect of Hydrogen on Chemisorbed Carbon Monoxide

A possible third factor of this type is the ability of the metal to dissolve hydrogen. All of the metals of Fig. 1 were reduced with hydrogen at elevated temperatures and cooled to room temperature before the hydrogen atmosphere was removed. It is certain that all of the hydrogen was not removed from the metals and it is likely that some of the metals retained more hydrogen than others.

The effect of treating carbon monoxide, which is chemisorbed on platinum, with hydrogen at room temperature is shown in Fig. 2. This treatment shifts the band due to linear

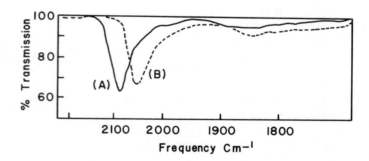

Fig. 2.   Effect of treating CO chemisorbed on silica-supported Pt with H_2: (A) Before treatment, (B) After H_2 treatment.

carbon monoxide to a lower frequency and increases the relative amount of bridged carbon monoxide. The change in the amount of bridged carbon monoxide is significant in the interpretation of Fig. 1 since it shows that the ratio of bridged and linear carbon monoxide can be influenced by factors other than the specific metal which is used as the adsorbent.

It had been found that removal of hydrogen from nickel at 350°C, instead of at room temperature, produced a profound difference in the properties of the nickel with respect to ethylene chemisorption (4). Therefore the chemisorption of carbon monoxide was repeated using nickel which had been degassed at 350°C. This produced a startling difference compared to the results shown in Fig. 1: now most of the carbon monoxide was chemisorbed in the linear structure (5). Similar experiments have not been made with palladium but it is reasonable to predict that the ratio of linear to bridged carbon monoxide would be increased by a more thorough removal of hydrogen from this metal.

The large amount of bridged carbon monoxide shown to be on nickel and palladium in Fig. 1 does not necessarily mean that in their pure state these metals have an inherent tendency to chemisorb carbon monoxide in the bridged form. Instead it appears likely that these metals retain hydrogen in a form effective in promoting the chemisorption of bridged carbon monoxide. For simplicity the hydrogen which is effective in promoting the formation of bridged carbon monoxide will be referred to as dissolved hydrogen with no attempt to consider its specific properties.

2.3 Dissolved Hydrogen and Catalytic Activity

Since dissolved hydrogen affects the mode of adsorption of carbon monoxide on nickel and palladium, it is necessary to consider whether the dissolved hydrogen is responsible for the high activity of these metals in the methanization reaction. If the activity is assumed to be due to dissolved hydrogen, there remains a question of whether this hydrogen is in a state best suited for hydrogenating carbon monoxide or whether the dissolved hydrogen influences the activity by modifying the properties of the catalytic metal.

There is important evidence that dissolved hydrogen modifies the activity of nickel for ethylene hydrogenation, that this modification involves changes in the electronic properties

of the nickel, and that these changes are similar to those produced by alloying with copper. The relationship between dissolved hydrogen and the activity of nickel for ethylene hydrogenation is complex and is not cited to imply a simple correlation
between the activity of nickel for ethylene hydrogenation and its
activity for the methanization reaction. Instead the objective is
to illustrate that dissolved hydrogen appears to be an important
factor in both types of reaction.

In 1955 Smith and co-workers (6) showed that decreasing the amount of dissolved hydrogen reduced the activity of
Raney nickel catalysts for ethylene hydrogenation. This work
was carried further by Kokes and Emmett (7) who found that
the activity of Raney nickel for ethylene hydrogenation first decreased as hydrogen was removed by pumping, reached a minimum when 60 cc/gram had been removed, and then increased
as a final 15 cc/gram were removed. The results are shown in
Fig. 3. The hydrogen discussed here is that formed as nascent

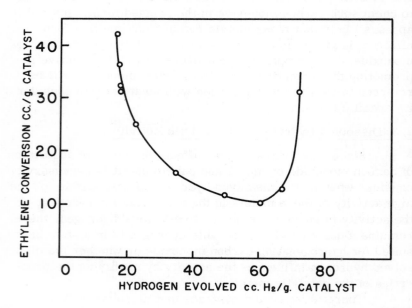

Fig. 3. The activity of Raney nickel for ethylene hydrogenation
        as a function of the amount of hydrogen removed by
        pumping.

hydrogen when aluminum is extracted from the nickel-aluminum alloy by a caustic solution. On the basis of magnetic measurements, differential thermal analysis, and density measurements, Kokes and Emmett conclude that the hydrogen is in solid solution with the nickel. The solid solutions are considered as hydrogen-nickel alloys and on this basis Kokes and Emmett plot the data of Fig. 4 to show the rate of ethylene hydrogenation as a function of the number of electrons in a unit

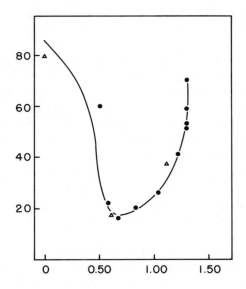

Fig. 4. Activities of Raney nickel for ethylene hydrogenation as a function of the number of electrons per unit cell.

cell. The number of electrons per unit cell was calculated on the basis that each hydrogen atom contributes one electron and each aluminum atom (about 10% of the Raney nickel catalyst is aluminum which has not been extracted) contributes three electrons. The triangular points on Fig. 4 were taken from previous work by Hall and Emmett (8) in which they studied ethylene hydrogenation as a function of the composition of copper-nickel alloys. Since the curve for hydrogen content versus activity is similar to that for copper content versus activity, Kokes and Emmett conclude that dissolved hydrogen modifies the electronic properties of the nickel.

The idea is not new that dissolved hydrogen can modify the activity of metal catalysts. Hall and Emmett (9) list a large number of workers who have supplied supporting evidence. Emmett, Kokes, and Hall showed that the behavior of dissolved hydrogen can be quantitatively related to the behavior of copper-nickel alloys. This important contribution bears directly on the present discussion because the effect of adding copper to nickel is also amenable to study by means of the spectra of chemisorbed carbon monoxide.

Early studies of carbon monoxide chemisorbed on copper-nickel alloys were complicated by the failure to realize the importance of dissolved hydrogen when the experiments were conducted (10). However recent infrared studies have shown that addition of 1 to 2% copper to nickel causes the band to shift to lower frequencies due to linear chemisorbed carbon monoxide (11). This shift supports the idea that copper and dissolved hydrogen have similar modifying effects on the electronic properties of the nickel. An argument developed below, based on the spectral changes, shows that these modifying effects are consistent with the view that electrons are transferred to the nickel.

The frequency region in which the bands due to linear carbon monoxide are found is consistent with either the single-triple bond species, M-C≡O, or the double-double bond species, M=C=O. The electronic structure of the former can be represented as M:C:::O: while that of the latter is M::C::O: . The single-triple bond structure requires 10 electrons while the double-double bond structure requires 12 electrons. Since gaseous carbon monoxide has 10 valence electrons, the single-triple bond structure could be formed without the metal's contributing electrons to the chemisorption bond. However, a contribution of electrons by the metal would be necessary for the double-double bond species. The structure of the linearly chemisorbed carbon monoxide is a mixture of these two forms. When shifts to lower frequency are observed it is reasonable to attribute these shifts to a decrease in the carbon-oxygen bond order, i. e. , to a greater contribution of the M=C=O form. The bridged form,

$$: \overset{..}{\underset{..}{O}} :$$
$$. \ C \ .$$
$$M \overset{.}{} \overset{.}{} M$$

also requires 12 electrons and therefore a contribution of electrons from the metal. On this basis it is concluded that factors which make it easier for the metal to contribute electrons to the chemisorption bonding will tend to shift the band that is due to linear carbon monoxide to a lower frequency and/or to increase the relative amount of bridged carbon monoxide. Thus the effect of dissolved hydrogen is due to the contribution of electrons to the metal, making it easier for the metal to contribute electrons to the carbon monoxide chemisorption bond.

Molecules, such as oxygen, which extract electrons from the metal during chemisorption cause the band due to linear carbon monoxide to be shifted to higher frequencies, as expected on the basis of the mechanism outlined above. Further support for this mechanism is provided by studies of the spectra of carbon monoxide on silica-supported platinum as a function of surface coverage (12). At surface coverages above 60% interactions between adjacently chemisorbed carbon monoxide molecules are the most important factor in producing shifts of the band due to linear carbon monoxide. However even at surface coverage of a few percent, shifts of the linear band to higher frequency are detected as the coverage is increased. The shifts can be explained on the basis that the first carbon monoxide added to the surface tends to chemisorb in the Pt=C=O structure. As more carbon monoxide is added it becomes more difficult for platinum to contribute bonding electrons; thus the proportion of the Pt-C≡O structure increases.

The foregoing discussion shows that the spectral pattern of chemisorbed carbon monoxide and the effect of adding constituents such as copper or dissolved hydrogen can be explained in a manner acceptable to most catalytic chemists. However it is not possible to outline a detailed mechanism for the methanization of carbon monoxide which similarly explains the high activity of nickel and palladium as compared to copper and platinum. As a consequence of the electronic mechanism it would be reasonable to assume that the rate controlling complex involves a contribution of electrons by the metal. But the concentration of this complex might never be high enough to make it detectable by infrared. Despite this limitation the spectral results are helpful in providing a general picture on which to base further experimentation. They suggest that the activity of nickel for the methanization reaction would be improved by alloying with copper, by promoting with K atoms, or by exposure to hydrogen at high temperature.

2.4 Spectrum of Chemisorbed Nitric Oxide

It has been emphasized that the infrared spectra of chemisorbed carbon monoxide are helpful for qualitative comparisons of the electronic properties of metal surfaces. A similar idea based on the infrared spectra of chemisorbed nitric oxide has been suggested by Terenin and co-workers (13,14). The nitrogen-oxygen stretching band is found in the 2000-2400 cm^{-1} region for the NO^+ ion, in the 1000-1100 cm^{-1} region for the NO^- ion, and at 1876 cm^{-1} for the neutral gaseous molecules. Thus the shift of the nitrogen-oxygen band produced by chemisorption provides a clue to whether nitric oxide has donated or accepted electrons. The spectrum of nitric oxide chemisorbed on alumina-supported iron at 20° C is shown in Fig. 5 (12). The strong band at 2010 cm^{-1}, attributed to the NO^+ ion, indicates that nitric oxide has donated electrons to the iron surface. The other bands in the spectrum of Fig. 5 are attributed to nitric oxide chemisorbed on iron oxide and on alumina and are not pertinent to the present discussion. This attempt to use the spectra of chemisorbed nitric oxide as a tool to study the electronic nature of metal surfaces is too limited to fully evaluate its usefulness. However the basic idea is of great interest and could be of vital importance if extended to systems such as copper-nickel alloys.

It is not clear whether Terenin visualizes the NO^+ ion as being chemisorbed by predominately ionic bonds. If so, it differs basically from the views expressed in the previous discussion of chemisorbed carbon monoxide. Although there would

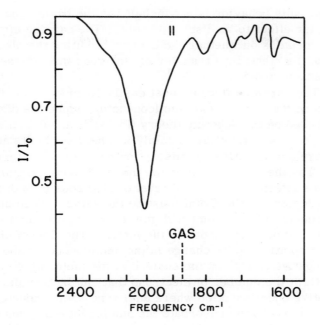

Fig. 5. Spectra of nitric oxide chemisorbed on alumina-
supported iron.

be a formal positive charge in the oxygen in the $\bar{M}:C:::\overset{+}{O}:$ structure, the bond between the carbon and the metal surface is vis-
ualized as being predominantly covalent.

3. CARRIER EFFECT IN CHEMISORPTION AND CATALYSIS

3.1 Theory of Metal-Semiconductor Interfaces

It is known from wide experience that the catalytic activity of supported metals is influenced by the nature of the support.
There is uncertainty, however, over the significance of these
findings. It is likely that in many cases the activity is influenced because the carrier contributes impurities, modifies the
particle size or crystal orientation of the supported metal, or
has catalytic properties of its own which alter the course of the

reaction. This behavior is not included in the basic concept of the carrier effect to be discussed here. The carrier effect question centers on whether the carrier modifies the electronic nature of the metal by a transfer of electrons through the carrier-metal interface.

The carrier effect is most easily considered for the case where the carrier is a semiconductor, since the discussion can be based on the Schottky theory (15,16) of metal-semiconductor contact, made familiar to catalytic chemists by its adaptation to explain depletive chemisorption on semiconductors (17, 18,19). The theory is based on the thermodynamic argument that at the interface the Fermi level of electrons in both the semiconductor and the metal must be the same. When an n-type semiconductor is in contact with the metal, equilibrium is attained by a flow of electrons to the metal. The flow of electrons sets up a positive space charge in the semiconductor and an induced negative charge on the surface of the metal which ultimately limit the number of electrons that can be transferred. In depletive chemisorption where an n-type semiconductor transfers electrons to the adsorbate the number of electrons that can be transferred is small. Thus this type of chemisorption is limited to about 1% of the semiconductor surface. Although the thermodynamic argument shows that a semiconductor type of carrier must have some influence on the electronic properties of the supported metal, there still remains a question of whether this influence is great enough to have any significance in the catalytic behavior of the metal. Further, it is not know what magnitude of effects of this type would be needed to affect catalytic activity. Thus the only route to further progress is by experimentation based on the general concepts of the metal-semiconductor contact theory.

The best example of an experimental study of the carrier effect is found in the work of Schwab, Block, and Schultze (20), who doped alumina with TiO_2 and GeO_2 to enhance its n-type conductivity and with BeO and NiO to decrease the conductivity. The doped alumina was then used as a carrier for Ni, Co, and Ag in studies of the formic acid decomposition. Samples of each metal were prepared by evaporating thin layers (10-110Å) onto pressed disks of the doped alumina. In previous studies of formic acid decomposition over Hume-Rothery alloys, Schwab had found that the activation energy for this reaction increased as the Brillouin zone was filled with electrons. From this he concluded that the rate controlling intermediate involved a transfer of electrons from the formic acid to the alloy, and that the increased activation energy resulted from the increased difficulty of this transfer when the electron number of the alloy was high. Thus it was expected that increasing the n-type conductivity of the carrier would increase the number of electrons transferred from the carrier to the metal and thereby would increase the activation energy for the formic acid decomposition.

The results of the experiments using doped alumina carriers are shown in Fig. 6. The predicted increase of activation energy with increasing conductivity of the carrier is observed for all three metals tested. The points at the conductivity of $4.2 \times 10^{-6} \ \Omega^{-1} \ cm^{-1}$ represent samples in which pure alumina was used as the carrier.

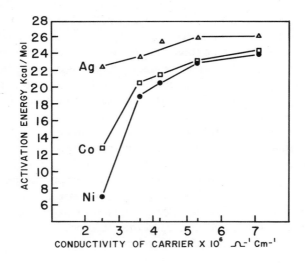

Fig. 6.   Activation energy for formic acid decomposition over Ni, Co, and Ag supported on doped alumina carriers.

The magnetic properties of supported nickel were also studied. It was found that the saturation magnetization, which

was 49 (Gauss) for nickel on pure alumina, was 44 on alumina
doped with 5% TiO_2 and 56 on alumina doped with 5% NiO. The
corresponding Bohr magneton values were 0.51, 0.46, and
0.59. These magnetic measurements indicate that the number
of unpaired electrons in the nickel was reduced by pairing with
electrons transferred from the carrier.

The results of Schwab's experiments indicate that there
is a carrier effect whose direction can be correlated with predictions based on the metal-semiconductor contact theory.
However in catalysis research there are many examples of
cases where attempts to reproduce complicated experiments of
this type have resulted in conflicting results. A question of
this basic importance will need confirming evidence before the
concept of the carrier effect is widely accepted.

On the basis of the mechanism used to explain the band
shifts and the ratio of bridged to linear carbon monoxide it is
evident that the infrared spectra of chemisorbed carbon monoxide would be useful in studies of the carrier effect. When alumina is used instead of silica as a carrier for platinum the resulting spectrum of chemisorbed carbon monoxide shows that
the band due to linear carbon monoxide has shifted to lower
frequency and the amount of bridged carbon monoxide is increased (4). This is interpreted as showing that the n-type
conductivity of the alumina is sufficient to modify the electronic properties of the platinum.

The carrier effect might also be amenable to studies of
the x-ray absorption edge of the supported metal. Experiments
of this type are being conducted by Lewis (22) of this laboratory.
He finds that the absorption edge of nickel supported on alumina
is identical to that of the pure metal. However in correlary
experiments he studied the chemisorption of oxygen and hydrogen on supported nickel and found that the total and relative
(to oxygen) amounts of hydrogen were reduced for alumina-
supported nickel. His finding is in line with predictions based
on the carrier effect theory.

3.2 Effect of Particle Size on Metal-Semiconductor Contacts

Schwab's experiments on the effect of doped alumina
carriers, the x-ray absorption edge experiments, and the study

of the effect of the carriers on the spectra of carbon monoxide chemisorbed on the supported metal have been considered in terms of concepts originating with the Schottky theory of metal-semiconductor contact. This theory provides an excellent basis for design of catalytic experiments; however there are questions concerning its validity when applied to the type of small particles of interest in catalytic work.

The alumina used to support the platinum in the infrared work mentioned above is composed of non-porous spheres with diameters in the 50-200Å range. The supported platinum particles are approximately 50Å in diameter. The platinum concentration is 9.1 wt %.

Particles of 50Å diameter have about one-fourth of their total number of atoms on the surface and 200Å particles have about one-fifteenth of their atoms on the surface. It is evident that the behavior of metal-alumina contacts could be influenced by surface states not presently understood. However even if this possibility is neglected, major complications can arise in applying the Schottky theory to small particles.

The depletion layer in the semiconductor at the metal-semiconductor interface of rectifiers has a depth of 100-1000Å (15, 16). Thus in catalysis one is often dealing with particles whose diameters are smaller than the normal depth of depletion layers. In many cases the volume of the particle is equivalent to the volume that might be expected to contain only a single charge carrier (10^{-17}-10^{-19} cc).

The small number of charge carriers in the semiconductor is partially compensated for by the small size of metal particles. By using Schwab's magnetic measurements as a clue to the number of electrons transferred to the nickel across the nickel-alumina interface it can be estimated that a change of 0.05 electron per atom would produce detectable catalytic effects. By extrapolation to the small dispersed type of metal particle being considered here, it is seen that for a particle containing 2000 atoms the equivalent transfer would be produced by 100 electrons. Despite this, if one considers contact between a 2000-atom platinum particle and a 100Å alumina particle (volume 4×10^{-18} cc) the flow of electrons to the metal would be drastically limited by the small number of charge carriers in the alumina.

When the diameter of the particle is small the depletion layer concept must be modified to consider the entire semiconductor particle as a depletion reservoir. This implies that the entire surface of the semiconductor particle would be affected by the point contact at the metal-semiconductor interface. A possibility for cooperative effects between the semiconductor particles is thus suggested. When the carrier particle in contact with a metal particle is also in contact with other carrier particles, the flow of electrons to the metal across the metal-semiconductor interface would be partially compensated for by a flow of electrons across the semiconductor-semiconductor interfaces. If this reasoning is valid the overall "carrier effect" would be a function of the composition of the sample with an increased effect being favored by a low metal concentration.

It is evident from the above discussion that unless cooperative effects between particles is assumed, the transfer of a significant number of electrons to metal particles from small particles of alumina is an unlikely possibility. These cooperative effects would be revealed through the effect of the concentration of the supported metal. This is a prime variable in catalyst preparation work and ideally experiments could be designed to test the concept.

The discussion of the carrier effect illustrates that the theories and concepts of the solid state physicist can be of great help to catalytic chemists. The theories would be even more helpful if the solid state physicist would consider the details of applying them to extremely small particles.

Acknowledgments

The author is grateful to Drs. L. C. Roess, W. A. Pliskin and P. H. Lewis for stimulating and helpful discussions during the preparation of this paper.

References

1. For examples see W. G. Frankenburg, V. I. Komarewsky, and E. K. Rideal, eds., Advances in Catalysis series, Academic Press.

2. R. P. Eischens, W. A. Pliskin and S. A. Francis, J. Chem. Phys., 22, 1786 (1954).
3. H. S. Taylor and P. V. McKinney, J. Am. Chem. Soc., 53, 3604 (1931).
4. R. P. Eischens and W. A. Pliskin, in W. G. Frankenburg, V. I. Komarewsky,and E. K. Rideal, eds., Advances in Catalysis, Vol. X, p. 1, Academic Press, 1958.
5. R. P. Eischens and W. A. Pliskin, unpublished results.
6. H. A. Smith, A. J. Chadwell, Jr., and S. J. Kirslis, J. Phys. Chem., 59, 820 (1955).
7. P. H. Emmett, J. Phys. Chem., 63, 449 (1959); R. J. Kokes and P. H. Emmett, to be published.
8. W. K. Hall and P. H. Emmett, J. Phys. Chem., 62, 816 (1958).
9. W. K. Hall and P. H. Emmett, J. Phys. Chem., 63, 1102 (1959).
10. R. P. Eischens, Z. Elektrochem., 60, 782 (1956).
11. R. A. Gardner and R. Petrucci, private communication.
12. R. P. Eischens, S. A. Francis and W. A. Pliskin, J. Phys. Chem., 64, 194 (1956).
13. A. Terenin and L. Roev, Spectrochim. Acta, 3, 274 (1959).
14. A. Terenin, V. Filimonov and D. Bystrov, Z. Elektrochem., 62, 180 (1958).
15. W. Schottky, Z. Physik, 113, 367 (1939).
16. N. F. Mott, Proc. Roy. Soc., A171, 25, 281 (1939).
17. P. Aigrain and C. Dugas, Z. Elektrochem., 56, 363 (1952).
18. K. Hauffe and H. J. Engel, Z. Elektrochem., 56, 366 (1952).
19. P. B. Weisz, J. chim. phys., 20, 1483 (1952).
20. G. M. Schwab, J. Block and D. Schultze, Angew. Chem., 71, 101 (1959).
21. G. M. Schwab, Trans. Faraday Soc., 42, 689 (1946).
22. P. H. Lewis, private communication.

DISCUSSION

J. F. DEWALD (Bell Telephone Laboratories): I do not believe that the effect of semiconductivity on catalysis is completely contained in either the Schottky or the Mott-Schottky approximations. Consider a supported metal catalyst. If one has an exhaustion layer on an n-type support then the total charge in the exhaustion layer would be very small. The potential, acting over so large a distance, would have very little effect on catalysis. If, however, you can cause an electron enrichment layer in the vicinity of the metal-n-type contact, you might expect very much larger catalytic effects, for there would be much larger electric fields near the point of contact.

K. HAUFFE (Kalle & Co. AG): I would like to comment on Dr. Dewald's discussion. Such a model would account for the increased rate for some, but not all, reactions. Whether an increase or a decrease was found in the reaction rate would depend on which step in a given reaction was the rate determining step. For example, if the rate determining step was the transfer of an electron from a molecule to the catalyst, then the overall reaction rate would decrease if one increases the concentration of free electrons in an n-type catalyst or if one decreases the concentration of holes in a p-type catalyst.

H. BASSECHES (Bell Telephone Laboratories): All of the supported catalysts you mentioned are polycrystalline. What the doping of such masses - especially tiny particles - means in terms of fundamental parameters is difficult for me to see. Could you elaborate on this point?

R. P. EISCHENS: This point also bothers me, but we know from Schwab's work [Trans. Faraday Soc. , 42, 689 (1946)] that doping the alumina does produce results that fit into the general picture that I mentioned.

M. BOUDART (Princeton University): I feel that the importance of electron transfer in catalysis is often exaggerated. Many catalytic reactions can be written in two ways, one that involves electron transfer and one that does not. In some cases one would expect that a reaction involving electron transfer with a surface would not proceed because of strong adsorption.

K. HAUFFE
Kalle & Co. AG

On the Mechanism
of the Oxidation
# of Metals

ABSTRACT

FOLLOWING A SHORT introduction dealing with the relationship between diffusion process and field transport phenomena in tarnishing layers on metals and alloys, the mechanism of oxidation of iron is discussed. Epitaxy plays an important role on the gradient of the concentration of lattice defects and, therefore, on the validity of the parabolic rate law. Classical examples of metal oxidation with a parabolic rate law are presented and the various reasons for the deviation observed are elucidated on the systems iron in CO/CO_2 and Cu_2O in O_2. In addition, the oxidation of alloys with interrupted oxide-metal interfaces is treated. Finally, attention is focussed on the difficulties in explaining the low temperature-oxidation mechanism.

1. INTRODUCTION (1)

If metals and alloys are brought in contact with gaseous, liquid or solid chemical agents, and if the thermodynamic conditions for a reaction are favorable, one observes a more or less rapid reaction with the metal in which the reaction products appear as a surface layer. The mechanism and rate of surface layer formation vary   depending upon the experimental conditions.

In order to limit the description of the multitude of possible ways in which reaction-product layers are formed, we shall deal in the present paper only with the mechanism of surface layer formation on pure metals in gaseous agents, with the further restriction of considering only compact and pore-free surface layers. Additional problems, such as occur in the oxidation of alloys, will be discussed only to the extent necessary for the interpretation of the metal oxidation.

Very thin surface layers formed on metals during oxidation are generally compact, adherent and pore-free. This is also observed if the reaction-product layers have a smaller molar volume than the atomic volume of the metallic phase, contrary to the rule of Pilling and Bedworth (2) which states that compact surface layers can only be expected if the ratio of molar volumes of the surface layer and the metal is greater than one. Detailed examination indicates the volume quotient does indeed play a role in the case of surface layers with greater thickness but not a decisive one. Schottky (3) was able to show recently that the essential prerequisite for the formation of a compact adherent surface layer is the readiness of both the metal and the oxide to undergo plastic flow and perhaps some elastic deformability of the lattice. Whereas in the metallic phase the shrinkage mechanism by hole emission at dislocations does not cause any conceptual difficulty, the appearance of shrinking in the oxide phase can be understood only if the oxygen ions diffuse also in addition to the metal ions; although according to Schottky (3) the transport of the oxygen ion may be by orders of magnitude smaller than the transport of the metal ion required for the growth of the layer. In the oxidation of iron, for example, the required flow process could be influenced decisively by the form of the metal specimen and thus by the form of the oxide layer formed (4, 5).

During the formation of a compact and pore free surface layer, the initial materials, metal and chemical agent, are separated from each other by the surface layer formed. Further reaction is possible only if the reacting constituents - at least one of them - migrate through this surface layer. In this connection the reaction front is displaced predominantly toward the metal/surface layer boundary or surface layer/gas depending upon the mobility of the reacting non-metal or metal.

Such systems require studying the diffusion and transport processes in ionic crystals which take place through defects in the lattice in the absence of pore and grain boundary diffusion. In this connection the question arises whether all defects are capable of migrating, or whether only certain kinds are favored because of their structure. This question was answered by Wagner (6) in his theory of tarnishing reactions in the sense that in the lattices to which the theory applies, usually highly heteropolar, only the excess and hole defects charged according to their lattice valency are capable of migrating; thus in ZnO with excess Zn only the $Zn^{..}$ defects migrate and in Cu_2O with Cu deficiency only the Cu vacancies $|Cu|'$ (7). However in Wagner's case the migration of $Zn^{.}$ and $Zn^{\times}$ defects partially or completely neutralized by electrons in ZnO or the migration of $Cu^{\times}$ defects neutralized by electron holes $|e|^{.}$ in Cu_2O is excluded, not as much by the assumption of immobility of the uncharged defects as by the concept that at the elevated temperatures in question the Zn is essentially present as $Zn^{..}$, and the $|Cu|$ is essentially present as $|Cu|'$. We shall substantially restrict the following considerations to the assumption that at higher temperatures only unneutralized defects whose charge agrees with the lattice valency of the corresponding ions contribute to the transport processes. It must be examined from case to case to what extent this assumption is still valid for very low temperatures, where the position of the neutralized levels relative to the Fermi potential is decisive for the existence of defects having a charge not corresponding to the lattice valency. For example, in the low temperature oxidation of zinc (8), univalent zinc ions as interstitials are predominantly present in the ZnO surface layer whereas the concentration of $Zn^{..}$ is negligible since at low temperatures the second donor level lies far below the Fermi potential of the partial neutralization process $Zn^{.} \rightleftarrows Zn^{..} + e'$.

With this precise concept it is easy to understand that

in the case of metal oxidation by gaseous oxygen the nature and
extent of particle transport must depend upon the defect model
of the oxide constituting the surface layer. For example, in
the case of Zn oxidation the ZnO surface layer which contains
Zn ions in interstitial lattice sites due to a metal excess, will
favor predominantly a migration of Zn ions through interstitial
lattice sites together with free electrons towards the outer ZnO
boundary; in the case of Cu oxidation to Cu_2O, where Cu ion
vacancies and electron holes are formed due to a metal deficien-
cy, outward migration of Cu ions and electrons will take place
through vacancies and holes. Conversely, anion migration will
always be favored whenever the anion sublattice is predominantly defective, which can be assumed for example in TiO_2 due
to the occurence of vacancies in the partial lattice of oxygen
ions. Naturally one must also assume a bilateral migration of
cations and anions whenever both sublattices are defective,
such as is the case of alkali halides, even though this case is
not of immediate interest in metal oxidation (9).

In order to establish the prerequisites for interpreting
surface layer formation on metals it appears necessary to deal
somewhat extensively with transport processes in crystalline
substances with lattice defects and to explore the relationship
between transport of defects and self-diffusion.

2. THE GENERAL NATURE OF TRANSPORT PROCESSES IN INORGANIC SURFACE LAYERS, PARTICULARLY OXIDES

We shall start with the basic concept that in the oxides
formed on metals, (the same also applies to sulfides and halides),
transport of material particles occurs only by the motion of inherent defects (Eigen-Störstellen) present in the lattice; these
defects are assumed to consist essentially of simple particles
in interstitial lattice sites or vacancies of the particles constituting the crystal. The free electrons or holes which are
present for reasons of electrical neutrality are coupled to the
migrating defects and move considerably more rapidly.

Preferential motion of these defects in a certain direction is caused either by a concentration gradient of the corresponding type of defect or by a local difference in their elemen-

tary energy. Transport processes in an electric field produced externally or by reaction are referred to as field transport. Even if one is only interested in the resultant material flux, it is necessary, for field transport and currentless diffusion processes within the oxide phase, to calculate individual defect fluxes within the framework of defect theory just as if one were interested in a general representation.

2.1 Defect Transport and Saddle Transitions

We shall consider as an individual process either the motion of an interstitial particle from a certain interstitial position i to one of a nearest neighbor position k or the transition of a particle A or B into a neighboring A or B vacancy. Under the assumption that in its new rest position the particle is always in equilibrium with its lattice neighbors, the overall system will again have the same energy after each jump. In the presence of an electric field, the initial and final states will differ in mean electrostatic energy by the amount zeV ($z \lessgtr 0$, charge of the particle). In all cases, however, the initial and final position is fixed by a sufficiently deep potential well. Between i and k the particle must then necessarily overcome a potential barrier. Since it will prefer those positions where the potential has a minimum along the direction perpendicular to the motion, although it has a maximum along the direction of motion of the particle, we may speak of a potential saddle which must be crossed; a particle transition between two valleys i and k may be denoted a saddle jump.

The time-sequence of any kinetic process is evidently determined if the particle population of certain valleys, i, in the crystal is known for the initial state, and if the elementary transition probabilities w_{ik} (transitions per unit time) into a valley k, neighboring i, can be given. Retaining the assumption that defect interactions are to be excluded, we shall limit ourselves here to i → k transitions of elementary particles located at a sufficient distance from all other defects. In formulating the theoretical expression for w_{ik} we can make use of the treatment by Jost (10) and that by Schottky (ref. 10, p. 155). It is found that w_{ik} can be represented as the product of a frequency constant $kT/h \approx 10^{14}\ sec^{-1}$ having the dimension of reciprocal time and an activation term containing the difference in Gibbs free energy ΔG between the saddle and the rest position at i:

$$w_{ik} = \frac{kT}{h}\ \exp\ (-\Delta G/A) \tag{1}$$

where A represents the voltage equivalent of temperature, kT/e, and h the Planck constant. Here as in all subsequent formulae, the free energies and chemical potentials are correspondingly expressed in eV, and the electrostatic term assumes the simple form zV. Lidiard (11) recently published a particularly clear derivation of the w_{ik} expression under simplifying classical assumptions. In the following it is expedient to express ΔG not as a difference between the free energies of the total crystal in the transition and ground state, but to subtract from both quantities the G_o values for a defect-free crystal. Then, for a crystal with interstitial defects, G_i - G_o represents the basic component η_i of the electrochemical potential for an excess particle at an interstitial site (without concentration term). and G_m - G_o represents the corresponding electrochemical potential η_m for the same excess particle located in the saddle. Instead of (1) we then obtain the following relation for the transition i → k:

$$w_{ik} = \frac{kT}{h}\ \exp\ \{-\ (\eta_m - \eta_i)/A\} \tag{2}$$

A corresponding expression is obtained for a transition k → i in the reverse direction.

It is well known that the particle current density s_{ik} in the direction i → k is given by the product of the homogeneous volume concentration n of the migrating particles and their mean velocity caused by the i → k transitions. This velocity, however, is equal to the number w_{ik} of i → k transitions per second multiplied by the path r_{ik} traversed during each transition. For the reverse transitions k → i one must substitute w_{ki}. The resultant particle current density s_{ik} in the direction i → k is thus

$$\bar{s}_{ik} = nr_{ik} (w_{ik} - w_{ki}) \tag{3}$$

or

$$\bar{s}_{ik} = nr_{ik} w_{ik} (1 - \exp \Delta\eta_{ik}/A) \tag{4}$$

where $\Delta\eta_{ik} \equiv \eta_k - \eta_i$. This difference involves only the elec trochemical potentials of the particles in the ground states i and k; if $z \gtrless 0$ represents the effective charge of the excess charge caused by the presence of the particular defect in question, then by definition

$$\eta = \mu + zV \tag{5}$$

where μ is the basic component of the chemical potential and V is the electrostatic potential caused by the presence of the field $\mathcal{E}$ which changes from i to k by an amount $-r_{ik} \mathcal{E} \cos (\mathcal{E}, r_{ik})$ ($\mathcal{E}$ and r are vectors of $\mathcal{E}$ and r). If $\Delta\eta \ll A$, then in Eq. (4)

$$1 - \exp \Delta\eta_{ik} /A = -\Delta\eta_{ik}/A \tag{6}$$

However, in view of (5), $\Delta\eta_{ik} = z\Delta V_{ik} = -z\mathcal{E}r_{ik} \cos (\mathcal{E}, r_{ik})$ and thus (4) assumes the form:

$$\bar{s}_{ik} = \left[nzr_{ik}^2 \ w_{ik} \cos (\mathcal{E}, r_{ik})/A \right] \mathcal{E}$$

In order to determine the current distribution of the i $\rightleftarrows$ k transitions in an arbitrary direction x, we must also multiply by $\cos (x, r_{ik})$ and we thus obtain:

$$s_x = (nz/A)\sum_k w_{ik} \ r_{ik}^2 \cos (\mathcal{E}, r_{ik})\cos (x, r_{ik}) \ \mathcal{E} \tag{7}$$

Thus in the general case, if $\Delta\eta_{ik} \ll A$, s_x is related with $\mathcal{E}$ by a tensor-like factor which depends both upon the direction of $\mathcal{E}$ with respect to the various w_{ik} and upon the angle between the chosen x direction and r_{ik}. In view of this, Eq. (7) also applies for transport processes in an irregular lattice.

In order to relate the diffusion coefficient D of the migrating particles under consideration to the w_{ik} values it is merely necessary to establish a direct relationship between the diffusion coefficient and the mobility. Neglecting the relation derived elsewhere (1) we obtain as an intermediate result for the resultant particle current in the $i \rightarrow k$ direction:

$$\bar{s}_{ik} = (- nr_{ik}^2 \ w_{ik}/A)grad_{ik}\eta \tag{8}$$

where the gradient of the electrochemical potential η acts on the particles under consideration as a general driving force. Under our assumptions η contains no grad μ component but is given only by grad $\zeta + z$ grad V, with the statistical position component $\zeta \equiv A \ln n/N$, where N is the total number of equivalent lattice sites for the rest position of n jumping particles. If we now rewrite Eq. (8) as follows

$$\bar{s}_{ik} = (- r_{ik}^2 w_{ik} \ grad \ n - nzr_{ik}^2 \ w_{ik}/A)grad \ V \tag{9}$$

or in more common notation

$$\bar{s}_{ik} = - D_{ik} \ grad_{ik} \ n - nb_{ik} \ grad_{ik} V \tag{10}$$

where b is the mobility ($cm^2 \ volt^{-1} \ sec^{-1}$), then the first component may be regarded as diffusion current and the second as field current. From this it follows that:

$$D_{ik} = \frac{A}{z} \ b_{ik} \tag{11}$$

With these definitions we may thus regard Eq. (11) as one of general validity within the framework of saddle transition theory, both for scalar and tensor character of b and D. This is in fact the well-known Einstein relation.

In applying this relation to transport processes in oxide crystals, we denote all types of ion defects by J and the free electrons or holes by n and p respectively, i.e., D_J, b_J, D_n, b_n, etc. In the D_J notation, using Eqs. (10) and (11) and writing

$\eta_J = \mu_J + z_J V$, as well as grad $V = -\mathcal{E}$, we obtain the following transport equations:

$$s_J = (- D_J/A)n_J \ \text{grad} \ \eta_J \tag{12a}$$

$$s_J = (- D_J/A)n_J \ (\text{grad} \ \mu_J - z_J \mathcal{E}) \tag{12b}$$

and

$$s_n = (- D_n/A)n \ \text{grad} \ \eta_n \tag{13a}$$

$$s_n = (- D_n/A)n \ (\text{grad} \ \mu_n + \mathcal{E}) \ \text{etc.} \tag{13b}$$

In later sections we shall discuss further the applications and limitations of these relations.

3. CURRENTLESS OXIDE LAYER FORMATION UNDER LOCAL DEFECT EQUILIBRIUM AND QUASINEUTRALITY

Except for the very early stages of surface layers, it is justified during practically the entire observable course of metal oxidation to assume that the concentration n_j of ionic and electronic defects is small compared to the concentrations N_A, N_B or N_M of the lattice constituents A and B or the lattice molecules. Consequently the particle currents will not contribute appreciably to a time-variation of defect concentrations, but almost exclusively to the layer formation. For defects we may thus write

$$\frac{\partial n_j}{\partial t} = 0 \tag{14}$$

In calculating the growth rate $d\xi/dt$ of a layer of thickness ξ , we shall assume quasi-planar arrangements and choose the transverse direction of the layer as the x direction, taking x = 0 at the metal and x = ξ at the gas boundary. The s_A flux which flows without divergence from the metal through the layer to the outside combines at the gas boundary with the reacting gas to form lattice molecules, requiring N_A/N_M A-particles; i.e., in the Cu_2O case two particles, to construct one lattice molecule of Cu_2O. Denoting the total number of lattice molecules per unit area of the layer by u_M, and letting $u_M = \xi N_M$, we obtain the total increase in s_A

$$\frac{d\xi}{dt} = \frac{s_A}{N_A} - \frac{s_B}{N_B} \tag{15}$$

If it is now possible to express s_A and s_B in terms of ξ and the chemical boundary conditions at both interfaces, then we have obtained the growth law for the layer from Eq. (15). Quasineutrality, however, is one of the most essential pre-requisites.

Since both ξ and n_j increase considerably with increasing temperature, one may expect the quasineutrality conditions, $n_\rho = 0$, to be fulfilled predominantly at high temperatures.

Correspondingly in Eq. (15), assuming internal defect equilibrium, we may express the s_A and s_B in terms of grad μ_A or grad μ_B and thus obtain (μ_A and μ_B are the chemical potentials of A and B of the crystal AB):

$$\frac{d\xi}{dt} = -\frac{1}{A}(D_A \text{ grad } \mu_A - D_B \text{ grad } \mu_B) \tag{16}$$

by transforming and integrating over x one finally obtains:

$$\xi \frac{d\xi}{dt} = -\frac{1}{A} \int_{\mu_A(0)}^{\mu_A(\xi)} (D_A + \frac{N_A}{N_B} D_B) d\mu_A \tag{17}$$

In this expression the right hand side represents a quantity depending only upon both limiting values of μ_A which is designated as the oxidation constant k' (>0) and which is independent of ξ. The time variation of ξ is thus given by:

$$\xi \frac{d\xi}{dt} = k'; \ \xi^2 = 2k't; \ \xi = (2k't)^{1/2} \tag{18}$$

This time dependence of ξ is known as parabolic oxidation law.

A law of this form was obtained in many cases and was first determined empirically in 1920 by Tammann (12). Wagner is responsible for its derivation under general assumptions.

Among special cases we shall first examine the case involving only one type of charged (metallic) defect and one electronic type. For the special case here considered we find:

$$k' = - \alpha_J (1 + |z_J|) D_J \int_{n_J(0)}^{n_J(\xi)} dn_J =$$

$$- \alpha_J (1 + |z_J|) D_J \left[n_J(\xi) - n_J(0) \right] \tag{19}$$

where α_J represents the number of A-particles at the defect J. This relation has an unexpected character only inasmuch as it no longer depends upon the exact value of the smaller of these two quantities for large relative differences in $n_J(\xi)$ and $n_J(0)$. The resultant particle current is practically the same as it would be if n_J actually vanished on one side.

As a special application of Eq. (19) we shall consider oxide formation on zinc. Here we may assume only Zn·ions on interstitial lattice sites and electrons e' at practically all temperatures. Consequently $\alpha_J = +1$ and $z_J = +1$. Moreover, $n_J(0) \gg n_J(\xi)$, or $n_{Zn\cdot}(0) \gg n_{Zn\cdot}(\xi)$. From Eq. (19) we thus obtain

$$k' = 2 D_{Zn\cdot} \left[n_{Zn\cdot}(0) - n_{Zn\cdot}(\xi) \right] \tag{20}$$

or $k' \approx 2 D_{Zn\cdot} \cdot n_{Zn\cdot}(0)$ \hfill (21)

To calculate k' it would thus be necessary to know $D_{Zn\cdot}$ and $n_{Zn\cdot}$ on the metal side. However it is not possible to evaluate either of these two magnitudes quantitatively on a purely theoretical basis. In order to verify k' it would be necessary to obtain $D_{Zn\cdot}$ and $n_{Zn\cdot}$ by independent measurements. It was possible to verify the oxygen pressure independence implied by Eq. (21) for the case of Zn oxidation (13).

A complimentary case to Eq. (20) is encountered in the

oxidation of Cu to Cu_2O at high temperatures. Since in this case a p-conducting oxide layer is formed which has Cu ion defects $|Cu|$ ' and holes $|e|$ ·, we have $\alpha_J = -1$ and $z_J = -1$. Eq. (19) can thus be rewritten as follows:

$$k' = 2D_{|Cu|} \cdot \left[n_{|Cu|} \cdot (\xi) - n_{|Cu|} \cdot (0) \right] \tag{22}$$

or, since $n_{|Cu|} \cdot (\xi) >> n_{|Cu|} \cdot (0)$,

$$k \approx 2D_{|Cu|} \cdot n_{|Cu|} \cdot (\xi) \tag{23}$$

An essential difference with respect to Eq. (20) consists in the dependence of the $n_{|Cu|} \cdot (\xi)$ term (which is the only determinative term in the case of O_2 pressures which are not too low) upon the oxygen pressure on the basis of the external equilibrium

$$1/2 \ O_2(g) \rightleftarrows Cu_2O + 2|Cu| ' + 2|e| \cdot \tag{24}$$

Considering that $n_{|e|} \cdot = n_{|Cu|}$ ', we obtain for $x = \xi$ $n^2_{|Cu|} \cdot n^2_{|e|} \cdot = n^4_{|Cu|} \cdot$ proportional to $p_{O_2}^{1/2}$, and thus k' is also proportional to $p_{O_2}^{1/8}$, which was verified experimentally (13) (Fig. 1). It should be pointed out that the linear concentration gradient in the boundary layer is rigorously limited to the special assumption that only one type of ion and electron defect is present. In all other cases, defining a single value of n_J together with the neutrality condition no longer suffices to calculate all defect concentrations n_J. In the space-charge case a linear gradient is no longer possible even for one ion and electron-defect type.

Neglecting the direct D_A and D_B measurements for all concentrations of interest, one can use the process employed by Wagner under quite generally valid assumptions to represent k' on the basis of electric conductivity and transfer measurements (14). Under simplified conditions one can arrive at a formula already obtained by Wagner (15) in a different way:

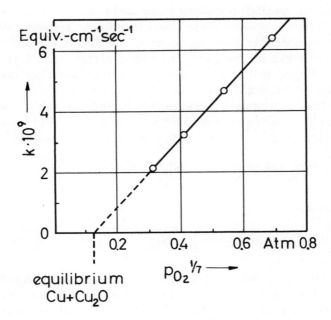

Fig. 1. Rational oxidation constant k for the oxidation of copper to Cu_2O at $1000^\circ C$ as a function of the seventh
root of oxygen pressure (13).

$$D_A + \frac{N_A}{N_B} D_B = \frac{1}{|z|} \frac{A}{e} \sigma t_{ion} t_{el} \tag{25}$$

where $|z|$ is the absolute value of the valency of the migrating
particle and t_{ion} and t_{el} are the transfer numbers of ions and
electrons, respectively.

3.1 Variation of Defect Concentration in the Surface Layer

As pointed out previously, one must assume a linear
concentration gradient of defects in surface layers containing
only one uniformly charged type of defects. It is now of interest to discuss the experimental verification of these assumptions. In view of the very low defect concentrations frequently

encountered, available analytical methods generally do not permit determination of these concentrations. However very high defect concentrations do occur in the FeO phase which is the bottom layer in iron oxidation within certain temperature ranges. Engell (16) succeeded in measuring the defect variation in an FeO layer by an electrochemical method (17). $Fe_{1-y}O$ may exhibit considerable iron deficiency, which manifests itself by the presence of Fe ion vacancies, $|Fe|''$, and holes $|e|^{\cdot}$, ($\equiv Fe^{+3}$). According to the disorder equation

$$1/2\ O_2\ (g) \rightleftarrows FeO + |Fe|'' + 2|e|^{\cdot} \tag{26}$$

it follows that:

$$y = n_{|Fe|''}/N_{Fe} = \frac{1}{2}\,p/N_{Fe}$$

The analytical method of Engell is based on determining the $p(\equiv Fe^{+3})$ concentration at any particular depth in the layer by simultaneously measuring the quantity of iron going differentially into solution, and the electrolytic current passing through. Fig. 2 shows the result of these experiments. The y values are plotted for two different layer thicknesses as a function of the distance x from the metal boundary (curves 1 and 2). It is seen that y at the metal side is not equal to zero but already has a relatively large value amounting to approximately 6% at the temperature in question. From this value y rises linearly to approximately 12% at the gas side. However such a variation agrees with the theory only as long as the FeO layer is in intimate contact with the metal phase. If this contact is interrupted due to plastic rigidity of the oxide layer (Fig. 3), then the Fe supply at these places virtually ceases and equilibrium with the Fe_3O_4 phase is established throughout the surface layer, which leads to a constant y concentration in these portions of the FeO layer (curve 3 in Fig. 2). It should also be emphasized that the y values of Engell are in agreement with the y determinations in homogeneous FeO specimens subjected for the same temperature range to various oxygen pressures within the stability region of the FeO phase (18). The variation

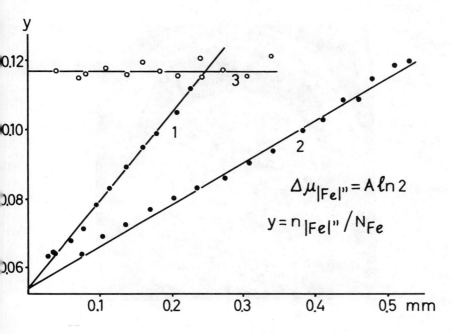

Fig. 2.   Variation of y in FeO layers of different thickness
formed in air at 900°C (16). Curve 3: poor adhesion
of FeO on Fe.

of y with oxygen pressure further implies that we must assume
$|Fe|''$ defects rather than $|Fe|'$. In agreement with Eq. (26),
it was found that $y \sim p_{O_2}^{1/6}$ (18).

It is rather remarkable that at these relatively high
defect concentrations one still does not observe any noticeable
deviations from the assumption $\mu_{|Fe|''}$ = constant + $A \ln$

$n_{|Fe|''}$ or μ_p = constant + $A \ln p$. For holes this is surprising
inasmuch as this case involves volume concentrations $\approx 10^{21}$/
cm^3 at which one should expect degeneracy.   In this connection
Schottky (1) points out the peculiar position assumed by the
transition metals, in particular Fe, Co, and Ni, and concludes
that there is an anomalously high effective mass for holes which
accordingly increases the degeneracy concentration.

Fig. 3. Metallographic section of a pure iron wire oxidized in
        oxygen at 750°C (16).

3.2 Some Experimental Results Concerning Surface Layer
Formation on Metals and Alloys

From Eqs. (25) and (17) and with the assumptions
stated above, we obtain an expression which is directly applicable to the experimental results, and which was derived by
Wagner in a different way:

$$\frac{dn}{dt} = \frac{q}{\xi} \left[\frac{300}{96500} \frac{1}{|z_B| N_L e} \int_{\mu_B^{(i)}}^{\mu_B^{(a)}} (t_A + t_B) t_{el} \, \sigma \, d\mu_B \right] \quad (27)$$

In this expression t_A, t_B, and t_{el} are the transfer numbers of the metal ions, anions, and electrons; μ_B is the chemical potential of the non-metal, N_L Loschmid's number and z_B the valency of the non-metal. The superscripts (a) and (i) denote the outer and inner boundary, respectively, of the surface layer. The surface to be oxidized, q, is constant only in cases such as metal sheets. The expression in brackets is constant in time under the given conditions and is referred to as the rational oxidation constant k in equivalents $cm^{-1} sec^{-1}$. It is equivalent to Tammann's parabolic oxidation constant.

In addition to the examples already mentioned we shall discuss the bromination of silver and Ag-Cd alloys. In all cases a parabolic rate law was observed above 200°C. Contrary to the previous example, the AgBr surface layer is an ionic conductor characterized by a Frenkel-type disorder, i.e., $n_{Ag^\cdot} = n_{|Ag|'}$; we must now write $t_A \equiv t_{Ag} \approx 1$, $t_B \equiv t_{Br} \approx 0$, and consequently t_{el} becomes the rate determining factor in Eq. (27). According to Frenkel:

$$\text{null} \rightleftharpoons Ag^\cdot + |Ag|' \qquad (28)$$

We must represent the effect of bromine on AgBr by the following two equations:

$$1/2\ Br_2(g) \rightleftharpoons AgBr + |Ag|' + |e|^\cdot \qquad (29)$$

and

$$1/2\ Br_2(g) + Ag \rightleftharpoons AgBr + |e|^\cdot \qquad (30)$$

Whereas the ionic defect concentration which is quite large from the outset is not changed noticeably by the action of Br_2, the change in hole concentration, $p \ll n_{|Ag|'} \approx n_{Ag^\cdot}$, however, follows the mass action law; then from Eqs. (29) or (30):

$$p = \text{constant } p_{Br_2}^{1/2} \qquad (31)$$

or

$$p = p \, (p_{Br_2} = 1) \, p_{Br_2}^{1/2} \quad \text{and thus}$$

$$\sigma_p = \sigma t_p (p_{Br_2} = 1) \, p_{Br_2}^{1/2}$$

(32)

From this we obtain the bromination rate of silver:

$$\frac{dn_{AgBr}}{dt} = \frac{q}{\xi} \left[\frac{300}{96500} \, \sigma_p \, (p_{Br_2} = 1) \, A \left(\sqrt{p_{Br_2}^{(a)}} - \sqrt{p_{Br_2}^{(i)}} \right) \right]$$

(33)

where $p_{Br_2}^{(a)}$ and $p_{Br_2}^{(i)}$ are the corresponding partial bromine pressures at the phase boundaries AgBr/Br$_2$ and AgBr/Ag, respectively. However since $p_{Br_2}^{(i)} \ll p_{Br_2}^{(a)}$, the expression in Eq. (33), i.e., the oxidation constant k^o, is:

$$k^o = \frac{300}{96500} \, \sigma_p \, (p_{Br_2} = 1) \, A \, p_{Br_2}^{1/2}$$

(34)

The proportionality to be expected between the rational oxidation constant k and the square root of the given partial pressure of bromine in the temperature range of 200 to 400°C was verified experimentally by Wagner (19). The experimental results are listed in Table I.

By incorporating divalent metal ions, such as Cd^{++}, in AgBr the concentration of $|Ag|$' is increased according to the expression

$$CdBr_2 \rightleftarrows Cd|Ag|^{\cdot} + |Ag|' + 2\,AgBr$$

(35)

Here $Cd|Ag|^{\cdot}$ represents a divalent Cd ion at an Ag ion lattice

TABLE I

Oxidation Rate of Silver in Bromide

$$k \times 10^{10} \text{ equiv. cm}^{-1} \text{ sec}^{-1}$$

Temp. ^{o}C	$p_{Br_2} = 0.09$ atm	$p_{Br_2} = 0.23$ atm	$\dfrac{k(p_{Br_2} = 0.09)}{k(p_{Br_2} = 0.23)}$
200	0.23	0.38	0.61
250	0.53	0.91	0.58
300	0.96	1.78	0.54
350	1.21	2.32	0.52
400	1.15	2.27	0.50

position. According to the mass action law implied by Eq. (29):

$$n_{|Ag|} \cdot p = K \qquad (T \text{ and } p_{Br_2} = \text{constant}) \tag{36}$$

the hole concentration p and thus the rate of bromination must decrease. This is obtained in the bromination of Ag-Cd alloys. The ratio of oxidation constants for alloys and pure silver is (20):

$$\frac{k}{k^o} = \left\{ \frac{n_{Cd}}{2 n^o_{|Ag|}} + \left[\left(\frac{n_{Cd}}{2 n^o_{|Ag|}} \right)^2 + 1 \right]^{1/2} \right\}^{-1} \tag{37}$$

where n_{Cd} represents the concentration of $CdBr_2$ in the layer. Fig. 4 shows satisfactory agreement of the measured ratio k/k^o (curve 1) and the ratio calculated according to Eq. (37)

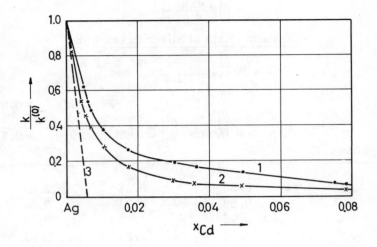

Fig. 4. Dependence of the ratio of oxidation constants k/k^o
upon the Cd content of the alloy at 330^oC and p_{Br_2} =
170 mm Hg (20). Curve 1 is obtained from experimental data, curve 2 is calculated according to
Eq. (37). The tangent to curve 1 at n_{Cd} = 0 inter-
sects the abscissa at $n_{Cd} \equiv n^o_{|Ag|}$ ' = 2. 9 x 10^{-3}.

(curve 2), calculated taking $n^o_{|Ag|}$ ' = 2. 9 x 10^{-3} given by
Teltow for 330^oC (21). A summary of studies on other alloy
systems has been published elsewhere (22).

3. 3 Deviations from Equilibrium at the Phase Boundaries

Deviations from equilibrium at the phase boundaries are
always to be expected when the transport of material and elec-

---

*n_{Cd} is the concentration in the alloy, which can be set equal to
the Cd concentration in the mixed crystal AgBr - $CdBr_2$ provided Cd goes into solution in the same proportion or has been
verified by analysis.

tronic charge carriers in the crystal is more rapid than one of
the possible phase boundary reactions. One then observes a
linear rate law of surface layer growth. Wilkins and Rideal
(23) have emphasized the decisive influence of the phase boundary reactions in the oxidation of copper. According to Tylecote
(24) the rate-determining phase boundary processes also take
place at the onset of copper oxidation. Such reactions can
occur particularly if oxygen is not used for the oxidation, but
an oxygen-supplying gas such as N_2O or CO_2. Such an example
is the oxidation of copper by N_2O at $150^\circ C$. On the basis of
the experimental results by Dell, Stone and Tiley (25) it seems
reasonable to assume that the slowest and thus rate-determining
step is the partial step (38c) in the following sequence of reactions:

$$N_2O(g) \rightarrow N_2O^\times (ads) \tag{38a}$$

$$N_2O^\times (ads) \rightarrow O^-(chem) + |e|^\cdot + N_2(g) \tag{38b}$$

$$O^-(chem) \rightarrow Cu_2O + 2\,|Cu|\,' + |e|^\cdot \tag{38c}$$

$$(|e|^\cdot + |Cu|\,')_{outward} \rightarrow (|Cu|\,' + |e|^\cdot)_{inward} \tag{38d}$$

$$Cu\ (metal) + |Cu|\,' + |e|^\cdot \rightarrow null \tag{38e}$$

This assumption is in agreement with the experimental observation that no gaseous oxygen can be detected. Moreover the
oxidation rate was found to be proportional to p_{N_2O}, which can
be understood only if an N_2O (gas) / $N_2O^\times$ (ads) equilibrium
prevails, and the $N_2O^\times$ (ads) concentration is small.

The oxidation of iron at high temperatures, where several iron oxide phases form, obeys the parabolic rate law whereas in CO-CO_2 mixtures above $900^\circ C$, it obeys a linear rate law
with the exclusive formation of an FeO layer (18). This result
is understandable if one considers the high defect concentration
in FeO of approximately 10%, which ensures high diffusion velocity. The linear rate constant $\mathscr{l}''$ exhibits the following de-

pendence upon gas pressure (18):

$$\mathscr{l}'' = \text{constant } (p_{CO_2}/p_{CO})^{2/3} = \text{constant}^* p_{O_2}^{1/3} \quad (39)$$

It was further observed that $\mathscr{l}''$ is proportional to the sum of the partial pressures, $P = p_{CO_2} + p_{CO}$, in a pressure range between 0.4 and 1 atmospheres (26) in agreement with the formula derived by Wagner (27)

$$\mathscr{l}'' = kP(1+K) \left[x_{CO_2} - x_{CO_2} \text{ (equilibrium)} \right] \quad (40)$$

where $K = p_{CO_2}/p_{CO}$ and $x_{CO_2} = p_{CO_2}/P$. On the other hand, a normal parabolic dependence of the oxidation of iron to FeO is observed in a H_2-H_2O atmosphere above $950°C$. Evidently, contrary to the CO_2/CO reaction, the corresponding processes with H_2O/H_2 proceed sufficiently rapidly so that the diffusion of Fe ions through the FeO layer represents the slower process, despite considerable defect concentration in the FeO lattice.

3.4 Multi-Phase Surface Layers

In principle, multi-phase surface layers may be expected on pure metals whenever the metal ion can occur in several valancies, such as in the sulfuridation or oxidation of iron, where the surface layers consist of FeS and FeS_2 or FeO, Fe_3O_4 and Fe_2O_3. The mechanism of surface layer formation can be described quantitatively under the assumption of a preferred parallel stratification of the individual oxides in the surface layer, the lowest oxidation step being located near the metal and the highest being in equilibrium with the gas atmosphere.

A parabolic oxidation law is assumed so that simple relations can be derived. Jost (28) as well as Valensi (29) and Wagner (quoted in 23) have discussed more general assumptions. These relations, which have been derived elsewhere (1) in somewhat modified and generalized form, are based on the similarity of the defect and the μ_A distributions in each individual partial surface layer with variable ξ value, and on the assumption that at the boundary of two partial layers a value of μ_A and μ_B, respecitvely, prevails which is independent of the overall ξ value, as, for example, in oxides near the equilibrium oxygen pressure (decomposition pressure). The transport currents s_A and s_B flowing through the partial layer, under steady-state conditions, are reciprocally proportional to the layer thickness and thus also reciprocally proportional to the number of lattice molecules $\mathscr{N}_M$ per unit surface area of the layer in question. Since the A and B currents are generally not equal in the two phases, lattice molecules from one phase are converted into those of the neighboring phase.

As a simple example of a multiple layer process we shall consider an arrangement: A(metal)/AF/AB$_2$/B$_2$(gas), such as is realized for example in the action of sulfur vapor on iron within certain ranges of pressure and temperature (Fig. 5). If the sulfur transport is assumed to be negligibly small, i. e. , $s_B \approx 0$ in both phases, then there can be no AB formation at the phase boundary A/AB, whereas at the gas boundary the AB$_2$ lattice structure is completely determined by s_{A2}. The formation of AB independently of the migration mechanism of the A particles involves only the A particles which do not migrate any further because of the reaction:

$$A + AB_2 \rightarrow 2 \, AB \tag{41}$$

Since the number of A particles becoming available is determined by $s_{A1} - s_{A2}$, we obtain the total formation rate of AB particles according to Eq. (41):

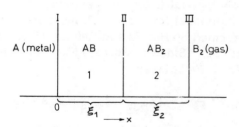

Oxidation system with two reaction-product layers

$$\xi_2/\xi_1 = 2 \, N_2/N_1 \cdot k_2' \, / \, k_1'$$

Fig. 5. Sequence of layers of an oxidation system with several reaction product layers. N is the number of lattice molecules per cm^2 at the layer.

$$\left(\frac{d\mathcal{M}_1}{dt} \right)_{total} = 2 \, (s_{A1} - s_{A2}) \tag{42}$$

$$\left(\frac{d\mathcal{M}_2}{dt} \right)_{total} = 2 \, s_{A2} - s_{A1} \tag{43}$$

and the ratio of s_A currents is found to be:

$$s_{A2}/s_{A1} = N_2^2 / N_1^2 \;\; k_2' / k_1' \;\; \mathcal{M}_2 / \mathcal{M}_1 \tag{44}$$

From this it follows that the quantitative ratio of lattice molecules in the two phases is determined to within a numerical factor by the ratio of their Tammann layer formation constants k'; the ratio of the partial layer thicknesses is:

$$\xi_2 / \xi_1 = \mathcal{M}_2 / N_2 \; \mathcal{M}_1 / N_1 = 2 N_2 N_1 \; k_2' / k_1' \tag{45}$$

This relation could be verified experimentally if, under a given external sulfur vapor pressure, one measured the thickness ratio of the two partial layers on the one hand, and k_2' and k_1' on the other with the μ_{Fe} or μ_S values. The latter can be determined for the partial layers by performing $d\xi/dt$ measurements on the individual layers. Such measurements have in fact been performed by Hauffe and Rahmel (30), and Meussner and Birchenall (31). Since in Eq.(45) $N_2 = N_1$, we obtain the ratio of the FeS - FeS_2 layer:

$$\xi_{FeS_2} / \xi_{FeS} = 2 k_{FeS_2} / k_{FeS} = 4.2 \times 10^{-4} \tag{46}$$

with the actual result $k_{FeS_2} = 0.7 \times 10^{-11}$ for $p_{S_2} = 1$ atmosphere and $k_{FeS} = 3.3 \times 10^{-8}$. Thus according to calculations the FeS_2 layer should be approximately 2000 times thinner than the FeS layer. Very thin FeS_2 layers have in fact been observed. No quantitative verification is as yet available, however.

A very interesting case involving several oxide layers is the oxidation of iron at high temperatures and oxygen pressures. It was possible in this case not only to prove the presence of the three oxide phases FeO, Fe_3O_4 and Fe_2O_3, but also to determine quantitatively their rate of formation (32). The calculation of the relative layer thickness ratio from the transport constants of the individual layers, formulated above, must be extended in two directions: on the one hand, more than two layers should be taken into consideration, and on the other, the assumption that s_B is zero in all partial layers must be eliminated. Actually, even in this extended case a calculation of the steady-state ζ ratio from the diffusion constants D_A and D_B of the individual layers is possible in a quite general way (1) under the assumptions of Wagner's theory. Additional complications arise in connection with the system $Cu/Cu_2O/CuO/O_2$ (33).

4. CURRENTLESS FORMATION OF SURFACE LAYERS FOR NON-DIVERGENT DEFECT TRANSPORT; SURFACE AND SPACE CHARGE EFFECTS

While at high temperatures and upon the formation of compact and pore-free surface layers growth of the layers is in most cases controlled by diffusion, leading to the parabolic rate law, at intermediate and low temperatures the above-mentioned ambipolar diffusion is often no more the rate-determining process. This is indicated by the rate laws of surface layer growth encountered in the oxidation of various metals. Thus among others one encounters the cubic, logarithmic and reciprocal logarithmic rate law. The parabolic rate law observed at low temperatures (oxidation of zinc at $400^\circ C$ with the formation of thin oxide layers) cannot be interpreted on the basis of rate-determining diffusion. All these rate laws can only be understood if one takes into account the electric fields caused by the electron transfer from the surface layer to the reacting gas, either in the presence or absence of space charge in the surface layer. Chemisorption of the reacting gas which initiates the oxidation will be considered below by first neglecting any changes caused by the growth process.

4.1 Space Charge Boundary Layers in Electrochemical Equilibrium with the Gas Phase; Chemisorption

During the action of oxygen on an oxide crystal, different distributions of the ion and electron defects will be established in the superficial regions of the oxide crystal because of the different chemical potential differences of the electrons and ions in the crystal and the oxygen they are in equilibrium with. This will cause the formation of space charge boundary layers (34). Owing to the transfer of electrons to the chemisorbing oxygen, an exhaustion of free electrons, e', will occur in an n-type oxide, for example ZnO, according to the overall equation

$$1/2 \ O_2 \ (gas) + e'^{(H)} \rightleftarrows O^{-(\sigma)} \tag{47}$$

An enrichment of holes $|e|^{\cdot}$ will occur in the case of a p-type oxide, for example NiO, according to the overall equation

$$1/2 \ O_2 \ (gas) \rightleftarrows O^{-(\sigma)} + |e|^{\cdot (R)} \tag{48}$$

The superscripts (R), (H) and (σ) characterize the boundary layer, the neutral interior of the semiconductor, and the chemisorption layer respectively. If we denote by n the number of defects per cubic centimeter, then we may write for the boundary layer of the n or p-type oxide (Fig. 6):

$$n^{(R)} < n_{Me}^{(R)} \quad ; \quad n^{(R)} < n_H \tag{49}$$

or

$$p^{(R)} > n_{|Me|}^{(R)} \quad ; \quad p^{(R)} > p_H \tag{50}$$

where n and p were used as symbols for the concentration of free electrons and holes, Me represents a cation at an interstitial lattice site and $|Me|$ represents a cation vacancy. The space charge density ρ (x) caused by the concentration difference of ion and electron defects in these boundary layers, at a distance x from the surface, for a p-type oxide, is given by:

$$\rho(x) = e[zn_{|Me|}(x) - p(x)] \tag{51}$$

where z is the valence of the cation vacancy or the excess charge. The density distribution of defects is governed by Boltzmann statistics and for a p-type oxide we have:

$$n_{|Me|}(x) = n_H \exp(-z V(x)/A) \tag{52}$$

$$p(x) = zn_H \exp(+ V(x)/A) \tag{53}$$

Here V is so chosen that $V_{x \to \infty} \approx 0$ sufficiently far in the interior and hence

$$p(\infty) = zn_{|Me|}(\infty) = zn_H$$

$$\rho(\infty) = 0$$

From Eqs. (52) and (53) one obtains the electrostatic potential difference between the surface with the chemisorbed gas and the crystal interior (35):

$$V(0) - V(\infty) \equiv V_D = \frac{A}{z+1} \ln \frac{p(0)}{zn_{|Me|}(0)} \tag{54}$$

By introducing the suitable Boltzmann assumptions for $n_{|Me|}(0)$ and $p(0)$ into Eq. (54), one finds that the potential difference over the boundary layer is essentially proportional to a difference between two energy quantities, customarily referred to as electron affinity of the chemisorbing gas. The potential variation as well as the spacial distribution of defects in the boundary layer can be calculated by integrating the Poisson equation:

$$\frac{d^2 V}{dx^2} = \frac{4\pi}{\epsilon} \rho(x) \tag{55}$$

where $\rho(x) = -e[n_{|Me|}(x) - p(x)]$ with z = 1. From this one

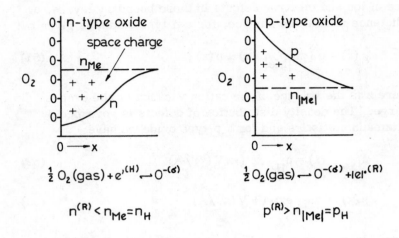

$$\tfrac{1}{2} O_2 (gas) + e'^{(H)} \rightharpoonup O^{-(\delta)}$$

$$\tfrac{1}{2} O_2 (gas) \rightharpoonup O^{-(\delta)} + |e|^{\cdot (R)}$$

$$n^{(R)} < n_{Me} = n_H$$

$$p^{(R)} > n_{|Me|} = p_H$$

Fig. 6. Concentration variation of defects n and p or n_{Me} and $n_{|Me|}$ respectively, in an n- and p-type oxide with a space charge boundary layer.

obtains a relation for monovalent ion defects, first theorized by Mott (36):

$$\frac{d^2 \Psi}{dx^2} = \frac{4}{x_o^2} \sin \Psi \qquad (56)$$

where $\Psi \equiv V/A$ and $x_o = (\epsilon kT/2\pi e^2 n_H)^{1/2}$ is a constant length analogous to the Debye length (ϵ = dielectric constant of the ionic crystal).

Undoubtedly the overall Eqs. (47) and (48) as well as the relations derived from them represent an approximate account of the electrochemical situation. However no information is obtained about the actual elementary steps of chemisorption which lead to creation of the field and space charge, or about the slow partial step. In the following we shall consider the kinetics of chemisorption on a p-type oxide on which electron-acceptor A particles are chemisorbed:

$$A\,(gas) + O^{(\sigma)} \frac{k_1}{k_1'} \quad A^{\times(\sigma)} \tag{57a}$$

$$A^{\times(\sigma)} \frac{k_2}{k_2'} \quad A^{-(\sigma)} + |e|\cdot \, ^{(R)} \tag{57b}$$

where O represents an unoccupied lattice site at the surface. From this we obtain the chemisorption rate of A particles:

$$\dot{M}_{A^-} = \frac{k_1}{k_1'} \, M_0 p_A \, \alpha_p p^o \, \exp\,(-\Delta E_A/A) -$$

$$k_2' p^o \exp\left\{ -(\Delta\eta_p - V_D)/A \right\} \tag{58}$$

where p^o is the degenerate concentration of holes and α_p is the statistical recombination coefficient of the $O^{-(\sigma)} - |e|\cdot$ reaction; M_0 is the surface concentration of unoccupied lattice sites. All other quantities can be obtained from Fig. 7.

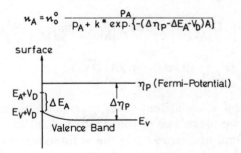

Fig. 7. Energy diagram of a p-type oxide with space charges near the surface, caused by chemisorption.

Having clarified the boundary layer formation mechanism, we will now deal with the transport processes in boundary layer fields and space charge zones.

4.2 General Ambipolar Diffusion Processes in Surface Layers Under Normal Ion and Electron Mobility

In thin surface layers forming during oxidation, even at higher temperatures, electric fields are generally present in the space charge boundary layers. At higher temperatures the electric fields in the boundary layers do not usually play any significant role because they are shortly overtaken upon the onset of oxidation; i.e., thicker surface layers are formed, and diffusion becomes rate determining (Wagner's case).

Even under exclusive formation of space charge boundary layers it is not justified to neglect the diffusion component (the first term on the right hand side of Eq. (12a) or (12b)) with respect to the electric field transport caused by space charges. This requirement is adequately known from the treatment of processes in the space charge regions in gas discharge electrodes (37). The treatment of transport processes in such space charge boundary layers requires taking into account Eq. (12) in its entirety. Considering a p-type layer with holes $|e|^{\cdot}$ and cation vacancies $|Me|$ of valence z, we can begin with Eqs. (12) and (13), derived in section 2.1:

$$s_{Me} = \left(- D_{|Me|} \quad grad \; n_{|Me|} + zn_{|Me|} \; /A\right)\mathcal{E}(x) \qquad (59a)$$

$$s_p = \left(- D_p \quad grad \; p - p \; /A\right)\mathcal{E}(x) \qquad (59b)$$

with the additional condition: $zs_{|Me|} = s_p = const.$ In evaluating Eq. (59) we make use of the first integral of Poisson's equation (55) and the expression there introduced for the space charge density $\rho(x)$ in order to eliminate the generally unknown field intensity $\mathcal{E}(x)$. The equations obtained in this way are too complex to be useful in the treatment of actual examples. Instead for each particular case it is necessary to find approximate solutions under simple assumptions. From the discussion of this section it becomes clear that one must always take into account both components - diffusion and electric field transport - in the discussion of oxidation processes involving even thin layers, regardless of whether or not space charge

occur within them. As Ilschner (38) has shown, the space
charge boundary layers occuring in growing oxide films are
caused not only by the different affinity of the individual phases,
but also by the different mobility of the electrically charged
defects during migration through the oxide layer. As numerical estimates indicate the space charge boundary layers caused
exclusively by the different rates of migration of defects are of
approximately the same magnitude as the statical space charge
regions caused by the electron affinity of oxygen.

4.3 Surface Boundary Equilibrium and Constant Field Intensity

Since space charge boundary layers make quantitative
treatment quite difficult, Cabrera and Mott (37) have attempted
to circumvent this difficulty in their well-known theory of
metal oxidation by making the following two simplifications,
whose applicability should first be discussed since they are not
always justified: (1) It is assumed that the space charge effects
can be neglected in layers which are not thicker than several
hundred Å. (2) The assumption is implied, although not explicitly stated, that the concentration of defects within the thin
oxide layer is constant. Simplification (1) is justified to a first
approximation in the formation of poorly conducting n-type
oxide layers but not in other cases.

Simplification (2) is questionable if it is assumed that
the reactions at the two phase boundaries are rapid and that
transport through the layer determines the rate of the overall
process. This implies that at the two phase boundaries steady-
state defect concentrations of different orders of magnitude
will set in which will in turn produce a considerable concentration gradient at the surface layer between the phase boundaries. This is neglected in the theory by Cabrera and Mott.

Hauffe and Ilschner (35, 39) showed that it is possible
to achieve the same result as Cabrera and Mott even without
making this physically unfounded simplification. For the experimental results of Moore and Lee (40) on the oxidation of
zinc, we will only employ simplification (1). For this case we
use a relation identical to Eq. (59) (with $\mathcal{E} = V/\xi$ and $s_{Me} \equiv s_{Zn}$):

$$s_{Zn} = - D_{Zn} \left(\text{grad } n_{Zn} + zn_{Zn} \frac{V}{A} \frac{1}{\xi} \right) \tag{60}$$

where n_{Zn} represents the concentration of Zn ions in interstitial lattice sites, and ξ represents the particular thickness of the ZnO layer in question.

Since the growth rate of the oxide surface layer, $d\xi/dt$, is proportional to the transport current s_{Zn}, by introducing an oxidation parameter with an oxide volume per metal ion Ω, we obtain with

$$k'_1 = \Omega \, D_{Zn} \, z \, n_{Zn}^{(i)} \, \frac{V}{A} \tag{61}$$

a quasi-parabolic rate law for thin layers:

$$\frac{d\xi}{dt} = k'_1 / \xi \tag{62}$$

The parabolic oxidation parameter k'_1 depends upon oxygen pressure through V. By using a suitable chemisorption equation we obtain the following expression for V (41):

$$V = \frac{A}{2} \ln \left(\frac{4\pi 2}{\epsilon \overline{V}} \, \xi \, K^2 \, p_{O_2} \right) \quad \text{or using (61)}$$

$$k'_1 = \text{constant} \, \ln p_{O_2} + \ln (\text{constant}' \, \xi) \tag{63}$$

With these relations it is possible to evaluate the experimental results of Moore and Lee (40). In addition to the parabolic rate law (Fig. 8) the layer constant k_1 is found to be proportional to the logarithm of the oxygen pressure (Fig. 9).

Even more complicated transport appears to take place in the surface layers of oxidation systems in which a cubic rate law is observed of the form

$$\frac{dx}{dt} = \frac{k_c}{x^2} \qquad (x \sim t^{1/3}) \tag{64}$$

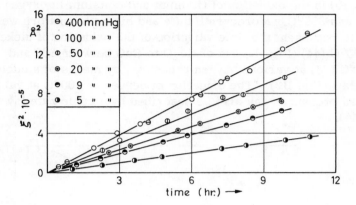

Fig. 8. Parabolic variation of Zn oxidation in the region of thin ZnO layers at 400°C and various oxygen pressures (40).

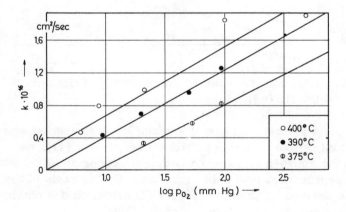

Fig. 9. Parabolic rate constant as a function of the logarithm of the oxygen pressure (40), evaluated by Engell and Hauffe.

Such a rate law was observed by Waber (42) and others (43)

(Fig. 10) in the oxidation of titanium and tantalum in oxygen at 216° and $350^{\circ}C$. Moreover Hauffe and his collaborators were able to represent the time variation of the oxidation of nickel at $400^{\circ}C$ (44) (Fig. 11) and of Cu_2O to CuO between 800 and $1000^{\circ}C$ (33) at various oxygen pressures by means of a cubic rate law (Fig. 12). The oxidation of copper at $100^{\circ}C$ at various oxygen pressures can also be described by a cubic rate law (45, 46).

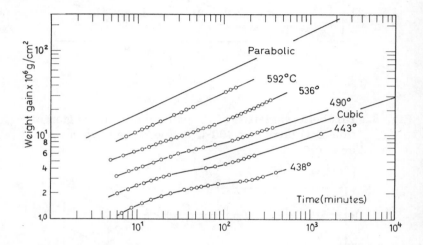

Fig. 10. The cubic rate law of the oxidation of titanium in dry air (43).

As a typical example of surface layer formation where significant space charges shall not be present (47), we choose the above-mentioned oxidation of copper at $100^{\circ}C$ which can be represented by a cubic rate law. On the basis of the relation derived by Grimley (48) for Cu oxidation one obtains an approximately cubic rate law of the form

$$\frac{d\xi}{dt} = \frac{1}{\xi^2} \left\{ D_i \, \Omega \, p_{O_2}^{1/4} \, \frac{\epsilon k T V^2}{4\pi e \mu^2 (\sigma)_{KA}^2} \right.$$

$$\left. \exp\left(- \Delta\mu / 2kT\right) \right\}$$

(65)

It was moreover shown that V/A increases very slowly with ξ. This cubic rate law is valid only as long as $b_{|Cu|}$, $\sim \mathscr{E}$. For oxide layers which are too thin or for very high field intensities, one obtains an exponential rate law.

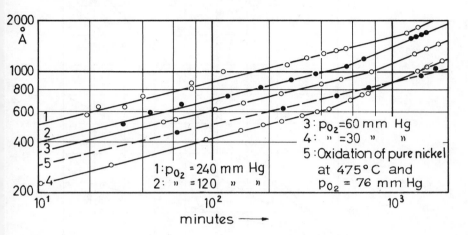

Fig. 11. Time variation of the oxidation of nickel at 400°C at various oxygen pressures (44).

4.4 Additional Role of Space Charge

The question has been considered (44) as to whether or not a cubic rate law can also be achieved by transport phenomena in p-type space charge boundary layers. These considerations were based on the assumption that the entire oxide layer constitutes a space charge boundary layer. In order to simplify the derivation of the rate law, we assume in the formation of p- and p-n type boundary layers that the electric field established in the surface layer is caused to a first approximation only by the distribution of holes, i.e., $p \gg n_{|Me|}$ and $p \gg n$. Under these assumptions, the derivation of the hole current leads to the following expression:

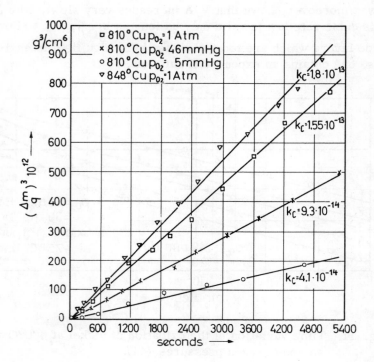

Fig. 12. Time variation of the oxidation of Cu_2O at 810 and 845°C at various oxygen pressures (33).

$$s_{|Ni|} = \frac{D_{|Ni|} \ K'}{(x_o' - \xi)^2}$$ (66)

Since the rate of layer growth $d\xi/dt$ is proportional to the hole current, it follows that

$$\frac{d\xi}{dt} = \frac{\text{constant}}{(x_o' - \xi)^2}$$ (67)

and by integration,

$$\xi(t) = x_o^i + k (t + t_o)^{1/3} \tag{68}$$

where x_o^i again is a characteristic length. From these considerations it appears that experimental observation of a cubic
rate law still does not permit any definitive conclusion concerning the reaction mechanism.

4.5 Very Thin Surface Layers With and Without Space Charge; Increased Ion Mobility and Electronic Tunnel Effect

Passing on to the discussion of very thin layers of 10 to
100 Å, such as those forming during oxidation of metals and
alloys and also passive layers such as those formed on iron in
nitric acid at low temperatures (0 to 200°C), one must consider
additional phenomena which are characteristic of the reaction
mechanisms involved. Our discussion of these phenomena are
based, with certain limitations, on the theory of Mott and
Cabrera.

As was recently discussed in more detail by Hauffe and
Ilschner (49), one must not only assume a rate-determining
field transport, but also a field-dependent, rate-determining
transfer or removal of cations or anions at the phase boundary
metal/metal oxide or metal oxide/oxygen. It was shown that,
regardless of whether the potential barrier at the surface and
in the interior U_1 and U_2, $U_1 > U_2$ or $U_1 < U_2$, the layer
growth rate is:

$$\frac{d\xi}{dt} = \text{constant} \exp(\xi_o/\xi) \tag{69}$$

where $\xi_o = za/2 \quad V/A$. After some transformations, the integral of this differential equation becomes:

$$\frac{1}{\xi} = \text{constant} - \frac{1}{\xi_o} \ln(t + t_o) \text{ for } \xi \ll \xi_o \tag{70}$$

where

$$\text{constant} = \frac{2}{\xi_o} \ln \left\{ (k'' \xi_o)^{-1/2} \xi \right\} \quad \text{and}$$

t_o is a constant of integration. We denote Eq. (70) as the reciprocal logarithmic rate law. According to Eq. (70) the growth rate of the surface layer slows down so rapidly that one can define a critical layer thickness ξ^* above which no increase can be observed within a reasonable time interval.[†] In this connection Cabrera and Mott compared the theoretical derivation with the experimental results of Gunterschulze and Betz (50) who observed the above discussed exponential dependence of layer growth rate on field strength $\mathcal{E}$ in the anodic polarization of aluminum.

However if one abandons the assumption introduced by Mott of a constant potential difference over the Al_2O_3 surface layer, and assumes according to Grimley and Trapnell (47) a constant field intensity independent of the layer thickness, and if a rate-determining field transport of Al ions through interstitial sites is retained, one obtains a linear rate law of the form:

$$\frac{dx}{dt} = b_{Al} \, \Omega \, \frac{A}{3a} \, n_{Al} \, \exp{(3a/x_o^2)} \tag{71}$$

Here b_{Al} and n_{Al} represent the mobility and concentration of Al ions on interstitial lattice sites, and Ω represents the oxide volume per metal ion; x_o is as defined in Eq. (56).

A rate-determining electron supply should be considered as a possibility in interpreting a logarithmic rate law. This can perhaps be discussed in connection with the low temperature oxidation of metals with p-type surface layers, in particular nickel (51). Experimental results by Scheuble (52) are available in this connection (Fig. 13). He observed a logarithmic rate law for the time dependence of oxygen consumption due to NiO-formation:

$$\xi = \xi_o \, \ln{(t + t_o)} - \xi_o \, \ln{t_o} \tag{72}$$

[†]Definition of Cabrera and Mott: The reaction reaches standstill when 10^5 sec are required for building up one lattice plane.

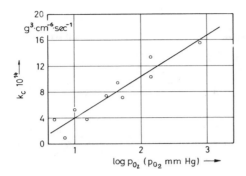

Fig. 13. Logarithmic rate law of the air oxidation of nickel at 200°C (51) according to data from ref. (52).

To interpret this observation, Hauffe and Ilschner (51) followed a concept which was already suggested by Mott (53) in a different connection, although it was hardly applicable in that case. In deriving the logarithmic rate law, Mott made the assumption that electron transport through the layer occurs by tunneling, and that, moreover, it takes place slowly with respect to ion transport. (This naturally does not refer to the velocity of electrons, which is high as usual, but the number of electrons passing through the surface per unit time and unit area.)

As shown schematically in Fig. 14, in the case of very small thicknesses (range I), not as many electrons tunnel through the layer as ions migrating through it under the influence of the fields, assuming there are sufficient electrons available. From the schematic representation of Fig. 14, it is possible to determine empirically the constants ξ_0 and t_0 on the right hand side of Eq. (72). In particular, ξ_0 is found to be approximately 1 to 2 Å. This quantity is related, in a known manner, to the height Φ of the potential barrier through which tunneling occurs (which we shall assume to be rectangular to a first approximation), and to the electron mass m (which to a first approximation is equal to the rest mass):

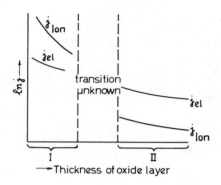

Fig. 14. Dependence of the ion and electron currents in very
          thin oxide layers. Rate is determined by electron
          transport in region I and by ion transport in region II.

$$\xi_o = \frac{h}{4\pi} \sqrt{2 m \Phi} \qquad (73)$$

For $\Phi \approx 1$ eV we also obtain $\xi_o \approx 1$ Å, in agreement with experiments.

Since ion and electron inhibition was employed in interpreting the reciprocal logarithmic and the logarithmic rate
laws, it appeared desirable to subject the assumptions and
limits of these inhibition phenomena to a critical examination
(1). It was found that the extrapolation from region II, previously performed by us (51), is not justified. Strictly speaking, therefore, it is not even certain that a region with predominant electron inhibition is involved at all. The counter potential which forces the electrons backwards in region II, in the
case of small ξ values, might decrease (and possibly even reverse) to such an extent that the tunnel current is cancelled by
a $V_{equil.} + A$ ion current, and the ion inhibition becomes de-
terminative even in the case of small ξ values. The observations in Fig. 13 certainly do not represent any decisive counter-
argument in this regard.

References

1. K. Hauffe and W. Schottky, Deckschichtbildung auf Metallen, in W. Schottky, ed., Halbleiterprobleme, Vol. V, Friedr. Vieweg and Sohn, 1959.
2. N. B. Pilling and R. E. Bedworth, J. Inst. Metals, 29, 529 (1923).
3. W. Schottky, Z. Elektrochem., 63, 784 (1959).
4. H. J. Engell and F. Wever, Acta Met., 5, 695 (1957).
5. D. W. Juenker, R. A. Meussner and C. E. Birchenall, Corrosion, 14, 57 (1958).
6. C. Wagner, Angew Chem., 49, 737 (1937); Z. physik. Chem., B, 21, 25 (1933); 32, 447 (1936).
7. W. Schottky, in W. Schottky, ed., Halbleiterprobleme, Vol. IV, p. 235, Friedr. Vieweg and Sohn, 1958.
8. D. G. Thomas, J. Phys. and Chem. Solids, 3, 229 (1957).
9. K. Hauffe, Reaktionen in und an festen Stoffen, Vol. II, p. 73, Springer-Verlag, 1955.
10. W. Jost, in W. Schottky, ed., Halbleiterprobleme, Vol. II, p. 145, Friedr. Vieweg and Sohn, 1955.
11. A. B. Lidiard, in S. Flügge, ed., Handbuch der Physik, Vol. 20, p. 246, Springer-Verlag, 1957.
12. G. Tammann, Z. anorg. u. allgem. Chem., 111, 79 (1920).
13. C. Wagner and K. Grünewald, Z. physik Chem., B, 40, 455 (1938).
14. C. Wagner, in Atom Movements, p. 153, American Society for Metals, 1951.
15. C. Wagner, Z. physik Chem., B, 21, 25 (1933).
16. H. J. Engell, Z. Elektrochem., 63, 835 (1959).
17. H. J. Engell, Arch. Eisenhüttenw., 28, 109 (1957).
18. K. Hauffe and H. Pfeiffer, Z. Metallk., 44, 27 (1953).
19. C. Wagner, Z. physik. Chem., B, 32, 447 (1936).
20. K. Hauffe and Ch. Gensch, Z. physik. Chem., 195, 116 (1959).
21. J. Teltow, Ann. Physik, Folge 6, 5, 63, 71 (1949).
22. K. Hauffe, Oxydation von Metallen und Metallegierungen, Springer-Verlag, 1956.
23. F. J. Wilkins and E. K. Rideal, Proc. Roy. Soc. (London), A, 128, 394, 407 (1930).
24. R. F. Tylecote, J. Inst. Metals, 81, 681 (1952-53).

25. R. M. Dell, F. S. Stone and P. F. Tiley, Trans. Faraday Soc., 49, 201 (1953).
26. F. Pettit, R. Yinger and J. B. Wagner, Acta Met., in press.
27. C. Wagner, Mimeographed Notes, Course 3.23 "Kinetics in Metallurgy," MIT, Cambridge, Spring 1955.
28. W. Jost, Diffusion und chemischen Reaktion an festen Stoffen, pp. 162, 167, Steinkopf, 1937.
29. G. Valensi, Intern. Conf. Surface Reactions, 1948, p. 156.
30. K. Hauffe and A. Rahmel, Z. physik Chem., 199, 152 (1952).
31. R. A. Meussner and C. E. Birchenall, Corrosion, 13, 677 (1957).
32. L. Himmel, R. F. Mehl and C. E. Birchenall, J. Metals, 5, 827 (1953).
33. K. Hauffe and P. Kofstad, Z. Elektrochem., 59, 399 (1955).
34. W. Schottky, Naturwissenschaften, 26, 843 (1938); Z. Physik, 113, 367 (1939); 118, 539 (1942); compare with N. F. Mott, Proc. Roy. Soc. (London), A, 171, 944 (1939).
35. K. Hauffe and B. Ilschner, Z. Elektrochem., 58, 467 (1954).
36. N. Cabrera and N. F. Mott, Repts. Progr. Phys., 12, 163 (1949).
37. W. Weizel and R. Rompe, Theorie der elektrischen Lichtbogen und Funken,p. 97, J. A. Barth, 1949.
38. B. Ilschner, Z. Elektrochem., 59, 542 (1955).
39. K. Hauffe, Oxydation von Metallen und Metallegierungen, p. 97, Springer-Verlag, 1956.
40. W. J. Moore and J. K. Lee, Trans. Faraday Soc., 47, 501 (1951).
41. H. J. Engell and K. Hauffe, Metall, 6, 285 (1952).
42. J. T. Waber, J. Chem. Phys., 20, 734 (1952).
43. P. Kofstad, K. Hauffe and H. Kjööesdal, Acta Chem. Scand., 12, 239 (1958).
44. H. J. Engell, K. Hauffe and B. Ilschner, Z. Elektrochem., 58, 478 (1954).
45. W. E. Campbell and U. B. Thomas, Trans. Electrochem. Soc., 91, 623 (1947); T. J. Rhodin, J. Am. Chem. Soc., 72, 5102 (1950).

46. M. A. H. Lanyon and B. M. W. Trapnell, Proc. Roy. Soc. (London), A, 227, 387 (1955).
47. T. B. Grimley and B. M. W. Trapnell, Proc. Roy. Soc. (London), A, 234, 406 (1956).
48. T. B. Grimley, in W. E. Garner, ed., Chemistry of the Solid State, p. 336, Academic Press, 1955.
49. K. Hauffe, Reaktionen in und an festen Stoffen, Vol. II, p. 565, Springer-Verlag, 1955.
50. A. Günterschulze and H. Betz, Z. Physik, 92, 367 (1934).
51. K. Hauffe and B. Ilschner, Z. Elektrochem., 58, 382 (1954).
52. W. Scheuble, Z. Physik, 135, 125 (1953).
53. N. F. Mott, J. Inst. Metals, 65, 333 (1939).

DISCUSSION

H. BASSECHES (Bell Telephone Laboratories): In your discussion on the oxidation of tantalum, you proposed that the migrating species was either Ta^+ or Ta^{++}. Since most of the evidence indicates that the oxide is Ta_2O_5, how can the migrating ions have these valences?

K. HAUFFE: It is difficult to understand how an ion with a plus five charge can go through a lattice. This apparent discrepancy can, perhaps, be resolved by the Schottky "fixation" effect. In the case of tantalum oxide this would mean that Ta^{+5} accompanied by three electrons migrates through the lattice giving an effective plus charge for the combination. As a further possibility we can assume an escort of an anion vacancy with a two or three minus charge. The anion vacancy would only be associated with the Ta^{+5} while it was moving; after it stops moving the anion vacancy leaves the tantalum ion.

D. A. VERMILYEA (General Electric): On this particular point, there is experimental evidence that allows one to put limits on the tantalum valence. In anodic oxidation, the equation for current flow contains an exponential term involving $q\lambda$ where q is the charge on the ion and 2λ is the width of the potential barrier that the ion must surmount. From transient experiments it is possible to determine the product $q\lambda$. The room temperature value of this product was found to be 4. 5, with λ in A^0. Presumably 2λ is about two or three angstroms, so that q should be between three and five electron changes. This is a little low, thus q will be a little less than five but probably not as low as one.

I would like to comment on the application of the Pilling-Bedworth rule. In most cases of oxidation, it is the metal ion that migrates in the oxide film. If this is true, then the metal ion will go through the oxide layer and form new oxide on the outer surface. Since this new oxide is not constrained, there seems to me to be no reason why the difference in the volume of the metal oxide to the volume of the metal should be used to predict the continuity of the oxide film. For example, for sodium, one would predict, by this rule, a porous oxide when actually a dense, protective oxide is found. For tungsten, one would predict a compact oxide while the opposite is found. It seems to me that the continuity of the oxide layer is determined more by the possible transformations or reactions of the film which forms initially.

H. C. GATOS (M. I. T.): In connection with Dr. Vermilyea's last comment, our results on the oxidation of germanium by nitric acid [J. Electrochem. Soc. , 105, 487 (1958)] would be of interest. We found that by merely changing the concentration of the nitric acid, we could obtain either an adherent protective film or a thick porous film. In this case the type of film appears to depend solely on the rate of formation.

E. A. GULBRANSEN (Westinghouse): In your model, you assume that nickel oxide is ionic. This may not be the case; the lattice may be only partly ionic. How would this change the oxidation mechanism?

K. HAUFFE: From our knowledge of the semiconducting properties of NiO, in particular the very low mobility of the holes, which is not understandable because of the unoccupied 3d level of the Ni ions, we believe that nickel oxide in contrast to other oxides has not a covalent but an overwhelmingly ionic structure. Nevertheless, under general conditions the charge carriers are the holes and not the nickel ions. Only under strong electric fields, at the very beginning of the oxide film formation at low temperatures, the electron transport via holes can become slower than the nickel ions.

A. T. GWATHMEY

K. R. LAWLESS

University of Virginia

The Influence
of Crystal Orientation
on the Oxidation of Metals

ABSTRACT

THE INFLUENCE OF CRYSTAL orientation on the oxidation of metals is critically discussed. Present experimental results are surveyed and some new ones are presented. Present results are largely on: the rate of oxidation of different faces of metallic single crystals; the epitaxial relationship of the oxide to underlying metal on different faces; the topography of the oxide films with emphasis on special structures as revealed by optical and electron microscopes.

1. INTRODUCTION

There have been no detailed theories of the influence of crystal face on oxidation. Both rates of oxidation and epitaxy are expected to vary with the different arrangement of atoms on the different faces, and theories of oxidation have included such variables as the work function which has been shown to vary with face. The information on rates, epitaxy,

and topography to be presented in this paper represent the
basic experimental properties of the unit crystal which must
be dealt with in an acceptable theory of oxidation. This paper
will be primarily concerned with oxide films of less than 3000
Å in thickness.

There are two experimental requirements which must
be met in basic studies of the formation of thin oxide films on
metals: (1) separate measurements must be carried out on
each of the important faces of each metal; and (2) the surfaces
on which the measurements are to be made must be carefully
prepared and accurately characterized.

With respect to the first requirement, a polycrystalline
metal as ordinarily used exposes at the surface many different
types of crystal structure (different crystal faces, edges, corners, and boundaries between crystals). Each type of structure
has its special chemical properties. Measurements made on
ordinary polycrystalline material are a composite quantity
which may be useful for technological purposes but which give
little information for an understanding of the basic process of
oxidation. It is not yet generally appreciated that for thin oxide
films the differences in rates and structures on the different
crystal faces are under many conditions quite large, as indicated below.

With respect to the preparation of the surface, a measurement of a surface property is obviously only as good as the
preparation of the surface on which the measurement is made.
Ideally one would desire to have a surface which was atomically
flat on a crystallographically perfect and chemically pure crystal. After reliable information had been obtained on such
ideal surfaces, it would then be necessary to determine the influence of surface roughness, of impurities, and of crystal
imperfections of various kinds on the oxidation process. Most
of the measurements to be described in this paper, however,
have been made on surfaces which were prepared by the best
methods available at this time. A convenient method of determining the important faces of a metal for detailed study involves
the initial use of the specimen in the form of a sphere exposing
all possible crystal faces; such methods have been previously
described. It should be emphasized that much additional work

must yet be done on the preparation and characterization of surfaces if the information obtained is to be used for a basic interpretation.

2. THE RATES OF OXIDATION

A number of methods for measuring the thickness of oxide films formed on metals have been described by Kubaschewski and Hopkins (1). Each method has its special advantages and limitations and it is highly important, wherever possible, to check results obtained by one method with those made by one or more of the other methods.

The gravimetric method employing a vacuum micro-balance, as developed by Gulbransen (2) and Rhodin (3) for the study of thin oxide films, has the special advantage of giving a direct measure of the increase in weight of the specimen. The interference color method, as developed by Evans, Winterbottom and others (4), is especially useful in determining the relative thicknesses of oxide films formed on the different faces of a single crystal in the form of a sphere exposing all possible faces. The electrolytic reduction method, as developed by Evans (4), Miley (5), and Campbell and Thomas (6), measures the weight of the oxide by determining the total quantity of electricity required for reduction of the oxide. Miley (5) used the electrometric method and Constable (7) an optical method to calibrate the interference colors of oxide films of different thicknesses. The elliptically polarized light method, developed by Tronstad (8) and Winterbottom (9) has the special advantage in that it gives a continuous non-destructive method of measuring the thickness of an oxide film. By determining the optical constants of a clean metal surface and a surface covered with an oxide film, it is possible to calculate the thickness of the film. The determination of the constants of the oxide is a laborious undertaking. All of these methods have the limitation that they give no information on the topography of the surface and are unable to identify special types of structures such as nuclei and relatively large blocks of oxide which are known to form in thin oxide films.

2.1   Copper (f.c.c.)

Tammann (10) was the first to record that the different
grains of a piece of oxidized copper showed different interference colors. With the advent of electrolytic polishing and with
the use of single crystals of copper in the form of a sphere, the
oxidation of large crystals of copper was studied by Gwathmey
and associates (11, 24), using interference colors as the means
of determining the relative thickness of oxide on the different
faces. It was concluded that the rate of oxidation differed
greatly with crystal face, as much as five-fold, and the relative
order of the rates on the various faces was, in decreasing order:
$\{100\} > \{210\} > \{111\} > \{110\} > \{311\}$. Lustman and Mehl (12)
measured the rate of oxidation of a number of orientations of
copper single crystals using a polarizing spectrometer as a
means of measuring film thickness. A complicated variation
of the rate of oxidation with orientation, temperature, and pressure of oxygen was found.

Rhodin (3) made very careful measurements of the rate
of oxidation of electropolished $\{100\}$, $\{111\}$, and $\{110\}$ faces of
copper in the temperature range of -195° to $+50^\circ C$ with the aid
of a vacuum microbalance. Good agreement was obtained between the experimental measurements and values calculated by
the theory proposed by Mott and Cabrera (13). Since at the
highest temperature and for the longer periods of time the agreement was not quite so good, it may be concluded that these
measurements confirm the Mott-Cabrera theory at least at relatively low temperatures. Rhodin cautions that the theory is
based on somewhat idealized surface conditions which are sel-
dom encountered. The order of the relative rates of oxidation
on the different faces was in decreasing order: $\{100\} > \{110\} >$
$\{111\}$. At the higher temperature the thickness on the $\{100\}$ face
was of the order of 2.5 times that on the $\{111\}$ face. No information was obtained on nucleation or the heterogeneous nature of
the films. The variation in rate of oxidation with face was interpreted in terms of the relative mismatching of oxide and
metal as proposed in the theory of Frank and Van der Merwe (14)

The thickness of oxide films formed with increasing
time on the $\{100\}$, $\{111\}$, $\{110\}$, and $\{311\}$ faces of a copper crys-

tal was determined by Young, Cathcart, and Gwathmey (15) in the temperature range of 70°C to 178°C with the aid of elliptically polarized light. Flat surfaces parallel to the desired planes were cut on single crystal spheres, and special care was taken with the preparation of the final surfaces. Electropolishing was used, followed by special washing to remove traces of the polishing bath and by annealing in hydrogen. In order to show the striking variations of rate of oxidation with face, an oxidation pattern of interference colors formed on a sphere heated in oxygen at 250°C is given in Fig. 1. This shows the different thicknesses of oxide formed on the different faces all under the same conditions of experiment. The different faces

Fig. 1.   Interference color pattern on a copper single crystal oxidized in an oxygen pressure of 10 mm of Hg for about 10 min. at 250°C.

can be located by the symmetry of the pattern. Such a pattern
is very sensitive to the presence of impurities on the surface,
and this sensitivity was used as a test to make sure that all
traces of the polishing bath had been removed. For example,
oxidation experiments were carried out with spheres in which
the surface had been finally prepared by several methods, including electrolytic polishing in phosphoric acid, electrolytic
polishing in nitric acid-ethyl alcohol solution, and cleaning by
hydrogen-ion bombardment. Essentially the same oxidation patterns were obtained. Fig. 2 shows a plot of film thickness
versus time at 178°C for the four different faces as determined
with the aid of elliptically polarized light. The ratio of the
thickness of the oxide on the {100} face to that on the {311} face
at the end of 10 minutes was approximately 12. The limitations
in these measurements will be discussed below. An attempt was
made to interpret the results in terms of the theory of Mott and
Cabrera (13). A general qualitative but not a quantitative agreement was found. In view of the fact that this theory assumes a
uniform oxide film and does not take into account the large differences in rate with face, the agreement is reasonably good.

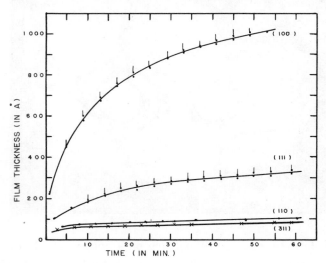

Fig. 2.   Oxidation of four faces of a copper single crystal at
178°C.   Thickness vs Time.

It might be expected that the differences between the rates of oxidation on different faces would decrease at the higher temperatures. Actually Benard and Talbott (16) reported that the rate of oxidation of copper differed with face by only a few percent at 900°C.

2.2 Nickel (f.c.c.)

The relative order of the rates of oxidation of the different faces of a nickel crystal in the form of a sphere was studied over the temperature range of 400-450°C with the aid of interference colors by Lawless, Young and Gwathmey (17). The crystal was polished mechanically and then electrolytically in 70% by weight sulphuric acid. It was carefully washed and cleaned by hydrogen bombardment. Reproducible rates of oxidation were obtained only when the crystal was outgassed to remove hydrogen by heating in a high vacuum to a temperature of at least 1000°C, at which temperature nickel will evaporate. The relative order of the different regions with respect to their oxidation rates was in decreasing order: the region in the vicinity of the (100) face in the [011] zone, the (310), (211), (100), and (111) faces. Small facets formed on the minor faces such as the {310} and {211} during evaporation and affected the rates of oxidation in these areas. This last result indicates the difficulties of outgassing a metal surface, especially of nickel; for if the metal is not thoroughly outgassed the oxidation rates are affected, while the high temperature destroys the smoothness of the crystal surface.

Otter (18) also obtained striking interference color patterns showing variation of rate of oxidation with face, when single crystal spheres of nickel were heated in oxygen at a pressure of 1 atmosphere and a temperature of 800°C for periods up to 15 minutes. The relative order of the rates of oxidation on the different faces and the smoothness of the starting surface were not given or discussed.

2.3 Iron (b.c.c.)

Mehl and McCandless (19) studied the rates of oxidation

in air of large grains in a cylindrical sample of Armco iron using interference colors. At 268°C after a half-hour the order
of relative rates on the different faces in decreasing order was:
{100} > {111} > {110}. The actual thicknesses reported under
these conditions were respectively 1800, 1000, and 430Å.

The rates of oxidation of the {100}, {111}, {110}, and
{320} faces on a single crystal made by the strain and anneal
method from Armco iron were studied by means of interference
colors for temperatures from 250 to 550°C and with pressures
of oxygen ranging from 10 to 760 mm Hg by Wagner, Lawless,
and Gwathmey (20). The surfaces were prepared by electropolishing and annealing in hydrogen, and the relative order of
the rates on the different faces in decreasing order was that
given above. At 250°C after 1 hour the thicknesses of the oxide
films on the (100), (111), and (320) were 1320, 730, and 530Å.

2.4 Niobium(b.c.c.)

Cathcart (21) oxidized single crystal spheres of niobium
and found large differences of rate with crystal face. The {111}
and {110} faces oxidized most rapidly and at about the same
rate, and the {100} face oxidized the most slowly. The time
required for crack formation in the oxide varied with face.

2.5 Cobalt (h.c.p.)

An interesting experiment on the oxidation of a single
crystal of cobalt, which has a phase change at 420°C, was
carried out by Kehrer and Leidheiser (22). Below 420°C cobalt
exists in the hexagonal close-packed structure, and above 420°C
in the face-centered cubic structure. After electropolishing in
orthophosphoric acid a cobalt sphere 5/16 inches in diameter,
it was oxidized in air in separate experiments both below and
above 420°C. At 400°C the symmetry of the oxidation pattern,
which indicates the variation of rate of oxidation with face,
followed the hexagonal structure, while at 450°C it followed the
symmetry of the face-centered cubic structure.

2.6   Magnesium (h. c. p.)

Separate single crystal slices of magnesium were prepared by Addiss (23) parallel to the prismatic (10$\bar{1}$0) and the
basal (0001) plane and oxidized in pure oxygen at a pressure
of 2.5 mm Hg and at temperatures of 400 and 440°C for periods
up to 8000 minutes. These were preliminary studies, and although no satisfactory method was found of removing the thin
oxide film initially present on magnesium, the basal (0001) face
oxidized at a greater rate than the prismatic (10$\bar{1}$0). The largest
difference between faces was of the order of a factor of two.
No single law described the oxidation rate.

2.7   Aluminum (f. c. c) and Chromium (b. c. c.)

A few preliminary experiments were carried out on the
oxidation of aluminum and chromium spherical single crystals
by Gwathmey, Leidheiser and Smith (24). Since the thin film
of oxide which formed on the surface after electropolishing
could not be removed before the oxidation experiment was
carried out, the results are not conclusive. An aluminum crystal heated in air for 15 hours at 550°C showed no apparent
change with the unaided eye. When it was heated, after electropolishing, in oxygen at 550°C for two days, a faint pattern of
foggy and bright regions appeared, indicating that regions
around the (100) and (110) poles oxidized the most rapidly and
regions around the (111) the least rapidly. When the chromium
crystal was heated in oxygen at 400°C for 3 to 10 hours or at
550°C for 10 minutes, a uniform interference color appeared
over the surface of the sphere, indicating a uniform rate of
oxidation for all faces. Possibly the initial film with a limiting
thickness obscured any variation of rate with face.

2.8   Germanium (diamond structure)

Oxidation rates of the {110}, {111}, and {100} faces of a
germanium crystal between 450 and 700°C and various oxygen
pressures were measured by Law and Meigs (25). At temperatures of 550°C and above, the oxidation rates of all faces were

inversely dependent on oxygen pressure, and no differences in behavior between faces were observed. At and above 550°C the oxidation process is controlled by the diffusion of germanium oxide away from the surface and no effect of crystalline orientation was found. At 500°C, only the {110} face oxidized appreciably, and it is proposed that at temperatures below 550°C the rate of oxidation is controlled by either the removal of a germanium ion from the lattice and/or its transport across the oxide film.

2.9   Other Studies

Bardolle and Benard (26) first showed in studies of the oxidation of iron that small nuclei formed in thin oxide films. More recently a number of studies have been carried out on nucleation and growth during the initial oxidation of iron (27), copper (28, 29, 30), nickel (31), nickel alloys (32, 33), and silver (34). Since the number, size and shape of the nuclei varied with the face exposed at the surface, these results support the above general conclusion that the nature and the rate of oxidation depend on the crystal face exposed at the surface. No estimates of the variation of rate with face have been made with this type of study. These results will be referred to later under Section 4 dealing with topography.

The relative rates of oxidation of the different faces of the above metals, for which meaningful rates are given, are summarized in Table I.

3.   THE EPITAXY OF THE OXIDE FILMS

The occurrence of different oxide orientations on different crystal faces is one of the most striking illustrations of the effect of crystal orientation on oxide growth. The determination of these epitaxial relationships between oxide and metal are important for an understanding of the mechanism of oxidation. Although numerous studies of the epitaxy of oxides on over a dozen different metals have been made (17-20, 23, 29, 34-71), only five of them have included more than a few major faces (18, 34, 35, 38, 53).

TABLE I

Relative Rates of Oxidation of Different Faces of Single Crystals

Metal	Ref.	$T^{o}C$	P in mm	Order of Rates in Decreasing Order
Copper (f. c. c.)	(15)	70-178	760	$\{100\} > \{111\} > \{110\} > \{311\}$
	(12)	80-300	760	Varied with temperature
	(3)	-195-+50	760	$\{100\} > \{110\} > \{111\}$
Nickel (f. c. c.)	(17)	400-450	760	Region near $\{100\}$ in [110] zone> $\{310\} > \{211\} > \{100\} > \{110\} > \{111\}$
Iron (b. c. c.)	(19)	268	760	$\{100\} > \{111\} > \{110\}$
	(20)	250-550	10-760	$\{100\} > \{111\} > \{110\} > \{320\}$
Niobium (b. c. c.)	(21)			$\{111\}$ and $\{110\} > \{100\}$
Magnesium (h. c. p.)	(23)	400-440	2.5	Basal $\{0001\} >$ prismatic $\{10\bar{1}0\}$
Germanium (diamond)	(25)	500	49-340	$\{110\} > \{111\}$ and $\{100\}$

The presence of an oriented oxide and the type of orientation are determined to a marked extent by the nature of the metal surface. Two factors in particular, the presence or absence of contaminating materials and the topography of the metal surface, have a very strong influence on the oxide formation. The presence of a contaminant in many cases leads to the formation of a randomly oriented polycrystalline oxide rather than an oriented one. A faceted or terraced surface can lead to the formation of orientations which are different from those found on a macroscopically smooth surface. It is obviously important to have well prepared and characterized surfaces if epitaxial studies are to have any real meaning. Despite this, there has been a notable lack of attention to this point and some authors have made no indication at all of the nature of the metal surface.

X-ray and electron diffraction techniques have been used to obtain the data on epitaxy. X-ray diffraction methods are particularly useful for thick oxide films and have the advantage of giving diffraction patterns from both the oxide film and the metal substrate. For oxide films less than several hundred Angstroms thick, electron diffraction techniques are necessary in most cases. In general, an electron diffraction pattern is not obtained from the metal substrate unless the oxide film is extremely thin, the surface is only partially covered with oxide, or the metal surface is rough. Reflection type diffraction techniques have been used with bulk specimens and transmission techniques with thin specimens and stripped oxide films from bulk metal specimens. Each technique has its special advantages and limitations, but these will not be discussed here.

A summary of data on the epitaxy of a number of metals and their oxides is given in Tables II and III. It is not possible to include all of the available data in this paper; in general only those which are considered the most reliable in terms of surface preparation are included for Cu, Ni, Fe, and Zn. Data on other metal-oxide systems are included although in some cases the nature of the surface is unknown. Information on the minor faces is not included in the tables but will be considered in the discussion, when such information is known.

TABLE II

Epitaxy of Oxide Films on Major Faces of Metals

Metal	Oxide	Surface Preparations	Oxidation Conditions	Parallel Planes		Parallel Axes		Ref.	Remarks	Misfit
				Metal	Oxide	Metal	Oxide			
Cu (f.c.c.)	Cu_2O (cubic)	Single crystal spheres and flat surfaces, electropolished, annealed in H_2.	O_2 at 150-350°C. 1-10 mm. 15 sec - 2 hrs.	{001}	{111}	[$\bar{1}$10]	[$\bar{1}\bar{1}$0]	(35)	Electron microscope observations indicate very smooth surfaces, free of facets or terraces.	18%
						[110]	[$\bar{1}$10]			
						[110]	[$\bar{1}\bar{1}$0]			
						[110]	[$\bar{1}$10]			
				{110}	{110}	[$\bar{1}$10]	[$\bar{1}\bar{1}$0]			
				{110}	{111}	[$\bar{1}\bar{1}$0]	[$\bar{1}\bar{1}$0]			
						[110]	[$\bar{1}$10]			
				{113}	{110}	[110]	[$\bar{1}$10]			
				{012}	{012}	[0$\bar{1}$1]	[110]			
						[01$\bar{1}$]	[110]			
Ag (f.c.c.)	Ag_2O (cubic)	Single crystal spherical surfaces, grown on W strip heater. No mechanical or	O_2 at 200-370°C. Pressures up to 100 atm. Times up	{001}	{111}	[$\bar{1}$10]	[$\bar{1}$10]	(34)	Parts of crystal surface show signs of terraces and facets.	-16%
				{110}	{110}	[$\bar{1}$10]	[$\bar{1}$10]			
				{111}	{111}	[$\bar{1}$10]	[$\bar{1}$10]			

TABLE II (Cont.)

Metal	Oxide	Surface Preparations	Oxidation Conditions	Parallel Planes Metal	Oxide	Parallel Axes Metal	Oxide	Ref.	Remarks	Misfit
		chemical polish or further anneal after growth.	to 9 hrs.	{113}	{110}	{1̄10}	{1̄10}			
Ni (f.c.c.)	NiO (cubic)	Single crystal spheres and flat surfaces, electropolished, annealed in H₂.	O₂ at 500°C. Atmospheric pressure; 10 min- 2 hrs.	{001}	{111}	[11̄0]	[11̄0]	(17, 49)	Surfaces smooth on microscopic basis.	19%
						[110]	[11̄0]			
						[110]	[11̄0]			
				{001}		[110]	[11̄0]		Otter observes only the (100) orientation on the {110} face.	
				{110}	{110}	[110]	[11̄0]		Otter observes a (115) orientation in addition to these two on the {111}.	
				{114}	{110}	[110]	[11̄0]		Otter's surfaces show terraces and	
				{111}	{111}	[110]	[11̄0]			
				{113}	{110}	[1ī0]	[1̄10]	[11̄0]	[11̄0]		

TABLE II (Cont.)

Metal	Oxide	Surface Preparations	Oxidation Conditions	Parallel Planes		Parallel Axes		Ref.	Remarks	Misfit
				Metal	Oxide	Metal	Oxide			
Pd (f.c.c.)	PdO (tetr.)	Single crystal film prepared by evaporation, or foil thinned down by etching.	O_2 at 600°C for 15 min. Slightly oxidized followed by anneal.	{001} {001}	{001} {001}	[110] [110]	[210] [100]	(50)	facets on microscopic basis. No information available on nature of the metal surface.	
Brass (f.c.c.)	Cu_2O (cubic)	Single crystal foil prepared by evaporation onto heated substrate.	O_2 at 300°C and 2 x 10^{-3} mm pressure.	{001}	{001} {111}	[010] [1$\bar{1}$0] [110]	[010] [1$\bar{1}$0] [110]	(51)	The (001) orientation was the major orientation observed. The nature of the surfaces was not known.	
	ZnO (hex.)		O_2 at 450°C and 2 x 10^{-3} mm pressure	{001}	{0001}	[1$\bar{1}$0] [110]	[11$\bar{2}$0] [11$\bar{2}$0]			

TABLE II (Cont.)

Metal	Oxide	Surface Preparations	Oxidation Conditions	Parallel Planes Metal	Parallel Planes Oxide	Parallel Axes Metal	Parallel Axes Oxide	Ref.	Remarks	Misfit
Fe (b.c.c.)	FeO (cubic)	Single crystal, flat surfaces. Electropolish-ed. Annealed 48 hrs at 850 °C in H$_2$. Then 8 hr vacuum anneal at 10^{-6} mm.	H$_2$+H$_2$O mixture at 750°C.	{001} {011}	{001} {111}	[100] [100]	[1$\bar{1}$0] [1$\bar{1}$0]	(53)	An (011) orientation on the {011} face of Fe was reported by Collins and Heavens.	6%
				{111}	1° of {021}	[1$\bar{1}$0]	[001]		A parallel (111) orientation on the {111} face of Fe was reported by Collins and Heavens.	
		Mechanically polished flats. Annealed 60 hrs at 850°C in vacuum. Some cases reduced in H$_2$.	H$_2$+H$_2$O mixture at 750°C.	{211} {311}	~{110} {310}	[110] [110]	[010] [010]	(52)		

TABLE II (Cont.)

Metal	Oxide	Surface Preparations	Oxidation Conditions	Parallel Planes		Parallel Axes		Ref.	Remarks	Mis-fit
				Metal	Oxide	Metal	Oxide			
Fe (b.c.c.)	Fe_3O_4 (cubic)	Single crystal spheres and flat surfaces. Electropolished. Annealed in H_2 at 500°C.	O_2 at 250-550°C 10-20 mm pressure.	{001} {011} {111} {211}	{001} {111} 2° of {210} {110}	[100] [100] [1̄10]	[1̄10] [1̄1̄0] [001]	(20)	Gulbransen and Ruka report mostly random Fe_3O_4 for similar oxidation temperatures.	
Zn (h.c.p.)	ZnO (hex.)	Single crystal, cleaved or electropolished. Not annealed.	Air at room temperature.	{0001} {101̄0} {101̄1}	{0001} {101̄0} {101̄1}	[101̄0] [0001] [21̄32]	[101̄0] [0001] [11̄00]	(57)	When facets are present other orientations occur.	22%
			Air at 300-400°C.	{0001}	{101̄0}	[0001]	[21̄32]	(59)	The same orientation as above was observed for room temperature oxidation.	
Cd (h.c.p.)	CdO (cubic)	Single crystal, flat surface, electropolished	Air at 200°C.	{0001} {101̄1} {101̄0}	{111} {111} {111}	[101̄0] [21̄32] [011̄0]	[1̄1̄0] [21̄1] [1̄10]	(57)	Growth on [101̄1] and	12%

TABLE II (Cont.)

Metal	Oxide	Surface Preparations	Oxidation Conditions	Parallel Planes Metal	Oxide	Parallel Axes Metal	Oxide	Ref.	Remarks	Misfit
		Not annealed.							[10$\bar{1}$1] facets was also observed even with the best electropolish.	
Mg (h.c.p.)	MgO (cubic)	Single crystal, flat surface. Electropolished. Oxide not removed.	O$_2$ at 400 °C.	{0001}	{111}	[10$\bar{1}$0]	[1$\bar{1}$0]	(23)	The amount of preferred orientation is small, most of the oxide being polycrystalline.	8%
Be (h.c.p.)	BeO (hex.)	Single crystal, cleaved surface.	Air at 300 °C.	{0001}	{0001}	[10$\bar{1}$0]	[10$\bar{1}$0]	(64)		22%
Co (h.c.p.)	Co$_3$O$_4$ (cubic)	Single crystal, flat surface. Cut mechanical and electropolish. No ann.	Air at 400 °C 30 min.	{0001}	{111}	[11$\bar{2}$0]	[1$\bar{1}$0]	(63)	The oxide is mostly polycrystalline with a preferred orientation.	12%

TABLE III - Miscellaneous Results on Epitaxy

Metal	Oxide	Surface Preparations	Oxidation Conditions	Oxide-Metal Relationships	Ref.
Pb (f.c.c.)	PbO (f.c. tetr.)	Single crystal flat surface. Electropolished.	Air at 150-350°C	The axes of the face centered tetragonal PbO are parallel to the cubic axes of Pb substrate in all possible permutations.	(65, 66)
Sb (rhomb)	Sb$_2$O$_3$ (cubic)	Single crystal. Cleaved (111) face.	Air at 400°C for 8 min.	(111) Sb$_2$O$_3$ // (111) Sb. The equilateral triangular array of lattice points in oxide and metal are parallel. The misfit is 83%.	(66)
Ta (b.c.c.)	Ta$_2$O$_5$ (ortho)	Single crystal	Air at 750°C	A fine grained oxide forms preferentially on {100} planes of Ta and in <100> directions with both surface and internal oxidation occurring. There is no definite indication of an epitaxial relationship.	(68)
Mn (cubic)	Mn$_2$O$_3$ (?)	Unknown	Unknown	Oxide forms with [111] direction normal to surface of metal.	(69)

TABLE III (Cont.)

Metal	Oxide	Surface Preparations	Oxidation Condition	Oxide-metal Relationships	Ref.
Fe-Ni (b.c.c.)	Fe_2O_3 (?)	Unknown	Air at 800°C.	$(10\bar{1})$ planes of oxide form parallel to metal surface. Needles grow normal to the surface.	(70)
Fe (b.c.c.)	α-Fe_2O_3	Unknown	Unknown	$(\bar{1}01)$ planes form parallel to substrate. No preferred orientation in first formed thin oxide.	(71)
U (ortho)	UO_2 (CaF_2)	Single crystal cylinder. Both abraded and electropolished surfaces.	Water vapor at 450°C., 15 mm pressure.	A (110) planar texture formed with no epitaxial relationship to the substrate.	(67)

3.1   Copper (f. c. c.)

More data has been published for copper (29, 35-46) than for any other metal, the most complete studies being those of Menzel (38) and of the authors (35). It is apparent from Table II that the most general feature is the parallelism of at least one close packed direction in the metal and the oxide. Recent studies of oxide formed on all possible faces on copper made by the authors indicated that the oxide orientations on the various faces of copper could be classified in four categories. They are indicated as regions on the stereographic plot shown in Fig. 3:

(1) A region about the $\{011\}$ faces, extending outward in an elliptically shaped area to approximately the $\{012\}$ and $\{133\}$ faces, in which the oxide was oriented completely parallel to the metal. Within this region there was only one orientation on any particular face. This region was one which oxidized slowly.

(2) A triangular shaped area about the $\{111\}$ faces, extending to near the $\{133\}$ faces with arms extending to the $\{012\}$ - $\{023\}$ areas, in which the anti-parallel (111) orientation occurred. The parallel twin orientation usually occurred in this region also. This was a region of intermediate oxidation rates.

(3) A large region about the $\{113\}$ faces, extending from the $\{111\}$ regions to the $\{100\}$ regions and to the boundaries connecting the $\{100\}$ and $\{012\}$ faces. In this region, from a point near the <111> poles to a point near the <100> poles, there was a continuous tilt of the oxide with respect to the metal lattice, the tilt being about the common [110] direction (Fig. 4). On any particular face in this region, which oxidized slowly, there was only one oxide orientation.

(4) A very small region about the <100> poles in which the (111) face of the oxide was parallel to the (001) face of the metal with four equivalent orientations occurring. This was the region which oxidized most rapidly.

It is interesting to note that the regions which oxidize slowly are those which show only one oxide orientation, the intermediate regions usually two orientations, and the fastest regions three or four orientations. The fast oxidizing regions, connecting the <100> and < 210> poles and surrounding the $\{110\}$

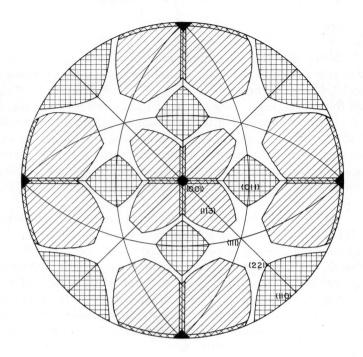

Fig. 3.   A stereographic plot of cuprous oxide orientation regions on a copper single crystal. 1. Regions cross-
hatched with vertical and horizontal lines: Oxide completely parallel to metal. One orientation. 2. Clear
regions: Anti-parallel orientation, (111)Cu$_2$O//(111)
Cu with [$\bar{1}$10] Cu$_2$O//[110] Cu. The twin of this orientation usually occurs in this region also, one or two
orientations. 3. Diagonally lined regions: One orientation on any one face, but this orientation varying
from point to point within the region. These regions
overlap along lines connecting <001> and <011> poles.
4. Solid regions: (111)Cu$_2$O//(001)Cu with four orientations.

areas, were boundaries between different orientations and two
or more orientations were usually present in these areas. The
similarity of the plot of orientations in Fig. 3 and the oxidation
pattern in Fig. 1 is striking.

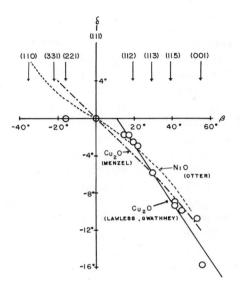

Fig. 4. Regular tilt of the antisymmetrical oxide lattice about the [1̄10] direction of the metal.

Orientations other than those listed in Table II have been observed by a number of workers (36, 39-41, 43). In general the occurrence of a parallel (100) orientation on the (100) face can be explained by assuming oxide growth on {110} or {111} facets. Menzel (38) showed that parallel growth was observed when {110} planes were exposed by an etch.

The degree of orientation depends markedly on the oxidizing conditions and on the thickness of oxide studied. For copper, oxidation at atmospheric pressure and temperatures up to 350°C formed an oxide in which the amount of orientation decreased rapidly for thicknesses over about 500Å (35). The occurrence of other orientations is not unexpected under those conditions. On the other hand, oxidation at reduced pressure (1-10mm) formed a highly oriented oxide which remained highly oriented even for thicknesses of several thousand Angstroms.

3. 2 Nickel (f. c. c.)

The epitaxy of NiO on Ni was studied by several workers (17, 18, 47-49). No complete study, however, was made as in the case of copper. Most studies were made in oxygen or air at atmospheric pressure, and under these conditions considerable disorientation was observed. Table II shows the best results available at present. Orientations very similar to those of Cu_2O on Cu occurred on the major faces with a close-packed [110] direction in the oxide and metal parallel. The parallel orientation on the {001} faces occurred even on smooth electropolished surfaces (49) but did not seem to be the major orientation. On rougher {100} surfaces (18, 47, 48) the parallel orientation seemed to be the major orientation. The major point of difference in the literature concerned the {110} faces for which Otter (18) reported only a (100) orientation, and the authors (17) observed a parallel (110) orientation with twinning occurring in the oxide on (111) and (11$\bar{1}$) faces. As in the case of Cu_2O on Cu, the oxide showed a continuous tilt about the common [110] direction with respect to the metal along the line connecting the {100} and {111} faces. This tilt is shown in Fig. 4. Otter (18) also observed a tilt of the oxide in the region between the {110} and {111} faces. This was not observed by the authors.

It is apparent both from published micrographs and from the method of surface preparation that the surfaces of Otter's crystals were faceted or terraced. This condition could possibly account for the differences observed. The twinning in the oxide on the {110} and {113} faces was apparently taking place on {111} planes of the oxide and was not related specifically to the metal surface. This twinning was not always present and its occurrence bears further investigation.

3. 3 Silver, Palladium, and α-Brass (f. c. c.)

Only limited data is available for the three face-centered cubic metals, Ag (34), Pd (50), and α-brass (51) (Table II). The orientations for the major faces of the system Ag_2O-Ag were exactly like those for Cu_2O-Cu. The data for both Pd and α-brass are subject to question since the nature of the surfaces of the evaporated films or etched foils used are unknown in these cases. The second orientation reported for Cu_2O on α-brass was in agreement with the results on copper.

3.4   Iron and Barium (b.c.c.)

Among the body-centered cubic metals, only iron has been studied thoroughly, and in general most of the results (19, 20, 52-55) are in agreement. The most complete study was made for the system FeO-Fe by Bardolle (53) using H_2-H_2O as the oxidizing atmosphere at a temperature of 750°C. Bardolle's study included the high index faces as well as the major faces and a method was proposed on the basis of his data for determining the orientation of FeO on any desired metal face. Oxidation at temperatures below 570°C led to the formation of Fe_3O_4 and the orientations observed under these conditions on the major faces of iron were the same as those reported for FeO (52). For air oxidation at 200°-500°C Gulbransen (52) reported completely random orientations for a wide thickness range. Wagner, Lawless, and Gwathmey (20) however found a strongly oriented Fe_3O_4 with the orientations shown in Table II. They are the same as the FeO orientation on the same faces, as shown in Table II.

It should be noted that results on the major faces of iron indicate that a close-packed [110] direction of the oxide is parallel to the second most closely packed [100] direction of the metal. The relationship, however, does not hold for oxide on some of the high index faces as shown by Bardolle's work. Bardolle (53) has proposed the general rule that FeO forms on the metal surface in such a way as to make the <111> directions of great atomic density of the metal correspond as closely as possible with the <110> directions of great density of iron ions in the oxide. It is not possible, however, to predict the orientation of oxide on any particular face from this rule alone.

From symmetry considerations, three orientations would be expected on the (111) face of iron and two on the (110) face. Bardolle (53) has determined that these are slowly oxidizing faces with respect to the (001) face which has only one oxide orientation.

A somewhat similar orientation relationship to that of

FeO on Fe has been reported for BaO on Ba (56), but the metal surface was not characterized and was probably not a single crystal.

3. 5   Zinc, Cadmium, Magnesium, Cobalt, and Beryllium (h. c. p.

A number of workers have studied the epitaxial relationships of ZnO on Zn (57-61). The earlier reports of pseudomorphism (58) have not been confirmed by later workers. The most careful study with attention to the surface preparation of the metal was that of Lucas (57) and his results for room temperature oxidation are included in Table II. This work emphasized the importance of surface preparation, and showed conclusively that different orientations could occur on a surface as a result of facet formation. At higher temperatures Raether (59) reported an orientation in which the (0001) planes of the ZnO were normal to the surface rather than parallel as in the case of room temperature oxidation. Yang (61), however, reported the usual parallel orientation at 350°C.

The formation of CdO on Cd was also studied by Lucas (57) and for each of the three faces of the metal examined a (111) plane of the oxide was parallel to the substrate face. Studied on the (0001) faces of Mg (23, 62), Co (63), and Be (64) oxidized at 300-400°C showed results which were exactly comparable to those on the (0001) face of cadmium and zinc for room temperature oxidation. No other faces were studied for these hexagonal close-packed metals.

The data on these five hexagonal metals are not complete enough to make any generalizations. There does seem to be, however, a definite tendency for the close packed planes of the oxide to form parallel to the hexagonal planes of the metal with the close packed rows of atoms in these planes parallel.

Table III includes information on a number of metals for which in general complete data is not available in the literature (65-71). In some cases only a brief reference to the presence or absence of epitaxy was made, and no details as to the oxide-metal relationships were available.

A number of observations indicated that the first formed

thin layer of oxide (20-50Å) was polycrystalline with in some cases a one degree orientation. This was reported by Harris, Ball, and Gwathmey (29) and by Gronlund (72) for Cu_2O on Cu, by Shimomura (71) for α-Fe_2O_3 on Fe, and by Gulbransen, McMillan, and Andrew for Fe_3O_4 on Fe (27). It should be noted that two of the observations (27, 29) were made on stripped oxide films and there is some question as to the formation of oxide or some structural change during the stripping process. Gronlund's observation was made by reflection electron diffraction on copper surfaces oxidized for 1 min. at temperatures of over 500°C and pressures of the order of several microns and indicated the formation of a thin polycrystalline oxide before oxide nuclei were visible. The authors have oxidized copper foils which were sufficiently thin for electron diffraction and microscopy, and preliminary results showed no evidence for an initial polycrystalline oxide. More experimental work on this point is needed to confirm the existence of this polycrystalline thin oxide.

The adherence of the oxide to the metal substrate may be related to the epitaxial relationships of the oxide-metal system. Bardolle (53) showed that the adherence of the oxide diminished with the multiplication of the epitaxial possibilities. Thus on iron the oxide was less adherent on the $\{011\}$ and $\{113\}$ faces than on the $\{001\}$ faces. The authors observed that when a copper single crystal sphere was heated in oxygen at a high temperature until a thick oxide scale formed on the high rate faces, the oxide cracked and flaked off easily on these faces but adhered tightly on the low rate faces. In this case the high rate faces show the greatest number of possible orientations, whereas the low rate faces show only one orientation. It should be noted that Bardolle's observations indicated that the faces with multiple orientations on iron were slow rate faces.

The possible relationship between the epitaxial growth and the relative rates of oxidation will be considered in a later section of this paper.

The various proposed theories of epitaxy have been considered in some detail by Pashley (73) and will not be discussed completely here. Enough reliable data on metal-oxide systems is not yet available to allow broad generalizations. In particular only limited data has been determined for high index faces, and too few metal-oxide systems have been studied. Several points should be made, however, which are important for a satisfactory theory of epitaxy.

There is considerable evidence that the alignment of close-packed directions in the metal and the oxide with a small misfit is a necessary condition for epitaxial growth (Table II). The work of Bardolle (53) on high index faces, however, indicates that an exact parallelism of these close-packed directions is not necessary for some metal-oxide systems. Likewise the large misfits observed in some cases indicate that the criterion of small misfit may not be a necessary one. Both the failure of the misfit criterion and the lack of evidence for a thin pseudomorphic oxide film throw doubt on the applicability of the theory of Frank and Van der Merwe (14). The numerous observed cases of epitaxial oxide growth on metals indicate that oriented growth is a general phenomenon and that the absence of an observable epitaxial growth is probably in most cases to be attributed to an unsatisfactory preparation of the metal surface or to special oxidizing conditions. An initial polycrystalline layer of oxide at the metal surface must also be considered in any theory of the oriented growth of oxide if the presence of this thin layer can be confirmed. It is by no means possible at this time to predict accurately what oxide orientation will occur on any particular metal face purely from crystallographic data on the structures of the oxide and metal concerned.

4. THE TOPOGRAPHY OF THE OXIDE FILMS

It has generally been assumed that thin oxide films formed on a polished metal had at any one time a constant thickness and smoothness over the surface. Both rate measurements and theories of oxidation for thin oxide films have generally been based on these assumptions.

In 1952 Bardolle and Benard (26) showed the existence of small nuclei and emphasized their importance in the formation of thin oxide films. Since that time a number of studied (27-34) (previously referred to in section 2), have been carried out in order to explain the origin and importance of nuclei and other structures in the initial oxidation process.

Many interesting questions immediately arise concerning these nuclei. Do the nuclei originate at imperfections of various kinds in the underlying metal (74), or are they related to imperfections in the oxide lattice, and does the number vary with crystal face, and temperature and pressure? Final answers to these questions have not yet been obtained, but recent studies indicate that nuclei of one type may be produced by controlling the pressure of oxygen, while other nuclei are related to dislocations in the underlying metal. The number of nuclei and their characteristics of growth are also a function of orientation, so that this subject does pertain to the influence of orientation on oxidation.

Only two recent studies will be discussed, one dealing with the influence of pressure of oxygen on the formation of nuclei and the other with the influence of dislocations in the metal. Benard, Gronlund, Oudar and Duret (75) studied the oxidation of the individual grains in a polycrystalline specimen of copper and proposed that the nucleation process is an intermediate stage in the formation of oxide films of uniform thickness as follows: there are three stages in the formation of the oxide film: (1) the incubation of nuclei, (2) the growth of nuclei, (3) the growth of the continuous film. The nucleation process can only be detected when the rate of the oxidation reaction is reduced by low temperature or low pressure, but it is believed that it takes place in a transitory state at higher rates of reaction. Experiments were carried out over a temperature range of 400 to 600°C and a pressure range of oxygen from $0.3x10^{-2}$ to $1.5x10^{-2}$ mm. At a constant pressure the number of nuclei increased as the temperature decreased, and at a constant temperature the number increased with an increase in pressure. The number of nuclei and their characteristics of growth varied with orientation. The rate of growth of the nuclei, defined as the increase in surface of all nuclei over a given element of surface, was independent of temperature in the range 450 - 600°C. The rate of growth was approximately proportional to pressure. At any given temperature and pressure the rate of growth of the nuclei was found to be constant throughout their development, and this was interpreted to mean that the radial growth of circular nuclei varied with the square root of the time.

The fact that at a given temperature and pressure all of the observable nuclei appeared in a few moments and their number remained constant during growth, suggested that each nucleus was surrounded by a sort of "zone of influence" within which new nuclei could form only with difficulty. The two-dimensional growth of the nuclei was compared to the growth of crystals in a homogeneous supersaturated environment which in this case was represented by the continuous oxide film. In such a system, if the pressure were increased, the rate of oxygen supply to the surface would be increased, the number of nuclei would increase, and the distance between them would decrease. If the temperature were increased, the rate of diffusion of oxygen in the base film would be greater, and the number of nuclei would decrease. The diffusion was thought to be surface diffusion.

With respect to the important question of whether the location of the nuclei was determined by the presence of such imperfections as dislocations and impurities, the authors did not rule out such possibilities, but stressed the fact that a variable number of nuclei on an element of surface can be produced by controlling the pressure of oxygen. Thus it is impossible with the present state of knowledge to use nuclei of this type to study imperfections and to draw conclusions about their number.

Young (76) has recently studied the relationship between known dislocations in copper single crystals and oxide nuclei which formed during oxidation. Specially prepared single crystals of 99.999% copper, and of copper impregnated or "doped" with tellurium, tin, or silicon, were bent in such a manner as to introduce regular arrays of dislocations. They were then oxidized by various methods at atmospheric pressure and temperatures of 200 to 325°C, and at an oxygen pressure of 1 to 10 microns and a temperature of 475°C. For crystals containing tellurium or tin and for crystals of oxygen-free high conductivity copper, it was found that oxide nuclei were formed at the known dislocations. For crystals of 99.999% copper and for copper containing silicon, there was no correlation between oxide nuclei and dislocations. Also other oxide nuclei, which were not related to dislocations, were formed on crystals of all purities. Thus dislocations in the metal were not necessary for the formation of oxide nuclei and apparently played no role in the oxidation of pure copper.

The other studies (27-34) previously referred to describe various conditions under which nuclei will form in oxide films and the influence of such factors as annealing and hydrogen in the metal lattice, but space will not allow a discussion of these results.

5. EVALUATION OF PRESENT STATE OF KNOWLEDGE OF INFLUENCE OF CRYSTAL ORIENTATION ON OXIDATION

Obviously, it cannot be claimed that the process of oxidation of metals is yet understood. However significant progress is being made in that many of the controlling factors have been identified, and discriminating questions may now be asked.

It is proposed that the studies described in this paper have shown that crystal orientation is a controlling factor and that its influence must be quantitatively determined before the process of oxidation can be understood. The experimental determination of the significant properties of the important faces for crystals of each of the metals in anything approaching their pure form is a major undertaking in itself. The importance of the careful growth of the crystals, and of the preparation and characterization of the desired surfaces has been emphasized. Although the authors place their faith in the study of well prepared and characterized specimens, it should be appreciated that much will continue to be learned from the study of more easily available specimens in which major emphasis is placed on determining the influence of existing impurities and imperfections on the properties of the metal.

A few general comments should be made about the three types of studies - rate, epitaxy, and topograph - which have been described in this paper. Some discussion of these studies has been given as the individual experiments were described.

The primary significance of rate measurements, in spite of the great difficulty of making accurate ones, is that they emphasize the different chemical activities of the different faces, and indicate the particular faces which should be selected for further study. Not only are the accuracies of the various methods of measuring film thickness not satisfactorily established, but thickness measurements by any one method are strikingly sensitive to impurities and surface preparation. For this and other reasons restraint must be exercised in attaching too much importance to the shapes of curves of thickness measurements, especially in confirming or disagreeing with some theory of oxidation. In spite of these discouraging limitations, measurements of film thickness, or rates, on the different faces are a primary requirement in themselves, and as a guide for other studies which must be carried out.

It should be expected that the epitaxial relations between oxide and metal, as determined with x-ray and electron diffraction, would be as reliable as any measurements made on surface films; but unfortunately it appears that too often even less care has been taken with surface preparation in structure studies than in rate measurements. In general it appears that the epitaxial relations on relatively smooth surfaces are different from those on etched surfaces. The general similarity between Fig. 1 showing an oxidation pattern on a sphere and Fig. 3 describing the epitaxial relationships, suggests that for copper the high rate faces are those having multiple orientations while the low rate faces show only a single orientation. These studies were carried out on the different faces of a single crystal. The results by Bardolle on separate grains of a polycrystalline sample of iron indicate the reverse relationship between rate and multiple orientations. If multiple orientations are important in determining oxidation rate, apparently the relationship is more complex than the simple suggestion made above. It is hoped that these results can be checked. Epitaxial relations should be important in controlling the breaking of the bond between oxide and metal as the film gets thicker. One general conclusion can be drawn from the orientation studies. The close-packed directions in oxide and metal in most cases are aligned with only a small misfit. Bardolle reports an exception on a high index face of iron. Although oriented overgrowths are a general phenomena, it is impossible to predict the complete

orientation of the oxide. Several points which are important
for a proper interpretation of epitaxial data in terms of oxidation rates cannot be discussed because of a scarcity of data.
These are the function of stresses in the oxide and their creation of dislocations during the growth process. The types of
grain boundaries produced in the oxide during growth may be a
function of the epitaxial growth and these boundaries may influence the diffusion of cations through the oxide. Sufficient
data on these points are not available at the present time to
warrant discussion.

The topographical studies of the oxide surface with the
aid of optical and electron microscopes have shown the necessity for understanding the several types of oxidation which take
place on any one face. The nature of these processes, such as
incubation and growth of nuclei of several types and the growth
of the base film, seem to vary with the face exposed, as well
as with other factors. The optical and electron microscopic
examinations of oxide surfaces have shown clearly the limitations of rate or epitaxial studies alone for fully elucidating the
oxidation process.

Since one of the stated purposes of the Symposium is to
suggest areas of interest for future investigations, the subject
of first importance experimentally, for the topic covered in
this paper, is obviously the preparation of specimens which approach as nearly as possible to crystallographic perfection,
chemical purity, and atomic flatness at the surface. Since the
best specimens will probably be far from perfect, it will be
necessary to characterize the surfaces with respect to both
dislocations, facets, and steps of various kinds. The dislocations may be identified by etching techniques and examination
with the optical microscope plus examination of replicas of the
surface with the electron microscope. Facets and larger steps
may be identified by examination of replicas. Possibly new
techniques for decorating atomic kinks on the surface and for
identifying them with the microscope can be developed. When
such surfaces have been prepared and characterized, it will
then be necessary to carry out the rate and epitaxial studies as previously described. Probably the most interesting studies which can
be carried out in the near future will be topographical studies
with aid of the electron microscope of the heterogeneous struc-

tures of very thin oxide films on the different faces. There
are many interesting questions. Are very thin films, 0 to 30Å
in thickness, amorphous, microcrystalline, or monocrystalline?
When do the nuclei form, and is their formation due to stresses
and dislocations in the oxide? How do the nuclei grow and what
is the role of surface diffusion? The nature of the base film
and its manner of growth offers an interesting subject for study.
The growth of both the nuclei and the base film appears to depend on crystal face. Electron microscopic studies of replicas
of thin oxide films and of stripped oxide films themselves will
answer some of these questions, as will also transmission
studies of oxide films formed on very thin metal foils. It almost
seems as if the surface chemistry of solids is becoming a question of observing increasingly small groups of atoms with the
aid of improved electron microscopes.

Unfortunately the study of three faces of a germanium
single crystal is the only one which has been made on the influence of crystal orientation on the oxidation of semiconductors.
The authors feel that results on semiconductors will probably
be similar to those reported here for other metals. It has not
been possible in this paper to discuss many subjects such as
adsorption, work function of the different faces, and surface
diffusion, all of which are important for a complete understanding of the influence of orientation on oxidation. There is
a scarcity of experimental data on these subjects and it is
hoped that future experimentation will alleviate this situation.

Acknowledgment

The authors would like to acknowledge a grant from the
Office of Naval Research supporting part of this work.

References

1. O. Kubaschewski and B. E. Hopkins, Oxidation of Metals
   and Alloys, Academic Press, 1953.
2. E. A. Gulbransen, in W. G. Frankenburg, V. I. Komarewsky
   and E. K. Rideal, eds., Advances in Catalysis, Vol.5, p. 119
   Academic Press, 1953.

3. T. N. Rhodin, in W. G. Frankenburg, V. I. Komarewsky, and E. K. Rideal, eds., Advances in Catalysis, Vol. 5, p. 39, Academic Press, 1953; J. Am. Chem. Soc., 72, 5102 (1950).

4. U. R. Evans, Metallic Corrosion Passivity and Protection, pp. 63, 802, Longmans, Green and Co., 1946.

5. H. A. Miley, J. Am. Chem. Soc., 59, 2626 (1937).

6. W. E. Campbell and U. B. Thomas, Trans. Electrochem. Soc., 76, 303 (1939).

7. F. H. Constable, Proc. Roy. Soc., A, 117, 376 (1928).

8. L. Tronstad, Trans. Faraday. Soc., 29, 502 (1933).

9. A. B. Winterbottom, J. Sci. Instr., 14, 502 (1933); Nature, 140, 364 (1937).

10. G. Tammann, J. Inst. Metals, 44, 29 (1930).

11. A. T. Gwathmey and A. F. Benton, J. Chem. Phys., 8, 431 (1940); J. Phys. Chem., 46, 969 (1942).

12. B. Lustman and R. F. Mehl, Trans. Am. Inst. Mining Met. Engrs., 145, 256 (1941).

13. N. F. Mott and N. Cabrera, Repts. Progr. in Phys., 12, 163 (1948-49).

14. F. C. Frank and J. H. Van der Merwe, Proc. Roy. Soc., A, 198, 205 (1949).

15. F. W. Young, Jr., J. V. Cathcart, and A. T. Gwathmey, Acta Met., 4, 145 (1956).

16. J. Benard and J. Talbott, Compt. rend., 225, 411 (1948).

17. K. R. Lawless, F. W. Young, Jr., and A. T. Gwathmey, J. chim. phys., 53, 667 (1956).

18. M. Otter, Z. Naturforsch., 14a, 355 (1959).

19. R. F. Mehl and E. L. McCandless, Trans. Am. Inst. Mining Met. Engrs., 125, 531 (1937).

20. J. B. Wagner, K. R. Lawless, and A. T. Gwathmey, submitted to Trans. Am. Inst. Mining, Met. Petrol. Engrs.

21. J. V. Cathcart, private communication; J. V. Cathcart, J. J. Campbell, and G. P. Smith, J. Electrochem. Soc., 105, 442 (1958).

22. V. J. Kehrer and H. Leidheiser, J. Chem. Phys., 21, 570, (1953).

23. R. R. Addiss, Jr., Technical Report No. 1, N-onr-401 (31), Metallurgy Branch 1958.

24. A. T. Gwathmey, H. Leidheiser, and G. P. Smith, Natl. Advisory Comm. Aeronaut. , Tech. Notes, No. 1460, (1948).

25. J. T. Law and P. S. Meigs, J. Electrochem. Soc. , 104, 154 (1957).

26. J. Bardolle and J. Benard, Rev. mét. , 49, 613 (1952); Compt. rend. , 232, 231 (1951).

27. E. A. Gulbransen, W. R. McMillan, and K. F. Andrew, Trans. Am. Inst. Mining Met. Engrs. , 200, 1027 (1954); E. A. Gulbransen and K. F. Andrew, J. Electrochem. Soc. 106, 511 (1959).

28. E. Menzel and W. Stossel, Naturwissenschaften, 41, 302 (1954).

29. W. W. Harris, F. R. Ball, and A. T. Gwathmey, Acta Met. , 5, 574 (1957).

30. F. Gronlund, J. chim. phys. , 53, 660 (1956).

31. U. M. Martius, Can. J. Phys. , 33, 466 (1955).

32. J. Moreau and J. Benard, J. Inst. Metals, 83, 87 (1954-55).

33. J. Moreau and J. Benard, J. chim. phys. , 53, 787 (1956).

34. E. Menzel and Chr. Menzel-Kopp, Z. Naturforsch. , 13a, 985 (1958).

35. K. R. Lawless and A. T. Gwathmey, Acta Met. , 4, 153 (1956).

36. Y. N. Trehan and A. Goswami, Trans. Faraday Soc. , 54, 1703 (1958); A. Goswami and Y. N. Trehan, Trans. Faraday Soc. , 52, 358 (1956).

37. P. A. Thiessen and H. Schütza, Z. anorg. u. allgem. Chem. , 233, 35 (1957).

38. E. Menzel, Ann. Physik. , 5, 163 (1949).

39. R. F. Mehl, E. L. McCandless and F. N. Rhines, Nature, 134, 1009 (1934).

40. L. Bruck, Ann. Physik. , 26, 233 (1936).

41. S. Shirai, J. Phys. Soc. Japan, 2, 81 (1947).

42. D. W. Pashley, Proc. Roy. Soc. , A, 210, 355 (1952).

43. T. Yamaguti, Proc. Phys. -Math. Soc. Japan, 20, 230 (1938).

44. H. Frisby, Compt. rend. , 228, 1291 (1949).

45. C. F. Elam, Trans. Faraday Soc. , 32, 1604 (1936).

46. Z. G. Pinsker, Electron Diffraction, p. 262, Butterworths Scientific Publications, 1953.

47. M. Schrank, Diplomarbeit, Darmstadt, 1958.

48. L. E. Collins and O. S. Heavens, Proc. Phys. Soc. , B, 70, 265 (1957).

49. K. R. Lawless and A. T. Gwathmey, unpublished results on Ni.
50. S. Fordham and R. G. Khalsa, J. Chem. Soc., 1939, 406.
51. N. Takahashi and J. J. Trillat, Acta Met., 4, 201 (1956).
52. E. A. Gulbransen and R. Ruka, J. Electrochem. Soc., 99, 360 (1952).
53. J. Bardolle, Publs. sci. et tech. ministère l'air, No. 327, (1957).
54. H. R. Nelson, Nature, 139, 30 (1937).
55. O. Haase, Z. Naturforsch., 11a, 46 (1956).
56. W. G. Burgers and P. van Amstel, Physica, 3, 1057 (1936).
57. L. N. D. Lucas, Proc. Phys. Soc., A, 64, 943 (1951); Proc. Roy. Soc., A, 215, 162 (1952).
58. G. I. Finch and A. G. Quarrell, Proc. Phys. Soc., 46, 148 (1934).
59. H. Raether, J. phys. radium,11, 11 (1950); H. Ehlers and H. Raether, Naturwissenschaften, 39, 487 (1952).
60. H. Ehlers, Z. Physik, 136, 379 (1953).
61. L. Yang, J. Electrochem. Soc., 97, 91C (1950).
62. R. Courtel, Métaux &corrosion, 25, 188 (1950).
63. J. B. Newkirk and W. G. Martin, private communication.
64. I. S. Kerr and H. Wilman, J. Inst. Metals, 84, 379 (1956).
65. H. Wilman, paper presented at Fourth International Congress, International Union of Crystallography, Montreal, 1957.
66. H. Wilman, J. chim. phys., 53, 607 (1956).
67. J. T. Waber, J. A. O'Rourke, and R. Kleinberg, J. Electrochem. Soc., 106, 96 (1959).
68. R. Bakish, J. Electrochem. Soc., 105, 71 (1958).
69. N. A. Shishakov and N. K. Andrushchenco, Zhur, Fiz. Khim., 30, 1966 (1956).
70. S. W. Kennedy, L. D. Calvert, and M. Cohen, Trans. Am. Inst. Mining, Met. Petrol. Engrs., 215, 64 (1959).
71. Y. Shimomura, Nippon Kinzoku Gakkaishi, 12, 9 (1948).
72. F. Gronlund, private communication.
73. D. W. Pashley, Advances in Physics, 5, 173 (1956).
74. N. Cabrera, in R. H. Kingston, ed., Semiconductor Surface Physics, p. 327, University of Pennsylvania Press, 1956.

75. J. Benard, F. Gronlund, J. Oudar, M. Duret, "Observations recentes sur le processus d'oxydation du cuivre par germination." Presented at meeting of Bunsen Gesellschaft, October, 1958.
76. F. W. Young, Acta Met., in press.

DISCUSSION

D. A. VERMILYEA (General Electric): I would like to echo your sentiments about the necessity for taking account of the fact that the surfaces of crystals are heterogeneous. This is all too often ignored. Not only surface reactions but also simple adsorption is a very heterogeneous process as shown by Ehrlich on tungsten [in C. A. Neugebauer, J. B. Newkirk, and D. A. Vermilyea, eds., Structure and Properties of Thin Films, p. 423, John Wiley & Sons, 1959]. I would like to point out, however, that there are some reactions that do not appear to depend upon the crystallography of the surface. For example the anodic oxidation of tantalum, and aluminum, and the formation of thin oxide films on nickel. These films appear to be of equal thickness on all crystal faces. Could the variation in rate with crystallographic planes possibly be due to a difference in probability of the transformation or nuclei formation on the various faces?

A. T. GWATHMEY: I have no significant comment to make except to mention from catalytic work the action of carbon monoxide on hot nickel. No carbon, or else very little, forms on some faces while on others carbon literally rains down. Whether this is due to the formation of a very thin layer or no reaction at all on some faces, I cannot say at present.

K. R. LAWLESS: In many cases, we do not know the specific structure of the first few layers of oxide that form. These can be very critical for the continued growth of oxide. For the oxidation of tantalum and chromium, apparently no difference in the rate of oxide growth on different crystallographic surfaces has been observed. This could be a result of the initial formation of the oxide. Much more work should be carried out to study the formation of the first few layers of oxide.

E. A. GULBRANSEN (Westinghouse): I would like to re-echo the comments on the importance of topography.   After measuring the kinetics of surface reactions for many years, we felt something was lacking and went to the examination of the surfaces.   We found much of vital interest which depends not only on the atmosphere but also on the metal structure.   Much can be gained from topographical studies not only in connection with the mechanism of oxidation but also in other processes such as fatigue and stress corrosion cracking.

SUBJECT INDEX

Abrasion damage
  see damaged surface layer
Activation
  in dissolution reactions, 315, 400
Adsorption
  activation barrier, 419
  chemisorption, 409-418
  entropy, 411
  kinetics, 414
  physical vs. chemical, 418
Aluminum
  electrolytic etching, 259
Anodic dissolution
  semiconductors, 286
Anodic insoluble products, 247
Anodic saturation current, 287
Beilby layer, 83
Carbon monoxide
  chemisorption of, 423
Catalysis-chemisorption, 421-437
Catalysis
  metal-semiconductor contacts, 434
CdO dissolution, 322
Chemisorption-adsorption, 409-418
Chemisorption-catalysis, 421-437
Chemisorption, infrared spectra, 422

Compounds, III-V
  dissolution in oxidizing solutions, 397
  effect of polar axis on etching, 149, 156
  hydrolysis, 395
  passivity, 402
  structure, 384
Copper
  electrolytic etching, 249
Covalent bonding in semiconductors, 382
Crystallographic polarity, 385, 398
Damage, mechanical, 100
Damaged surface layer
  depth of,
    metals, 98
    semiconductors, 120, 123
  electron spin resonance, 127
  metals, 82-106
  recombination of carriers, 115
  semiconductors, 107-130
Debye length
  electrolytes, 12
  semiconductors, 12
Deformation, plastic, of surfaces, 84
Depolarizers (dissolution), 360

523